THE Ultimate 1001 PUZZLE BOOK

© 2007 by Carlton Books Limited.

This 2008 edition published by Metro Books, by arrangement with
Carlton Books Limited.

All rights reserved. No part of this publication may be reproduced,
stored in a retrieval system, or transmitted, in any form or by any
means, electronic, mechanical, photocopying, recording, or otherwise,
without prior written permission from the publisher.

Puzzles by Tim Dedopulos
Illustrations by Moran Campbell Da Vinci

All photographs supplied by Jupiter Images (Royalty Free Unlimited)

Metro Books
122 Fifth Avenue
New York, NY 10011

ISBN-13: 978-1-4351-1038-0

Printed and bound in Singapore

10 9 8 7 6 5 4 3 2 1

THE Ultimate 1001 PUZZLE BOOK

Tim Dedopulos & Moran Campbell Da Vinci

METRO BOOKS
NEW YORK

INTRODUCTION

Enjoying a good puzzle is one of the few things that all societies can agree on. All Earth's cultures use puzzles, and from archaeological evidence, always have done. The first puzzle known is only a little younger than the first piece of writing. There's a very special satisfaction to be had from beating a puzzle – and the feeling is addictive.

It turns out to be a good thing that it is, too. Recent research has proven that mental exercise is as important for your mind as physical exercise is for the body. If we don't use our brains, our ability to think actually shrinks; if we keep them active, even dementia can be staved off. So it's lucky that puzzles are so much fun!

You won't need any special knowledge to tackle this book. The puzzles don't rely on mathematical or linguistic skills. You just need to think logically. Don't expect an easy ride, though! These puzzles will test your abilities, and although the book is not divided into difficulty levels, you may find that later puzzles are tougher than earlier ones.

Finally, I'd like to say a special thank you to Paul Moran and Guy Campbell, the talented artists who created the visual puzzles. This book would be a poorer thing without their efforts.

Now, let the trials begin!

Tim Dedopulos

1 Sudoku 1

Fill in the grid below so that the numbers 1–9 appear exactly once in each row, column and 3x3 box. For answer see page 272.

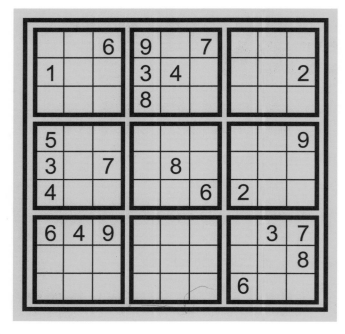

2 Kin-kon-kan 1

In the grid below, some cells contain diagonal mirrors which reflect light on both sides. One mirror is hidden in each room.

The coloured boxes around the edge indicate the start and finish of a coloured beam of light fired into the grid. These beams always travel in a straight line, but are reflected through a 90-degree angle when hitting a mirror. The number in each box shows how many grid cells its beam of light travels through before exiting again.

Where are the mirrors, and how are they placed? For solution see page 273.

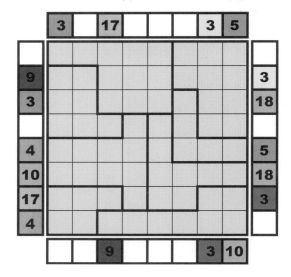

3 Futoshiki 1

Fill in the grid below so that the numbers 1 to 7 appear exactly once in each row and column. Red arrows indicate that a number is greater than its neighbour.
For answer see page 273.

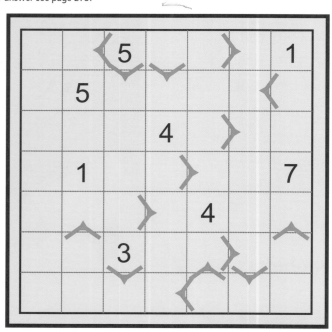

4 Minesweeper 1

The grid below contains a number of bombs hidden in empty squares. Each red flag tells you how many bombs are in the eight cells around it. Where are the bombs?
For answer see page 275.

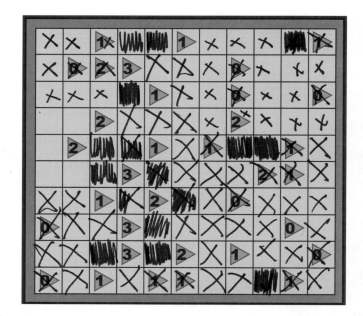

5 Gokigen Naname 1

Each cell in the grid below contains one diagonal line from corner to corner. The numbered circles show how many lines touch that corner. Fill in the grid so that the lines never form a closed circuit of any size. For answer see page 275.

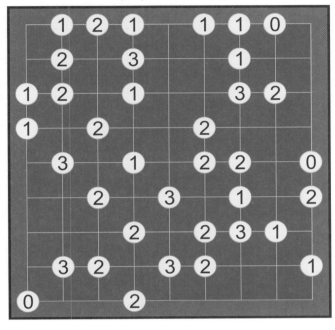

6 Sikaku 1

Divide the grid below into a number of rectangular rooms. Each room must contain exactly one number, equal to the number of cells that make up the room. Answer on page 277.

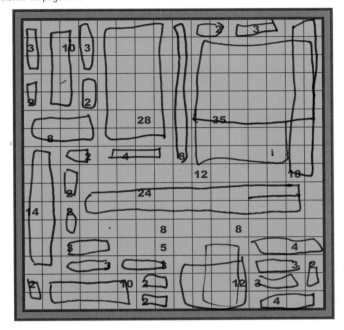

7 Slitherlink 1

A number of the intersection lines in the grid below have to be joined together to make one single complete loop. The numbers in the cell indicate how many of that cell's sides form part of the loop. Answer on page 278.

2	3	2	1					2
1			2	3	2	3	3	
1	2					0		
3		2	2	2	1			3
	2		1	3	3	2	3	
3	1	1	2				1	2
			2	2		2	2	2
	2	2	3			2		2
1	2		1		2	2		2
	3			3	2		2	3

8 Dominoes 1

A full set of dominoes containing all possible pairs of numbers from (0,0) to (9,9) is laid together in one solid rectangle. The dominoes may be placed horizontally or vertically. The numbers in the grid below indicate the value of each half of each domino. How are the dominoes arranged? Answer on page 279.

0	0	7	0	4	2	1	2	0	6	3
9	1	4	5	8	8	9	3	5	6	7
1	1	3	8	0	0	6	2	4	5	1
6	0	3	8	1	4	4	9	7	7	1
5	6	8	2	5	7	3	9	8	0	1
9	9	5	5	8	7	3	7	1	7	5
7	2	8	2	9	9	5	5	3	6	7
6	6	3	0	9	7	9	6	4	4	0
3	4	3	5	9	2	6	8	4	2	6
8	3	4	4	2	2	1	0	2	8	1

9 Bijutsukan 1

The bright cells and dark cells in the grid below represent corridors and walls respectively. Light sources shine a horizontal and vertical beam of light. A corridor cell becomes illuminated if it is in the same row or column as a light source and there is no wall cell in between them. Place light sources in the corridor cells so that every corridor cell is illuminated, and no light source illuminates another light source. The numbers in some walls tell you how many light sources are touching that wall horizontally or vertically. Answer on page 281.

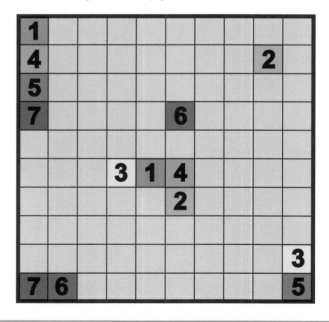

10 Domino placing 1

A set of dominoes containing all possible pairs of numbers from (0,0) to (7,7) is laid out vertically as shown in the blank grid below so that the larger number of each domino is on the top. The numbers above each column are from the top half of the dominoes in that column.

The numbers below each column are from the bottom half of the dominoes in that column.

The numbers to the left of each row are from the respective half-dominoes in that row.

All the numbers are given to you sorted into descending numerical order. How are the dominoes laid out? Answer on page 282.

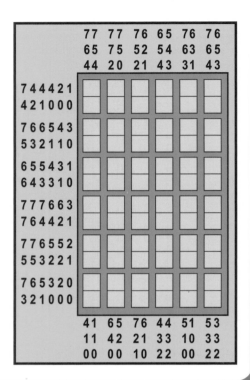

11 Number Link 1

The numbered cells in the grid below indicate the start and end points of single continuous paths. These paths fill the grid completely, and do not branch, cross each other, or touch themselves to form any pool of cells (2x2 or greater).
How are the paths arranged? Answer on page 284.

12 Tents 1

The grid below indicates a patch of woodland. Some cells contain grass, and others contain trees. Tents are placed on grass cells so that each tree has one tent next to it horizontally or vertically, although note that tents may be adjacent to more than one tree. No tent may be horizontally, vertically or diagonally adjacent to another tent. The numbers beside each row and column tell you how many tents are in that row or column. Where are the tents? Answer on page 285.

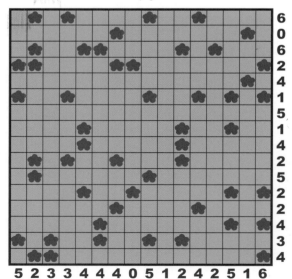

13 Hitori 1

Shade out cells in the grid below so that no number appears more than once in any row or column. Shaded cells cannot touch each other horizontally or vertically, and cannot cut the unshaded cells into two or more groups – the unshaded cells must remain connected horizontally or vertically into one complex branching chain. Which cells are shaded? Answer on page 286.

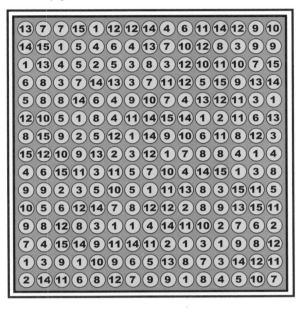

14 Fillomino 1

Each value shown in the grid below is part of a group of cells equal in number to that given value. A '6' is part of a group of six cells, for example. Groups may take any shape, but no two groups of the same size may touch each other horizontally or vertically at any point, and there are no blank cells. Not all groups need have a given value. How are the groups arranged? Answer on page 288.

4				7		5
6	4	4				
	6	5			7	
6				6	6	
5						2
			4			6
3		3	1			

15 Battleships 1

A number of ships of various sizes are hidden in the grid below. The numbers next to each row and column indicate how many ship segments are in that row or column. Some ship segments have already been filled in. Where are the ships? Answer on page 289.

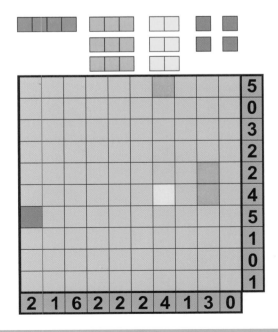

16 Colourminoes 1

In the grid below, each colour has a unique integer value from 0 to 6. The numbers next to each row and column indicate the total value of the cells in that row or column. The values of the cells of the grid correspond in turn to the numbers shown on a half-set of dominoes containing all possible pairs of numbers from (0,0) to (6,6) which has been laid together in one solid rectangle. Dominoes in this rectangle may be placed horizontally or vertically. What number does each colour correspond to, and how are the corresponding dominoes arranged? Answer on page 290.

19	23	21	20	20	20	23	22	
								21
								36
								14
								24
								22
								29
								22

17 Tentai 1

The grid below is divided into a number of shapes. Each shape has a star at its centre, and is made up of one continuous group of cells connected horizontally and/or vertically. The shapes are all symmetrical – they stay the same when rotated by 180 degrees – but may get quite complicated. Where are the shapes? Answer on page 291.

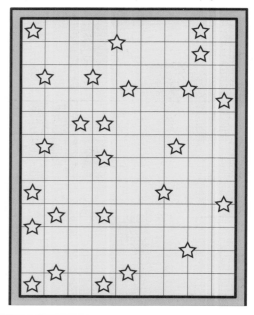

19 Kakuro 1

The empty squares in this grid contain digits from 1 to 9 so that each continuous unbroken line of numbers adds up to the clue value in the filled segment to its left (for horizontal lines) or above it (for vertical lines). No number may be used more than once in any unbroken line. How is the grid filled? Answer on page 293.

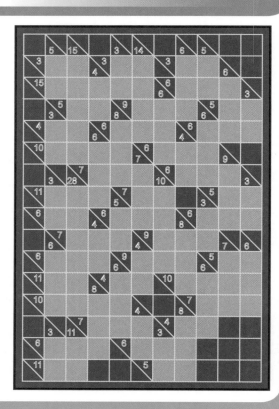

18 Missing Landmarks 1

Which famous landmark is blurred out of this photo? Answer on page 292.

20 Nonogram 1

A number of cells in the grid below are to be shaded. Each row and column may contain one or more continuous lines of shaded cells ('blocks'). The numbers adjacent to the row or column indicate the lengths of the different blocks contained. Blocks are separated from others in the same row or column by at least one empty cell. Where are the shaded cells? A picture will emerge when the cells are shaded correctly. Answer on page 294.

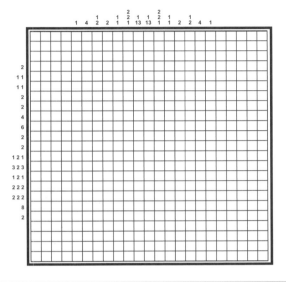

21 Map Colouring 1

The rooms of the grid are coloured so that no two rooms of the same colour ever touch. How are the rooms coloured? Answer on page 295.

22 Sudoku

Fill in the grid below so that the numbers 1–9 appear exactly once in each row, column and 3x3 box. For answer see page 272.

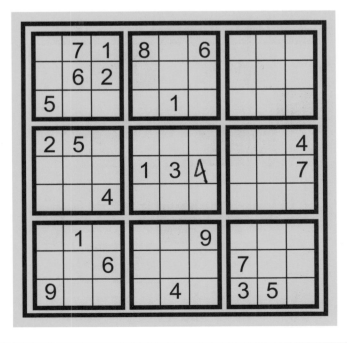

23 Battlehex 1

A number of ships of various sizes are hidden in the hexagonal grid below. The numbers next to each edge indicate how many ship segments are in the rows indicated by the directional arrows. Some ship segments and/or empty water cells have already been filled in. Where are the ships? Answer on page 296.

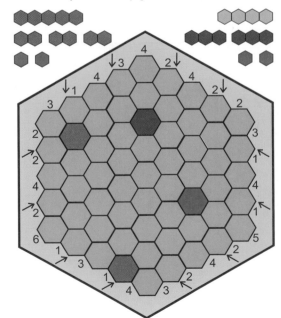

24 Futoshiki 2

Fill in the grid below so that the numbers 1 to 7 appear exactly once in each row and column. Red arrows indicate that a number is greater than its neighbour. For answer see page 273.

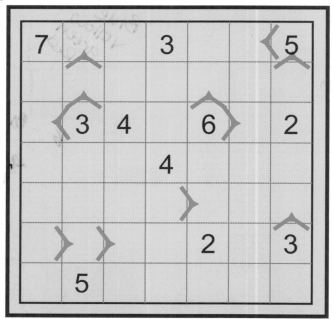

25 Hashiwokakero 1

A number of straight horizontal and vertical bridges connect the islands shown. The number on each island shows how many bridges touch that island. Bridges may not cross each other, and no more than 2 bridges may connect a pair of islands.
Where are the bridges?
Answer on page 297.

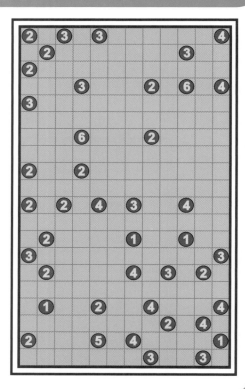

26 Tents 2

The grid below indicates a patch of woodland. Some cells contain grass, and others contain trees. Tents are placed on grass cells so that each tree has one tent next to it horizontally or vertically, although note that tents may be adjacent to more than one tree. No tent may be horizontally, vertically or diagonally adjacent to another tent. The numbers beside each row and column tell you how many tents are in that row or column. Where are the tents? Answer on page 285.

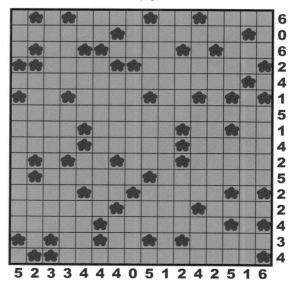

27 Fillomino 2

Each value shown in the grid below is part of a group of cells equal in number to that given value. A '6' is part of a group of six cells, for example. Groups may take any shape, but no two groups of the same size may touch each other horizontally or vertically at any point, and there are no blank cells. Not all groups need have a given value. How are the groups arranged? Answer on page 288.

28 Match One 1

Which of the jumbled images is identical to the one below the box? Answer on page 298.

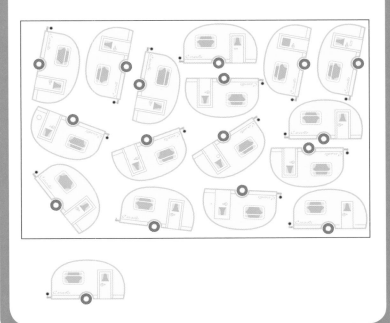

30 Dominoes 2

A full set of dominoes containing all possible pairs of numbers from (0,0) to (9,9) is laid together in one solid rectangle. The dominoes may be placed horizontally or vertically. The numbers in the grid below indicate the value of each half of each domino. How are the dominoes arranged? Answer on page 279.

4	4	8	7	7	6	8	8	5	2	4
2	8	5	7	4	9	5	0	4	2	3
7	2	1	3	6	7	4	1	4	9	7
5	4	8	9	2	5	0	8	0	1	4
8	3	5	5	3	9	6	6	8	9	6
2	1	5	4	0	7	1	3	8	7	8
7	3	0	2	9	6	9	0	4	6	5
2	0	0	0	2	2	9	1	3	3	2
0	1	3	6	0	3	9	6	5	1	6
9	8	7	7	1	3	1	9	6	1	5

29 Suiri 1

Legends tell of five evil vampires who terrorised the Romanian towns they ruled. Each one had a specific preference for victims. From the clues below, can you work out each vampire's name (1), title (2), city (3) and favourite food (4)?

1. The vampire who ruled Celanu liked wealthy victims, but he was not the duke, who was called Georghe.

2. The count of Tilead was neither Janos nor Vlad. The vampire who killed criminals was not named Iancu or Mihas.

3. The town of Vinatori was ruled by the vampire who enjoyed the taste of foreigners.

4. Cicea was not ruled by a baron.

5. Mihas, a lord, was not interested in the wealthy.

6. Janos liked to feed on the elderly, and was not a prince.

7. One of the vampires preferred to drink the blood of women.

8. One of the vampires had his lair in Napoca.

Answer on page 298.

		2					3				4				
---	---	Prince	Lord	Duke	Count	Baron	Vinatori	Tilead	Napoca	Cicea	Celanu	Women	Wealthy	Foreigners	Elderly	Criminals
1	Gheorghe															
	Iancu															
	Janos															
	Mihas															
	Vlad															
4	Criminals															
	Elderly															
	Foreigners															
	Wealthy															
	Women															
3	Celanu															
	Cicea															
	Napoca															
	Tilead															
	Vinatori															

31 Detail Scene 1

The three enlarged squares appear somewhere in the large picture. Can you find them? Answer on page 299.

32 Gokigen Naname 2

Each cell in the grid below contains one diagonal line from corner to corner. The numbered circles show how many lines touch that corner. Fill in the grid so that the lines never form a closed circuit of any size. For answer see page 275.

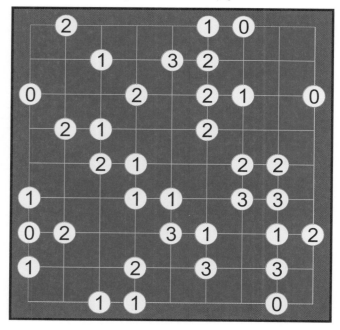

33 Bijutsukan 2

The bright cells and dark cells in the grid below represent corridors and walls respectively. Light sources shine a horizontal and vertical beam of light. A corridor cell becomes illuminated if it is in the same row or column as a light source and there is no wall cell in between them. Place light sources in the corridor cells so that every corridor cell is illuminated, and no light source illuminates another light source. The numbers in some walls tell you how many light sources are touching that wall horizontally or vertically. Answer on page 281.

34 Identicals 1

Which pair of images is identical? Answer on page 299.

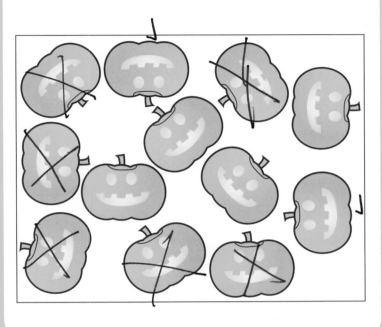

35 Hitori 2

Shade out cells in the grid below so that no number appears more than once in any row or column. Shaded cells cannot touch each other horizontally or vertically, and cannot cut the unshaded cells into two or more groups – the unshaded cells must remain connected horizontally or vertically into one complex branching chain. Which cells are shaded? Answer on page 286.

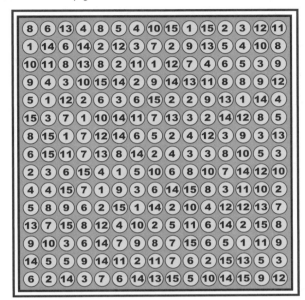

36 Mirror Image 1

Which of the five images below is an identical mirror image of the one above? Answer on page 300.

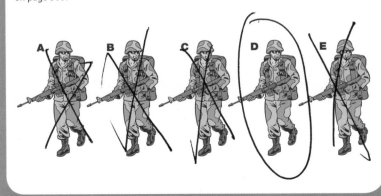

37 Sikaku 2

Divide the grid below into a number of rectangular rooms. Each room must contain exactly one number, equal to the number of cells that make up the room. Answer on page 277.

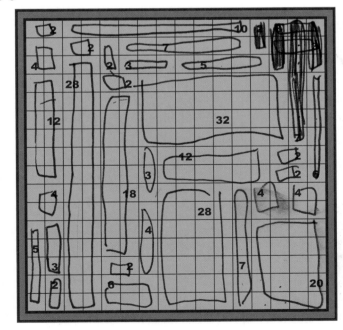

38 Slitherlink 2

A number of the intersection lines in the grid below have to be joined together to make one single complete loop. The numbers in the cell indicate how many of that cell's sides form part of the loop. Answer on page 278.

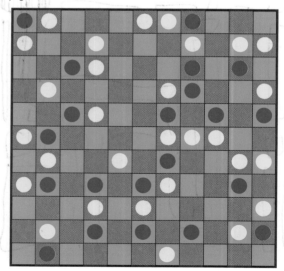

39 Number Link 2

The numbered cells in the grid below indicate the start and end points of single continuous paths. These paths fill the grid completely, and do not branch, cross each other, or touch themselves to form any pool of cells (2x2 or greater).
How are the paths arranged? Answer on page 284.

40 Masyu 1

A line passes through some or all of the cells in the grid below in such a way that it forms a single continuous non-intersecting loop. The line always exits a cell by a different side to the one it entered by, and passes through all cells containing a circle. The line travels straight through a cell with a light circle but turns in the previous and/or following cells in its path. The line turns in a cell containing a dark cell, but travels straight through both the previous and following cells in its path. Where is the line?
Answer on page 300.

41 Domino placing 2

A set of dominoes containing all possible pairs of numbers from (0,0) to (7,7) is laid out vertically as shown in the blank grid below so that the larger number of each domino is on the top.
The numbers above each column are from the top half of the dominoes in that column.
The numbers below each column are from the bottom half of the dominoes in that column.
The numbers to the left of each row are from the respective half-dominoes in that row.
All the numbers are given to you sorted into descending numerical order. How are the dominoes laid out? Answer on page 282.

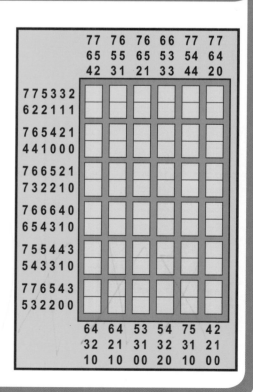

	77	76	76	66	77	77
	65	55	65	53	54	64
	42	31	21	33	44	20
775332 622111						
765421 441000						
766521 732210						
766640 654310						
755443 543310						
776543 532200						
	64	64	53	54	75	42
	32	21	31	32	31	21
	10	10	00	20	10	00

42 Yudoku 1

Fill in the grid below so that the letters s, p, a, r, k, l, i, n and g appear exactly once in each row, column and 3x3 box. Answer on page 301.

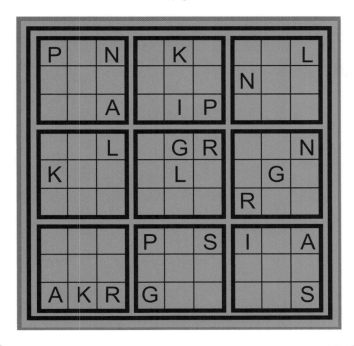

43 Battleships 2

A number of ships of various sizes are hidden in the grid below. The numbers next to each row and column indicate how many ship segments are in that row or column. Some ship segments have already been filled in. Where are the ships? Answer on page 289.

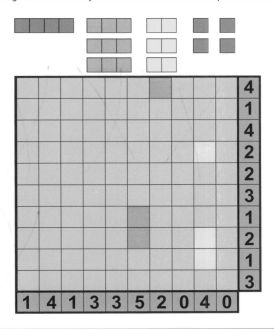

44 Colourminoes 2

In the grid below, each colour has a unique integer value from 0 to 6. The numbers next to each row and column indicate the total value of the cells in that row or column. The values of the cells of the grid correspond in turn to the numbers shown on a half-set of dominoes containing all possible pairs of numbers from (0,0) to (6,6) which has been laid together in one solid rectangle. Dominoes in this rectangle may be placed horizontally or vertically. What number does each colour correspond to, and how are the corresponding dominoes arranged? Answer on page 290.

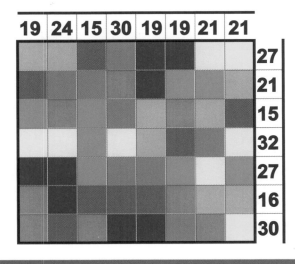

45 Sudoku

Fill in the grid below so that the numbers 1–9 appear exactly once in each row, column and 3x3 box. For solution see page 272.

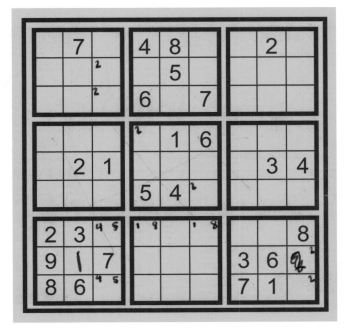

46 Silhouettes 1

Which of the six images fits the silhouette? Answer on page 302.

47 Tentai 2

The grid below is divided into a number of shapes. Each shape has a star at its centre, and is made up of one continuous group of cells connected horizontally and/or vertically. The shapes are all symmetrical – they stay the same when rotated by 180 degrees – but may get quite complicated. Where are the shapes? Answer on page 291.

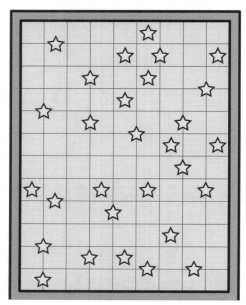

48 Who's Who 1

From the information given, can you match each owner to his or her pet? Answer on p302.

I'm Bob. My pet is called Jessie.

I'm Carol, my pet is called Ella.

I'm Alice, my cat, Georgie, has a collar.

I'm Ted, my pet is called Beth.

Clue: my owner is a woman.

clue: My owner wears glasses.

49 Futoshiki 3

Fill in the grid below so that the numbers 1 to 7 appear exactly once in each row and column. Red arrows indicate that a number is greater than its neighbour. For answer see page 273.

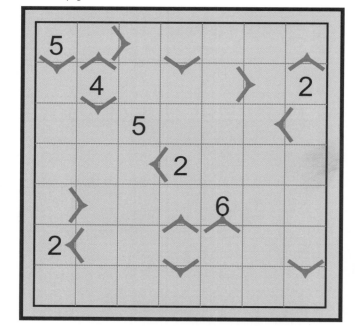

50 Missing Landmarks 2

Which famous landmark is blurred out of this photo? Answer on page 292.

51 Nonogram 2

A number of cells in the grid below are to be shaded. Each row and column may contain one or more continuous lines of shaded cells ('blocks'). The numbers adjacent to the row or column indicate the lengths of the different blocks contained. Blocks are separated from others in the same row or column by at least one empty cell. Where are the shaded cells? A picture will emerge when the cells are shaded correctly. Answer on page 294.

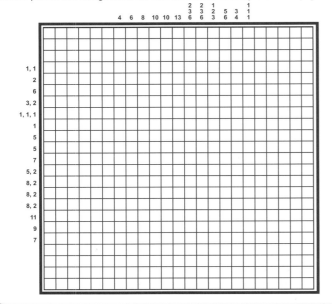

52 Kakuro 2

The empty squares in this grid contain digits from 1 to 9 so that each continuous unbroken line of numbers adds up to the clue value in the filled segment to its left (for horizontal lines) or above it (for vertical lines). No number may be used more than once in any unbroken line. How is the grid filled? Answer on page 293.

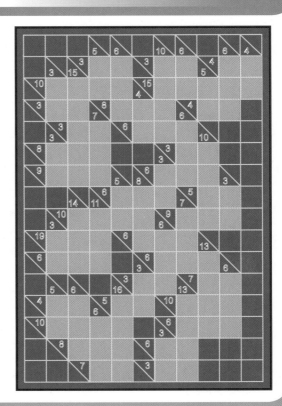

53 Slitherlink 3

A number of the intersection lines in the grid below have to be joined together to make one single complete loop. The numbers in the cell indicate how many of that cell's sides form part of the loop. Answer on page 278.

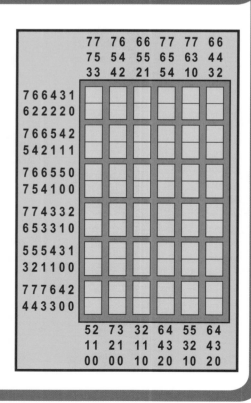

54 Bijutsukan 3

The bright cells and dark cells in the grid below represent corridors and walls respectively. Light sources shine a horizontal and vertical beam of light. A corridor cell becomes illuminated if it is in the same row or column as a light source and there is no wall cell in between them. Place light sources in the corridor cells so that every corridor cell is illuminated, and no light source illuminates another light source. The numbers in some walls tell you how many light sources are touching that wall horizontally or vertically. Answer on page 281.

55 Domino placing 3

A set of dominoes containing all possible pairs of numbers from (0,0) to (7,7) is laid out vertically as shown in the blank grid below so that the larger number of each domino is on the top. The numbers above each column are from the top half of the dominoes in that column.
The numbers below each column are from the bottom half of the dominoes in that column.
The numbers to the left of each row are from the respective half-dominoes in that row.

All the numbers are given to you sorted into descending numerical order. How are the dominoes laid out? Answer on page 282.

			77	76	66	77	77	66
			75	54	55	65	63	44
			33	42	21	54	10	32
766431	622220							
766542	542111							
766550	754100							
774332	653310							
555431	321100							
777642	443300							

			52	73	32	64	55	64
			11	21	11	43	32	43
			00	00	10	20	10	20

56 Dominoes 3

A full set of dominoes containing all possible pairs of numbers from (0,0) to (9,9) is laid together in one solid rectangle. The dominoes may be placed horizontally or vertically. The numbers in the grid below indicate the value of each half of each domino. How are the dominoes arranged? Answer on page 279.

7	8	7	0	9	4	7	1	3	0	1
8	6	1	5	6	6	7	4	0	4	9
3	5	9	0	7	4	6	2	1	2	9
1	1	4	0	3	0	2	5	4	2	3
7	6	4	9	2	7	1	5	8	8	3
8	0	3	6	3	7	9	3	9	1	5
2	6	5	2	5	8	9	1	8	2	7
6	8	5	7	0	0	0	0	0	3	6
5	5	1	4	2	9	3	2	5	9
6	4	2	8	4	9	6	4	3	8

57 Gokigen Naname 3

Each cell in the grid below contains one diagonal line from corner to corner. The numbered circles show how many lines touch that corner. Fill in the grid so that the lines never form a closed circuit of any size. For answer see page 275.

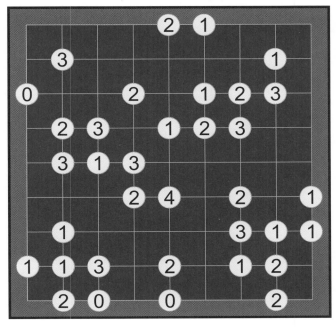

58 Fillomino 3

Each value shown in the grid below is part of a group of cells equal in number to that given value. A '6' is part of a group of six cells, for example. Groups may take any shape, but no two groups of the same size may touch each other horizontally or vertically at any point, and there are no blank cells. Not all groups need have a given value. How are the groups arranged? Answer on page 288.

7						3
7	4		6			1
	1		7	5		
					2	
	1					
5				1	5	
	1			4		

59 Hitori 3

Shade out cells in the grid below so that no number appears more than once in any row or column. Shaded cells cannot touch each other horizontally or vertically, and cannot cut the unshaded cells into two or more groups – the unshaded cells must remain connected horizontally or vertically into one complex branching chain. Which cells are shaded? Answer on page 286.

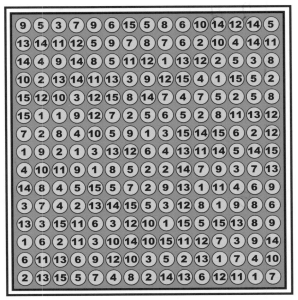

60 Tents 3

The grid below indicates a patch of woodland. Some cells contain grass, and others contain trees. Tents are placed on grass cells so that each tree has one tent next to it horizontally or vertically, although note that tents may be adjacent to more than one tree. No tent may be horizontally, vertically or diagonally adjacent to another tent. The numbers beside each row and column tell you how many tents are in that row or column. Where are the tents? Answer on page 285.

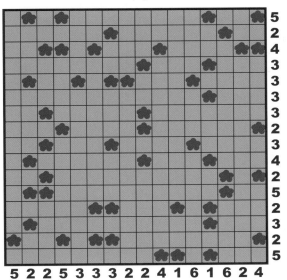

61 Sikaku 3

Divide the grid below into a number of rectangular rooms. Each room must contain exactly one number, equal to the number of cells that make up the room.
Answer on page 277.

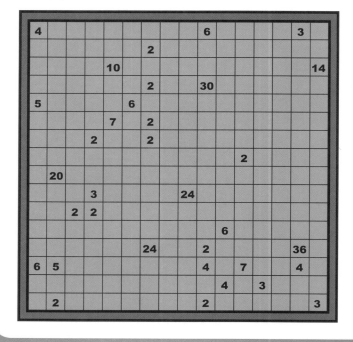

62 Number Link 3

The numbered cells in the grid below indicate the start and end points of single continuous paths. These paths fill the grid completely, and do not branch, cross each other, or touch themselves to form any pool of cells (2x2 or greater).
How are the paths arranged? Answer on page 284.

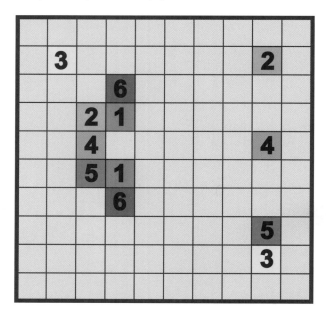

63 Battlehex 2

A number of ships of various sizes are hidden in the hexagonal grid below. The numbers next to each edge indicate how many ship segments are in the rows indicated by the directional arrows. Some ship segments and/or empty water cells have already been filled in. Where are the ships? Answer on page 296.

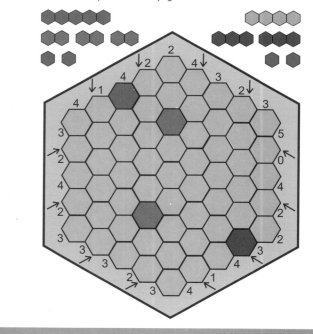

64 Sudoku 4

Fill in the grid below so that the numbers 1–9 appear exactly once in each row, column and 3x3 box. For solution see page 272.

65 Map Colouring 2

The rooms of the grid are coloured so that no two rooms of the same colour ever touch. How are the rooms coloured? Answer on page 295.

66 Battleships 3

A number of ships of various sizes are hidden in the grid below. The numbers next to each row and column indicate how many ship segments are in that row or column. Some ship segments have already been filled in. Where are the ships? Answer on page 289.

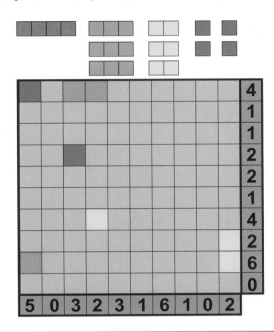

67 Colourminoes 3

In the grid below, each colour has a unique integer value from 0 to 6. The numbers next to each row and column indicate the total value of the cells in that row or column. The values of the cells of the grid correspond in turn to the numbers shown on a half-set of dominoes containing all possible pairs of numbers from (0,0) to (6,6) which has been laid together in one solid rectangle. Dominoes in this rectangle may be placed horizontally or vertically. What number does each colour correspond to, and how are the corresponding dominoes arranged? Answer on page 290.

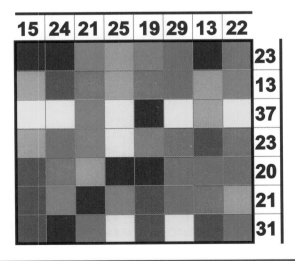

68 Futoshiki 4

Fill in the grid below so that the numbers 1 to 7 appear exactly once in each row and column. Red arrows indicate that a number is greater than its neighbour. For answer see page 273.

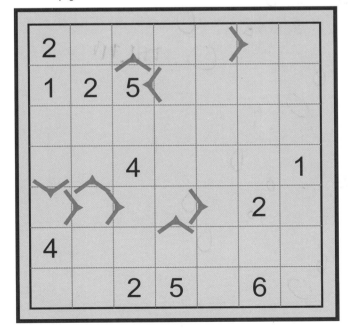

69 Tentai 3

The grid below is divided into a number of shapes. Each shape has a star at its centre, and is made up of one continuous group of cells connected horizontally and/or vertically. The shapes are all symmetrical – they stay the same when rotated by 180 degrees – but may get quite complicated. Where are the shapes? Answer on page 291.

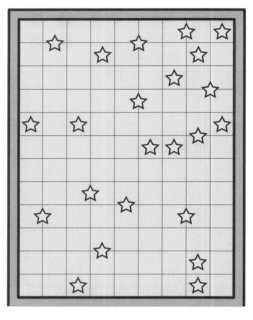

70 Killer Sudoku 1

Fill in the grid below so that the numbers 1–9 appear exactly once in each row, column and 3x3 block, and that the numbers in each dotted room add up to the value in its top right corner. Answer on page 303.

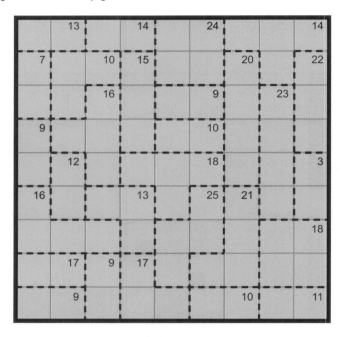

71 Spot the Difference

There are eight differences between the two pictures. Can you find them all? Answer on page 302.

72 Domino placing 4

A set of dominoes containing all possible pairs of numbers from (0,0) to (7,7) is laid out vertically as shown in the blank grid below so that the larger number of each domino is on the top. The numbers above each column are from the top half of the dominoes in that column.

The numbers below each column are from the bottom half of the dominoes in that column. The numbers to the left of each row are from the respective half-dominoes in that row.

All the numbers are given to you sorted into descending numerical order. How are the dominoes laid out? Answer on page 282.

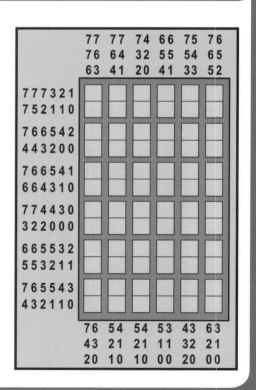

24

73 Bijutsukan 4

The bright cells and dark cells in the grid below represent corridors and walls respectively. Light sources shine a horizontal and vertical beam of light. A corridor cell becomes illuminated if it is in the same row or column as a light source and there is no wall cell in between them. Place light sources in the corridor cells so that every corridor cell is illuminated, and no light source illuminates another light source. The numbers in some walls tell you how many light sources are touching that wall horizontally or vertically. Answer on page 281.

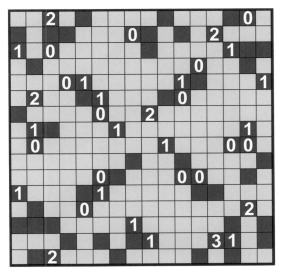

74 Hitori 4

Shade out cells in the grid below so that no number appears more than once in any row or column. Shaded cells cannot touch each other horizontally or vertically, and cannot cut the unshaded cells into two or more groups – the unshaded cells must remain connected horizontally or vertically into one complex branching chain. Which cells are shaded? Answer on page 286.

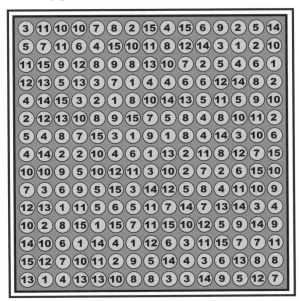

75 Masyu 2

A line passes through some or all of the cells in the grid below in such a way that it forms a single continuous non-intersecting loop. The line always exits a cell by a different side to the one it entered by, and passes through all cells containing a circle. The line travels straight through a cell with a light circle but turns in the previous and/or following cells in its path. The line turns in a cell containing a dark cell, but travels straight through both the previous and following cells in its path. Where is the line? Answer on page 300.

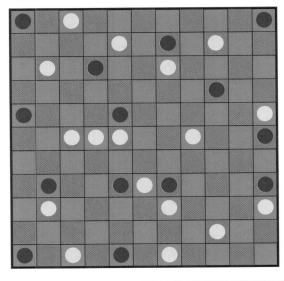

76 Number Link 4

The numbered cells in the grid below indicate the start and end points of single continuous paths. These paths fill the grid completely, and do not branch, cross each other, or touch themselves to form any pool of cells (2x2 or greater).
How are the paths arranged? Answer on page 284.

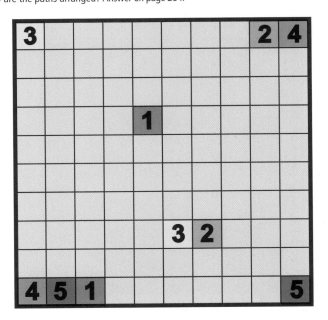

77 Sikaku 4

Divide the grid below into a number of rectangular rooms. Each room must contain exactly one number, equal to the number of cells that make up the room. Answer on page 277.

		12					2						14	
				8				8						
									2			2		2
									2		10			
					2									
					2		16		5				4	
		2			3				3		2			
								2	5					3
											7		21	
	12				7			21			3	5		
13										15				
			2											
		2	6											13
4											2			
				4					2		4		2	

78 Identicals 2

Which pair of images is identical? Answer on page 299.

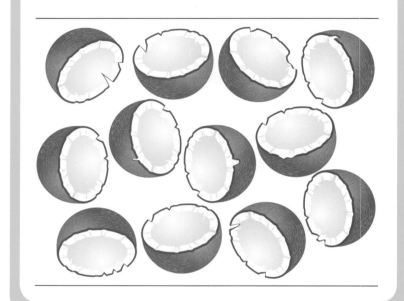

79 Tents 4

The grid below indicates a patch of woodland. Some cells contain grass, and others contain trees. Tents are placed on grass cells so that each tree has one tent next to it horizontally or vertically, although note that tents may be adjacent to more than one tree. No tent may be horizontally, vertically or diagonally adjacent to another tent. The numbers beside each row and column tell you how many tents are in that row or column. Where are the tents? Answer on page 285.

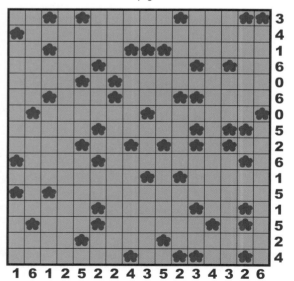

80 Samurai Sudoku 1

Fill in each 9x9 grid below so that the numbers 1–9 appear exactly once in each row, column and 3x3 block. Numbers in overlapping blocks count identically towards both grids. Answer on page 303.

81 Suiri 2

Five teenagers are starting rock bands. From the information given below, can you work out each kid's (1) band name (2), first track (3) and musical style (4)?

1. Steve is starting Red Lime, but not to record the Prog Rock song, which is called "Black Box".
2. Neck's song, "Sudden", is not Gothic Rock or Alternative Rock.
3. Bruce's band is not The Cult of the Void. Megan is not calling her band The Cult of the Void either, and she won't be playing Prog Rock.
5. Bellathon are an Emo band, but their song is not called "Juliette".
6. Leath is starting an Indie band.
7. Rael's band is recording "Kill the World", which is not an Emo song.
8. There is a band called Slopedown. There is a song called "Canvas Tragedy".
Answer on page 298.

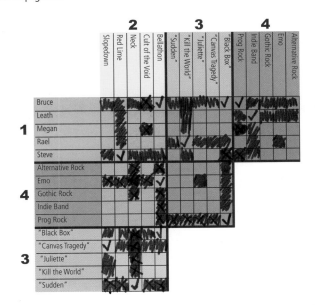

82 Gokigen Naname 4

Each cell in the grid below contains one diagonal line from corner to corner. The numbered circles show how many lines touch that corner. Fill in the grid so that the lines never form a closed circuit of any size. For answer see page 275.

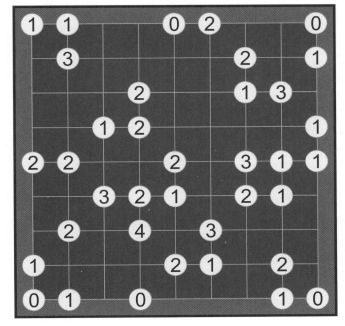

83 Sudoku 5

Fill in the grid below so that the numbers 1–9 appear exactly once in each row, column and 3x3 box. For solution see page 272.

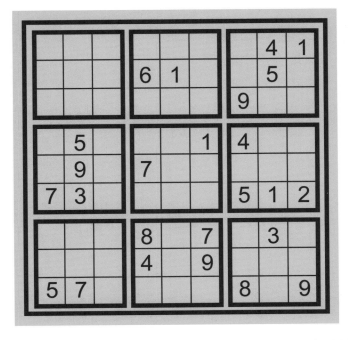

84 Detail Scene 2

The three enlarged squares appear somewhere in the large picture. Can you find them? Answer on page 299.

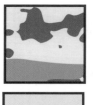

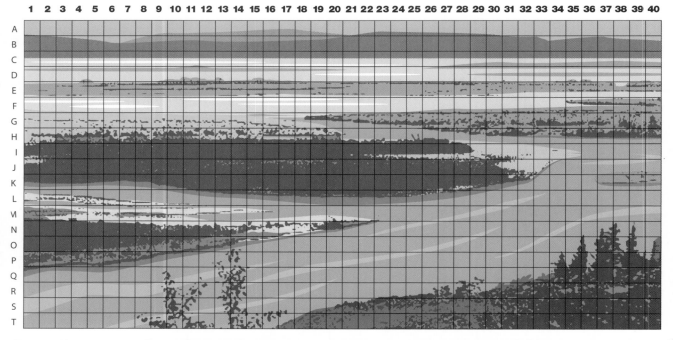

85 Super Sudoku 1

Fill in the grid below so that the digits 1, 2, 3, 4, 5, 6, 7, 8, 9, a, b, c, d, e, f and g appear exactly once in each row and column. Answer on page 303.

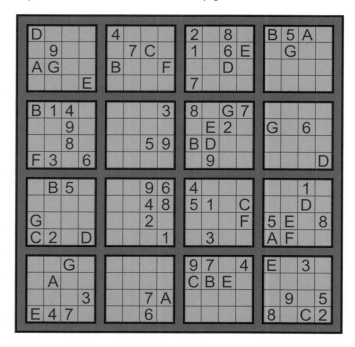

86 Differences

Each copy of the picture has one flaw that none of the others share. Can you find them all? Answer on page 304.

87 Match One 2

Which of the jumbled images is identical to the one presented here? Answer on page 298.

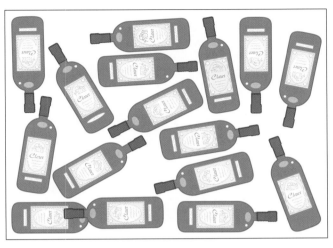

88 Fillomino 4

Each value shown in the grid below is part of a group of cells equal in number to that given value. A '6' is part of a group of six cells, for example. Groups may take any shape, but no two groups of the same size may touch each other horizontally or vertically at any point, and there are no blank cells. Not all groups need have a given value. How are the groups arranged? Answer on page 288.

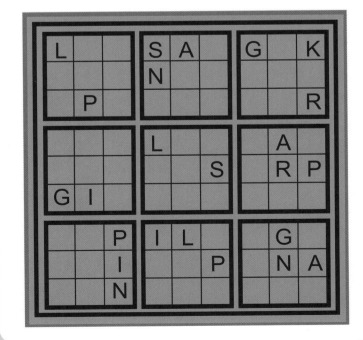

89 Mirror Image 2

Which of the five images below is an identical mirror image of the one above? Answer on page 300.

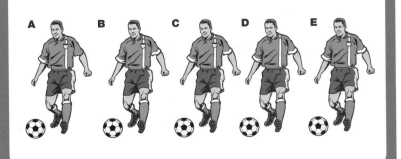

90 Yudoku 2

Fill in the grid below so that the letters s, p, a, r, k, l, i, n and g appear exactly once in each row, column and 3x3 box. Answer on page 301.

Slitherlink 4

A number of the intersection lines in the grid below have to be joined together to make one single complete loop. The numbers in the cell indicate how many of that cell's sides form part of the loop. Answer on page 278.

2	3		1				2	2
2				2			1	3
2		3	1		2			2
2					2	3	2	2
2			2	1		2	2	0
2		2	2			1		3
1			2	0		2	2	
	3		1				3	
	1		1		3	2	2	2
2	3	3	3	3	2			2

Hashiwokakero 2

A number of straight horizontal and vertical bridges connect the islands shown. The number on each island shows how many bridges touch that island. Bridges may not cross each other, and no more than 2 bridges may connect a pair of islands.
Where are the bridges?
Answer on page 297.

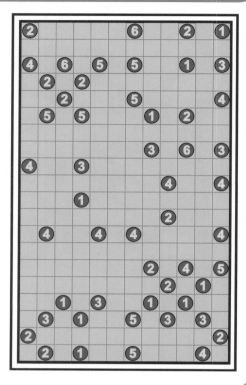

Spot the Set

There are four different versions of the picture in the group below, each one reproduced three times. Can you identify the four sets?
Answer on page 304.

Dominoes 4

A full set of dominoes containing all possible pairs of numbers from (0,0) to (9,9) is laid together in one solid rectangle. The dominoes may be placed horizontally or vertically. The numbers in the grid below indicate the value of each half of each domino. How are the dominoes arranged? Answer on page 279.

0	1	7	5	0	3	9	8	2	6	7
2	1	7	9	1	8	9	4	8	3	8
9	1	5	5	0	7	7	0	8	2	9
0	0	3	6	8	6	1	5	5	1	9
6	2	2	9	0	3	1	6	9	5	4
4	7	1	6	6	2	4	8	0	7	5
9	9	2	4	3	7	3	3	7	0	0
2	6	5	7	1	4	2	4	5	1	
4	4	7	8	8	2	3	0	9	6	
8	5	4	3	8	2	3	6	0	5	4

95 Missing Landmarks 3

Which famous landmark is blurred out of this photo? Answer on page 292.

96 Battleships 4

A number of ships of various sizes are hidden in the grid below. The numbers next to each row and column indicate how many ship segments are in that row or column. Some ship segments have already been filled in. Where are the ships? Answer on page 289.

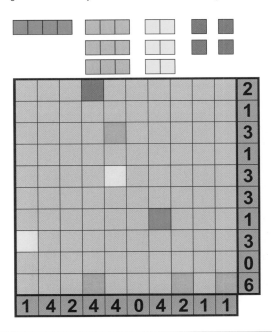

97 Futoshiki 5

Fill in the grid below so that the numbers 1 to 7 appear exactly once in each row and column. Red arrows indicate that a number is greater than its neighbour. For answer see page 273.

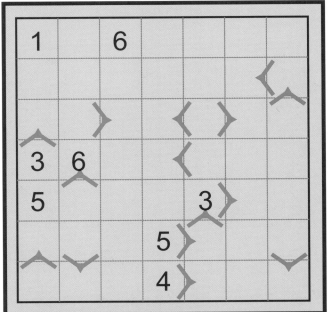

98 Kakuro 3

The empty squares in this grid contain digits from 1 to 9 so that each continuous unbroken line of numbers adds up to the clue value in the filled segment to its left (for horizontal lines) or above it (for vertical lines). No number may be used more than once in any unbroken line. How is the grid filled? Answer on page 293.

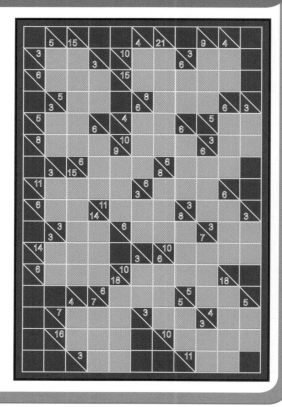

99 Artist's Errors

The artist drawing this scene has made a number of visual, conceptual and logical errors. Can you find them all?
Answer on page 304.

100 Nonogram 3

A number of cells in the grid below are to be shaded. Each row and column may contain one or more continuous lines of shaded cells ('blocks'). The numbers adjacent to the row or column indicate the lengths of the different blocks contained. Blocks are separated from others in the same row or column by at least one empty cell. Where are the shaded cells? A picture will emerge when the cells are shaded correctly. Answer on page 294.

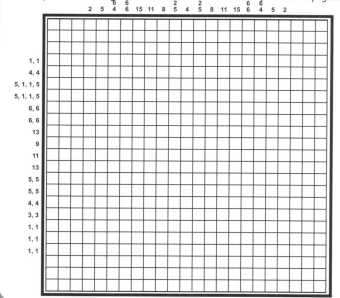

101 Colourminoes 4

In the grid below, each colour has a unique integer value from 0 to 6. The numbers next to each row and column indicate the total value of the cells in that row or column. The values of the cells of the grid correspond in turn to the numbers shown on a half-set of dominoes containing all possible pairs of numbers from (0,0) to (6,6) which has been laid together in one solid rectangle. Dominoes in this rectangle may be placed horizontally or vertically. What number does each colour correspond to, and how are the corresponding dominoes arranged? Answer on page 290.

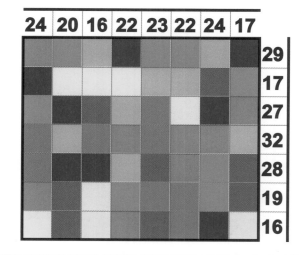

102 Battlehex 3

A number of ships of various sizes are hidden in the hexagonal grid below. The numbers next to each edge indicate how many ship segments are in the rows indicated by the directional arrows. Some ship segments and/or empty water cells have already been filled in. Where are the ships? Answer on page 296.

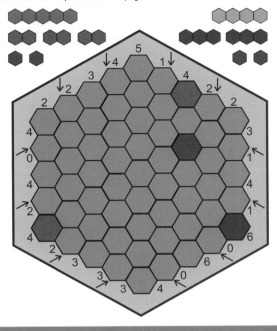

103 Map Colouring 3

The rooms of the grid are coloured so that no two rooms of the same colour ever touch. How are the rooms coloured? Answer on page 295.

104 Sudoku 6

Fill in the grid below so that the numbers 1–9 appear exactly once in each row, column and 3x3 box. For solution see page 272.

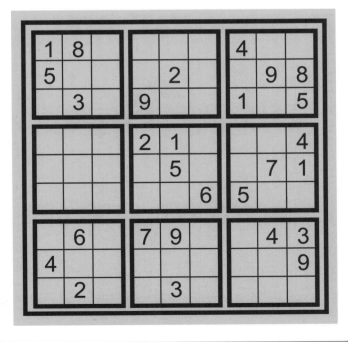

105 Gokigen Naname 5

Each cell in the grid below contains one diagonal line from corner to corner. The numbered circles show how many lines touch that corner. Fill in the grid so that the lines never form a closed circuit of any size. For answer see page 275.

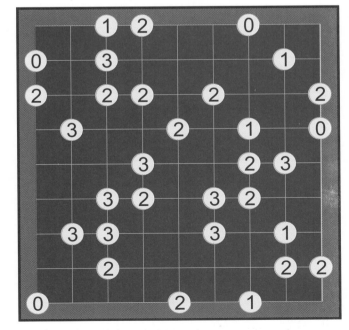

106 Number Link 5

The numbered cells in the grid below indicate the start and end points of single continuous paths. These paths fill the grid completely, and do not branch, cross each other, or touch themselves to form any pool of cells (2x2 or greater).

How are the paths arranged? Answer on page 284.

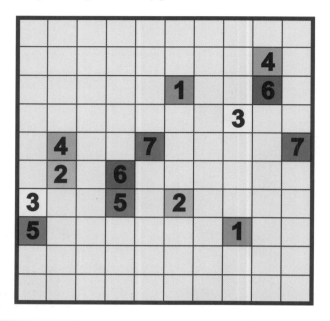

107 Minesweeper 2

The grid below contains a number of bombs hidden in empty squares. Each red flag tells you how many bombs are in the eight cells around it. Where are the bombs? For answer see page 275.

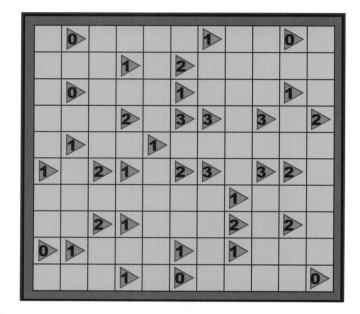

108 Bijutsukan 5

The bright cells and dark cells in the grid below represent corridors and walls respectively. Light sources shine a horizontal and vertical beam of light. A corridor cell becomes illuminated if it is in the same row or column as a light source and there is no wall cell in between them. Place light sources in the corridor cells so that every corridor cell is illuminated, and no light source illuminates another light source. The numbers in some walls tell you how many light sources are touching that wall horizontally or vertically. Answer on page 281.

109 Slitherlink 5

A number of the intersection lines in the grid below have to be joined together to make one single complete loop. The numbers in the cell indicate how many of that cell's sides form part of the loop. Answer on page 278.

	2	3						3
		3	2	3	2	2	3	2
	2	2	1		2	1		2
2				2			2	1
					1		1	3	3
3		3					2		2
3	0	2	2		1		2	2	3
	3				3	3	3	
1			3	1		0		1	3
				3	3	3	2

110 Dominoes 5

A full set of dominoes containing all possible pairs of numbers from (0,0) to (9,9) is laid together in one solid rectangle. The dominoes may be placed horizontally or vertically. The numbers in the grid below indicate the value of each half of each domino. How are the dominoes arranged? Answer on page 279.

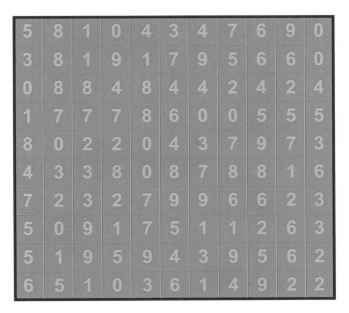

5	8	1	0	4	3	4	7	6	9	0
3	8	1	9	1	7	9	5	6	6	0
0	8	8	4	8	4	4	2	4	2	4
1	7	7	7	8	6	0	0	5	5	5
8	0	2	2	0	4	3	7	9	7	3
4	3	3	8	0	8	7	8	8	1	6
7	2	3	2	7	9	9	6	6	2	3
5	0	9	1	7	5	1	1	2	6	3
5	1	9	5	9	4	3	9	5	6	2
6	5	1	0	3	6	1	4	9	2	2

111 Domino placing 5

A set of dominoes containing all possible pairs of numbers from (0,0) to (7,7) is laid out vertically as shown in the blank grid below so that the larger number of each domino is on the top. The numbers above each column are from the top half of the dominoes in that column. The numbers below each column are from the bottom half of the dominoes in that column. The numbers to the left of each row are from the respective half-dominoes in that row. All the numbers are given to you sorted into descending numerical order. How are the dominoes laid out? Answer on page 282.

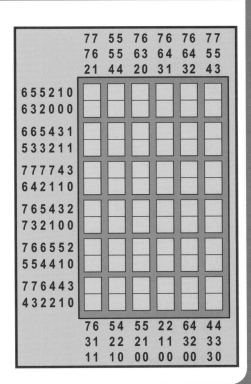

112 Hitori 5

Shade out cells in the grid below so that no number appears more than once in any row or column. Shaded cells cannot touch each other horizontally or vertically, and cannot cut the unshaded cells into two or more groups – the unshaded cells must remain connected horizontally or vertically into one complex branching chain. Which cells are shaded? Answer on page 286.

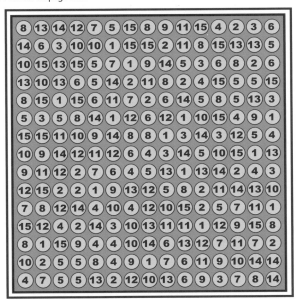

113 Tents 5

The grid below indicates a patch of woodland. Some cells contain grass, and others contain trees. Tents are placed on grass cells so that each tree has one tent next to it horizontally or vertically, although note that tents may be adjacent to more than one tree. No tent may be horizontally, vertically or diagonally adjacent to another tent. The numbers beside each row and column tell you how many tents are in that row or column. Where are the tents? Answer on page 285.

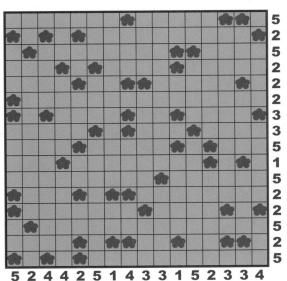

114 Sikaku 5

Divide the grid below into a number of rectangular rooms. Each room must contain exactly one number, equal to the number of cells that make up the room. Answer on page 277.

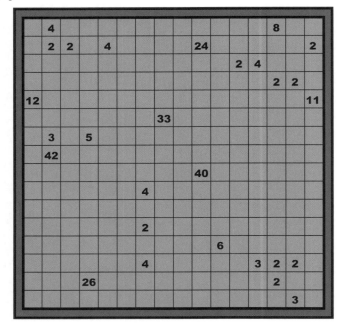

115 Fillomino 5

Each value shown in the grid below is part of a group of cells equal in number to that given value. A '6' is part of a group of six cells, for example. Groups may take any shape, but no two groups of the same size may touch each other horizontally or vertically at any point, and there are no blank cells. Not all groups need have a given value. How are the groups arranged? Answer on page 288.

			4	5	
7		5			5
6					
		2	3	4	
1					3
5					1
2	6				

116 Who's Who 2

From the information given, can you match each mother to her daughter? Answer on p302.

117 Tentai 4

The grid below is divided into a number of shapes. Each shape has a star at its centre, and is made up of one continuous group of cells connected horizontally and/or vertically. The shapes are all symmetrical – they stay the same when rotated by 180 degrees – but may get quite complicated. Where are the shapes? Answer on page 291.

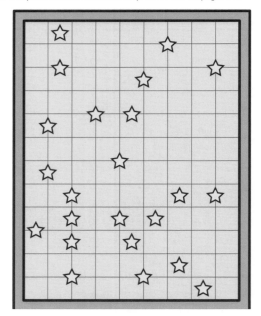

118 Futoshiki 6

Fill in the grid below so that the numbers 1 to 7 appear exactly once in each row and column. Red arrows indicate that a number is greater than its neighbour. For answer see page 274.

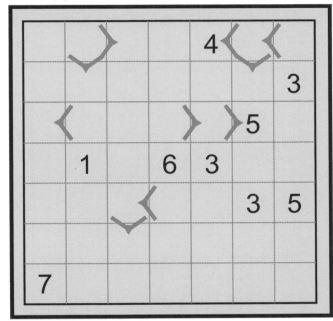

119 Silhouettes 2

Which of the six images fits the silhouette? Answer on page 302.

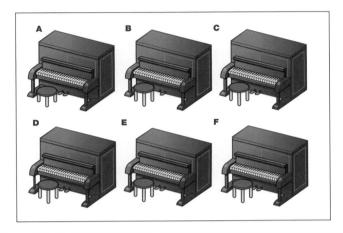

120 Battleships 5

A number of ships of various sizes are hidden in the grid below. The numbers next to each row and column indicate how many ship segments are in that row or column. Some ship segments have already been filled in. Where are the ships? Answer on page 289.

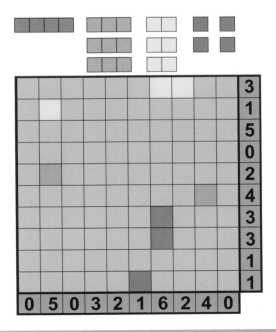

121 Sudoku 7

Fill in the grid below so that the numbers 1–9 appear exactly once in each row, column and 3x3 box. For solution see page 272.

7				1	8			
			6	5	4	8		
	8	5						3
	7			6				
	9					4	6	7
		3	5	7	1			
4			8					
		7		5			1	
			3					

122 Colourminoes 5

In the grid below, each colour has a unique integer value from 0 to 6. The numbers next to each row and column indicate the total value of the cells in that row or column. The values of the cells of the grid correspond in turn to the numbers shown on a half-set of dominoes containing all possible pairs of numbers from (0,0) to (6,6) which has been laid together in one solid rectangle. Dominoes in this rectangle may be placed horizontally or vertically. What number does each colour correspond to, and how are the corresponding dominoes arranged? Answer on page 290.

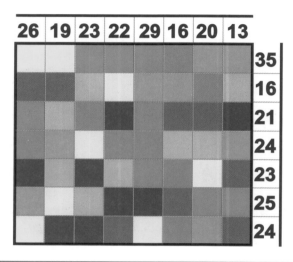

124 Nonogram 4

A number of cells in the grid below are to be shaded. Each row and column may contain one or more continuous lines of shaded cells ('blocks'). The numbers adjacent to the row or column indicate the lengths of the different blocks contained. Blocks are separated from others in the same row or column by at least one empty cell. Where are the shaded cells? A picture will emerge when the cells are shaded correctly. Answer on page 294.

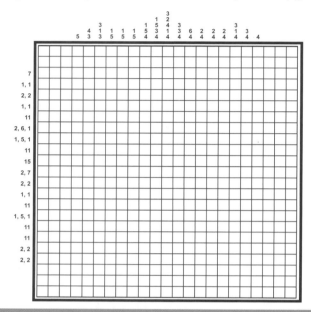

123 Detail Scene 3

The three enlarged squares appear somewhere in the large picture. Can you find them?
Answer on page 299.

125 Kakuro 4

The empty squares in this grid contain digits from 1 to 9 so that each continuous unbroken line of numbers adds up to the clue value in the filled segment to its left (for horizontal lines) or above it (for vertical lines). No number may be used more than once in any unbroken line. How is the grid filled? Answer on page 293.

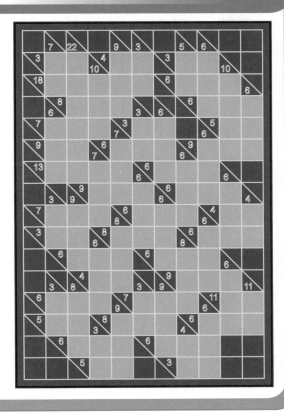

126 Masyu 3

A line passes through some or all of the cells in the grid below in such a way that it forms a single continuous non-intersecting loop. The line always exits a cell by a different side to the one it entered by, and passes through all cells containing a circle. The line travels straight through a cell with a light circle but turns in the previous and/or following cells in its path. The line turns in a cell containing a dark cell, but travels straight through both the previous and following cells in its path. Where is the line? Answer on page 300.

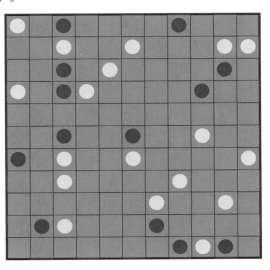

127 Match One 3

Which of the jumbled images is identical to the one presented here? Answer on page 298.

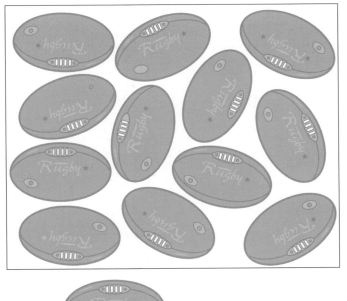

128 Hashiwokakero 3

A number of straight horizontal and vertical bridges connect the islands shown. The number on each island shows how many bridges touch that island. Bridges may not cross each other, and no more than 2 bridges may connect a pair of islands. Where are the bridges? Answer on page 297.

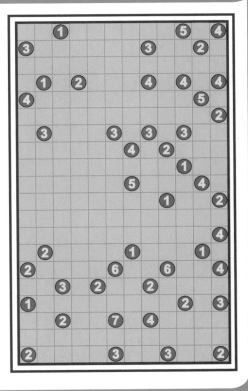

129 Gokigen Naname 6

Each cell in the grid below contains one diagonal line from corner to corner. The numbered circles show how many lines touch that corner. Fill in the grid so that the lines never form a closed circuit of any size. For answer see page 275.

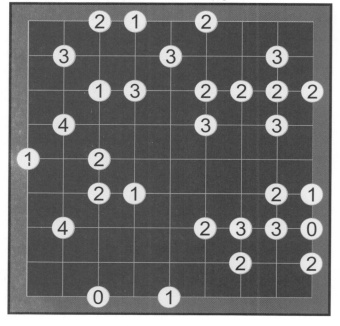

130 Bijutsukan 6

The bright cells and dark cells in the grid below represent corridors and walls respectively. Light sources shine a horizontal and vertical beam of light. A corridor cell becomes illuminated if it is in the same row or column as a light source and there is no wall cell in between them. Place light sources in the corridor cells so that every corridor cell is illuminated, and no light source illuminates another light source. The numbers in some walls tell you how many light sources are touching that wall horizontally or vertically. Answer on page 281.

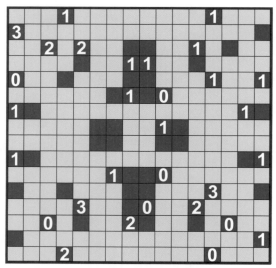

131 Mirror Image 3

Which of the five images below is an identical mirror image of the one above? Answer on page 300.

132 Yudoku 3

Fill in the grid below so that the letters s, p, a, r, k, l, i, n and g appear exactly once in each row, column and 3x3 box. Answer on page 301.

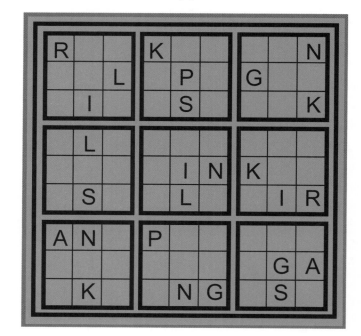

133 Fillomino 6

Each value shown in the grid below is part of a group of cells equal in number to that given value. A '6' is part of a group of six cells, for example. Groups may take any shape, but no two groups of the same size may touch each other horizontally or vertically at any point, and there are no blank cells. Not all groups need have a given value. How are the groups arranged? Answer on page 288.

				3	7	
	4		6			
4	1			6		7
		7	6	6		1
	1				7	
	4		5		1	
	2	1		1		3

134 Suiri 3

Five budget airlines run services around some major european cities, but you do get what you pay for. Given the information below, can you work out which airlines (1) are based in which country (2), what cities they fly to (3), and what the major problem with their service (4) is?

1. Simplejet are based in Holland or Portugal, and fly to Frankfurt or Paris.
2. Herta Airways fly to Barcelona or Prague.
3. The Belgian airline either has very expensive food, or does not allow children.
4. The airline with the cramped seats is either Baby Air or EFD, and is either Portugese or Belgian.
5. The airline that always has delayed departures flies to either Prague or Frankfurt.
6. The airline that flies to London either allows no children or only flies every other day.
7. Connor Airways flies to Barcelona or Frankfurt, is based in Portugal or Italy, and either suffers from delayed departures or very expensive food.
8. EFD flies to London or Frankfurt, and either has cramped seats or delayed departures.
9. There is an airline that is based in Denmark.
Answer on page 298.

135 Dominoes 6

A full set of dominoes containing all possible pairs of numbers from (0,0) to (9,9) is laid together in one solid rectangle. The dominoes may be placed horizontally or vertically. The numbers in the grid below indicate the value of each half of each domino. How are the dominoes arranged? Answer on page 279.

3	8	8	3	4	2	2	3	3	1	5
5	5	5	4	7	1	1	0	4	5	2
4	8	7	4	6	2	7	1	2	9	4
4	1	3	6	4	2	3	1	6	6	6
7	0	0	3	9	6	5	7	0	0	9
0	9	9	3	1	7	8	7	8	3	0
8	1	2	5	8	5	1	9	1	9	1
5	5	6	6	3	6	7	8	3	9	2
0	7	8	9	0	8	0	9	2	0	6
6	4	7	4	7	9	5	4	2	8	2

136 Missing Landmarks 4

Which famous landmark is blurred out of this photo? Answer on page 292.

137 Domino placing 6

A set of dominoes containing all possible pairs of numbers from (0,0) to (7,7) is laid out vertically as shown in the blank grid below so that the larger number of each domino is on the top. The numbers above each column are from the top half of the dominoes in that column.
The numbers below each column are from the bottom half of the dominoes in that column.
The numbers to the left of each row are from the respective half-dominoes in that row.
All the numbers are given to you sorted into descending numerical order. How are the dominoes laid out?
Answer on page 282.

	66	76	77	77	66	77
	53	54	66	75	42	55
	32	30	43	41	21	54
775522
764310
754441
432110
766432
222100
766533
653110
654310
543200
777665
543210
	33	74	66	33	52	54
	20	21	54	31	21	42
	00	00	21	00	11	10

138 Identicals 3

Which pair of images is identical? Answer on page 299.

139 Slitherlink 6

A number of the intersection lines in the grid below have to be joined together to make one single complete loop. The numbers in the cell indicate how many of that cell's sides form part of the loop. Answer on page 278.

140 Number Link 6

The numbered cells in the grid below indicate the start and end points of single continuous paths. These paths fill the grid completely, and do not branch, cross each other, or touch themselves to form any pool of cells (2x2 or greater).
How are the paths arranged? Answer on page 284.

141 Sikaku 6

Divide the grid below into a number of rectangular rooms. Each room must contain exactly one number, equal to the number of cells that make up the room. Answer on page 277.

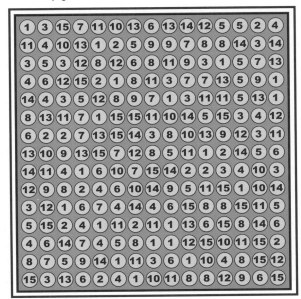

142 Tents 6

The grid below indicates a patch of woodland. Some cells contain grass, and others contain trees. Tents are placed on grass cells so that each tree has one tent next to it horizontally or vertically, although note that tents may be adjacent to more than one tree. No tent may be horizontally, vertically or diagonally adjacent to another tent. The numbers beside each row and column tell you how many tents are in that row or column. Where are the tents? Answer on page 285.

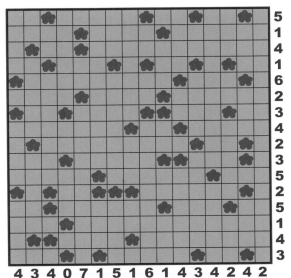

143 Hitori 6

Shade out cells in the grid below so that no number appears more than once in any row or column. Shaded cells cannot touch each other horizontally or vertically, and cannot cut the unshaded cells into two or more groups – the unshaded cells must remain connected horizontally or vertically into one complex branching chain. Which cells are shaded? Answer on page 286.

144 Futoshiki 7

Fill in the grid below so that the numbers 1 to 7 appear exactly once in each row and column. Red arrows indicate that a number is greater than its neighbour.
For answer see page 274.

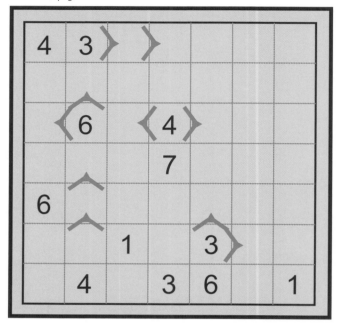

145 Battlehex 4

A number of ships of various sizes are hidden in the hexagonal grid below. The numbers next to each edge indicate how many ship segments are in the rows indicated by the directional arrows. Some ship segments and/or empty water cells have already been filled in. Where are the ships? Answer on page 296.

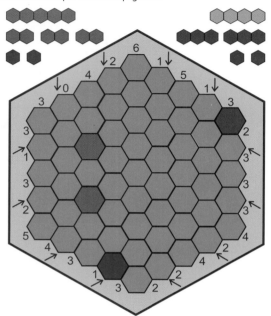

146 Sudoku 8

Fill in the grid below so that the numbers 1–9 appear exactly once in each row, column and 3x3 box. For solution see page 272.

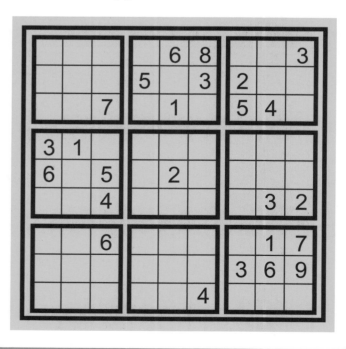

147 Map Colouring 4

The rooms of the grid are coloured so that no two rooms of the same colour ever touch. How are the rooms coloured? Answer on page 295.

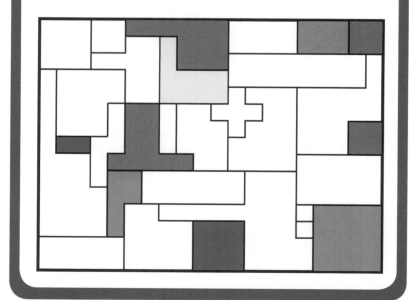

148 Battleships 6

A number of ships of various sizes are hidden in the grid below. The numbers next to each row and column indicate how many ship segments are in that row or column. Some ship segments have already been filled in. Where are the ships? Answer on page 289.

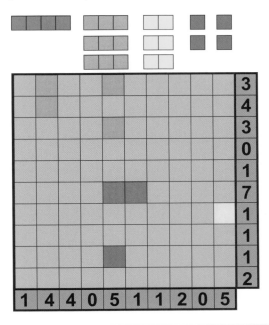

149 Tentai 5

The grid below is divided into a number of shapes. Each shape has a star at its centre, and is made up of one continuous group of cells connected horizontally and/or vertically. The shapes are all symmetrical – they stay the same when rotated by 180 degrees – but may get quite complicated. Where are the shapes? Answer on page 291.

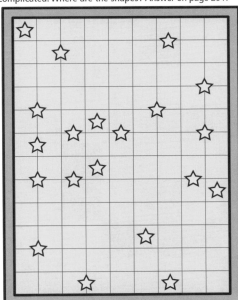

150 Colourminoes 6

In the grid below, each colour has a unique integer value from 0 to 6. The numbers next to each row and column indicate the total value of the cells in that row or column. The values of the cells of the grid correspond in turn to the numbers shown on a half-set of dominoes containing all possible pairs of numbers from (0,0) to (6,6) which has been laid together in one solid rectangle. Dominoes in this rectangle may be placed horizontally or vertically. What number does each colour correspond to, and how are the corresponding dominoes arranged? Answer on page 290.

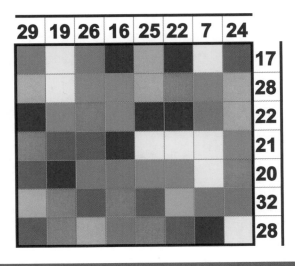

151 Tents 7

The grid below indicates a patch of woodland. Some cells contain grass, and others contain trees. Tents are placed on grass cells so that each tree has one tent next to it horizontally or vertically, although note that tents may be adjacent to more than one tree. No tent may be horizontally, vertically or diagonally adjacent to another tent. The numbers beside each row and column tell you how many tents are in that row or column. Where are the tents? Answer on page 285.

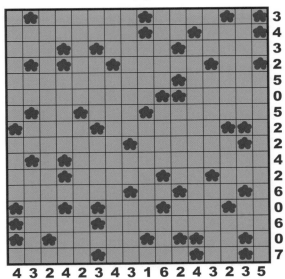

152 Fillomino 7

Each value shown in the grid below is part of a group of cells equal in number to that given value. A '6' is part of a group of six cells, for example. Groups may take any shape, but no two groups of the same size may touch each other horizontally or vertically at any point, and there are no blank cells. Not all groups need have a given value. How are the groups arranged? Answer on page 288.

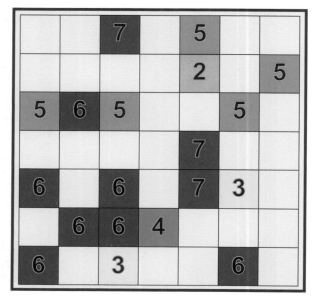

153 Hitori 7

Shade out cells in the grid below so that no number appears more than once in any row or column. Shaded cells cannot touch each other horizontally or vertically, and cannot cut the unshaded cells into two or more groups – the unshaded cells must remain connected horizontally or vertically into one complex branching chain. Which cells are shaded? Answer on page 286.

4	3	8	13	11	9	7	6	10	3	15	6	8	12	12
7	4	9	15	6	8	14	15	11	11	10	1	3	5	12
13	13	7	14	3	7	8	5	7	9	2	12	15	2	11
10	14	2	3	2	7	11	3	8	9	13	15	14	4	11
15	13	11	4	2	3	13	2	11	9	6	4	8	9	14
8	10	8	12	11	1	4	8	15	9	14	4	7	9	3
5	13	7	10	2	3	7	11	1	4	15	8	6	2	2
13	15	12	11	9	1	2	2	6	11	3	9	7	10	
9	2	10	8	14	15	12	13	7	2	12	7	6	11	4
2	8	11	7	11	14	5	10	11	7	6	3	8	10	6
14	5	6	11	7	2	12	4	5	10	8	9	6	6	15
2	2	5	6	13	15	11	3	9	9	10	11	7	8	
8	15	3	15	11	9	8	6	11	4	14	2	10	14	10
3	7	15	9	8	6	13	12	4	14	5	3	11	1	2
11	14	14	1	12	9	14	10	4	5	11	12	13	12	6

154 Bijutsukan 7

The bright cells and dark cells in the grid below represent corridors and walls respectively. Light sources shine a horizontal and vertical beam of light. A corridor cell becomes illuminated if it is in the same row or column as a light source and there is no wall cell in between them. Place light sources in the corridor cells so that every corridor cell is illuminated, and no light source illuminates another light source. The numbers in some walls tell you how many light sources are touching that wall horizontally or vertically. Answer on page 281.

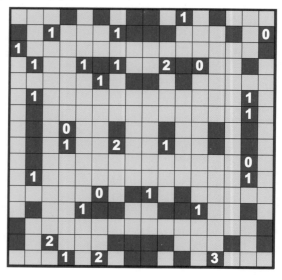

155 Slitherlink 7

A number of the intersection lines in the grid below have to be joined together to make one single complete loop. The numbers in the cell indicate how many of that cell's sides form part of the loop. Answer on page 278.

		3	2	3	1				
2	3	2	2			3	0	3	
	1	1	2		2		3		2
	2		2						
1		1	2	3		2			1
		2				2	2		2
		1				3			
3			3			2	1		
2	0		0		1	3			
	2		3		3	2	3	3	

156 Number Link 7

The numbered cells in the grid below indicate the start and end points of single continuous paths. These paths fill the grid completely, and do not branch, cross each other, or touch themselves to form any pool of cells (2x2 or greater).
How are the paths arranged? Answer on page 284.

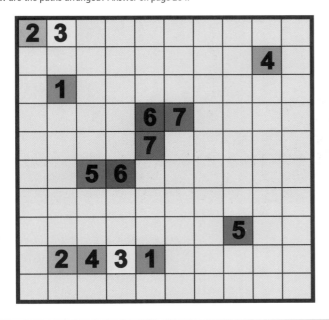

157 Gokigen Naname 7

Each cell in the grid below contains one diagonal line from corner to corner. The numbered circles show how many lines touch that corner. Fill in the grid so that the lines never form a closed circuit of any size. For answer see page 275.

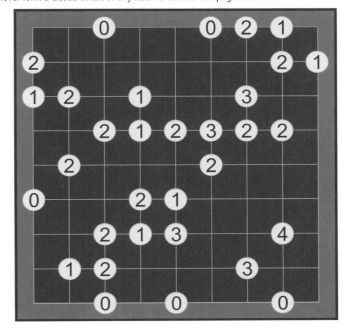

158 Dominoes 7

A full set of dominoes containing all possible pairs of numbers from (0,0) to (9,9) is laid together in one solid rectangle. The dominoes may be placed horizontally or vertically. The numbers in the grid below indicate the value of each half of each domino. How are the dominoes arranged? Answer on page 279.

5	9	0	6	2	8	1	8	0	7	0
0	7	1	5	2	4	1	0	0	5	2
7	4	5	4	3	9	5	5	1	9	2
3	0	1	1	8	6	8	3	3	6	2
6	9	8	9	5	9	8	4	5	2	7
7	5	7	6	2	0	9	2	4	8	2
7	7	7	3	4	6	4	1	4	8	0
0	8	8	6	4	3	2	1	6	8	3
4	3	3	3	7	1	1	1	3	4	9
9	9	6	0	5	9	7	5	2	6	6

159 Domino placing 7

A set of dominoes containing all possible pairs of numbers from (0,0) to (7,7) is laid out vertically as shown in the blank grid below so that the larger number of each domino is on the top. The numbers above each column are from the top half of the dominoes in that column. The numbers below each column are from the bottom half of the dominoes in that column. The numbers to the left of each row are from the respective half-dominoes in that row.

All the numbers are given to you sorted into descending numerical order. How are the dominoes laid out? Answer on page 282.

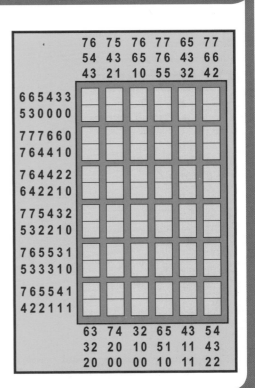

47

160 Sikaku 7

Divide the grid below into a number of rectangular rooms. Each room must contain exactly one number, equal to the number of cells that make up the room. Answer on page 277.

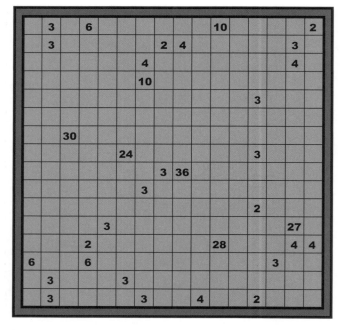

161 Missing Landmarks 5

Which famous landmark is blurred out of this photo? Answer on page 292.

162 Futoshiki 8

Fill in the grid below so that the numbers 1 to 7 appear exactly once in each row and column. Red arrows indicate that a number is greater than its neighbour. For answer see page 274.

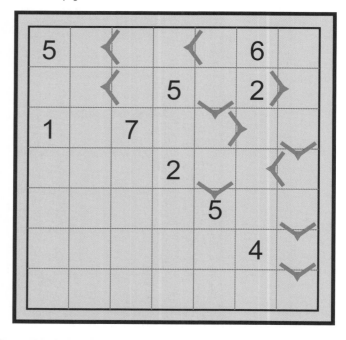

163 Sudoku 9

Fill in the grid below so that the numbers 1–9 appear exactly once in each row, column and 3x3 box. For solution see page 272.

								7
4								
3			4		7	5		
				5				1
6		8	2	1				
	7					1	9	
	3			9				6
	4	5			2	7		
				1			5	8
7				5		3	2	

164 Nonogram 5

A number of cells in the grid below are to be shaded. Each row and column may contain one or more continuous lines of shaded cells ('blocks'). The numbers adjacent to the row or column indicate the lengths of the different blocks contained. Blocks are separated from others in the same row or column by at least one empty cell. Where are the shaded cells? A picture will emerge when the cells are shaded correctly. Answer on page 294.

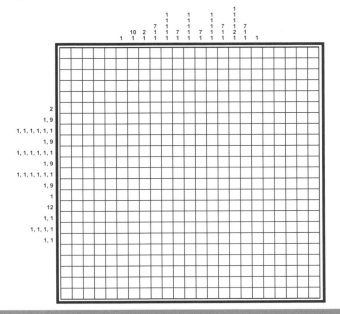

165 Kakuro 5

The empty squares in this grid contain digits from 1 to 9 so that each continuous unbroken line of numbers adds up to the clue value in the filled segment to its left (for horizontal lines) or above it (for vertical lines). No number may be used more than once in any unbroken line. How is the grid filled? Answer on page 293.

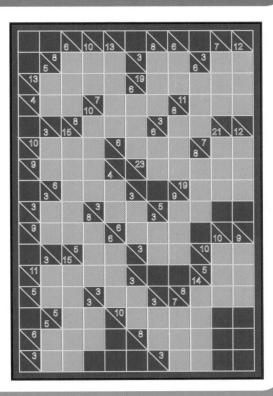

166 Battleships 7

A number of ships of various sizes are hidden in the grid below. The numbers next to each row and column indicate how many ship segments are in that row or column. Some ship segments have already been filled in. Where are the ships? Answer on page 289.

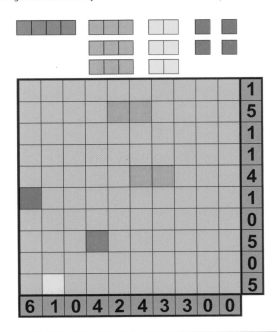

167 Colourminoes 7

In the grid below, each colour has a unique integer value from 0 to 6. The numbers next to each row and column indicate the total value of the cells in that row or column. The values of the cells of the grid correspond in turn to the numbers shown on a half-set of dominoes containing all possible pairs of numbers from (0,0) to (6,6) which has been laid together in one solid rectangle. Dominoes in this rectangle may be placed horizontally or vertically. What number does each colour correspond to, and how are the corresponding dominoes arranged? Answer on page 290.

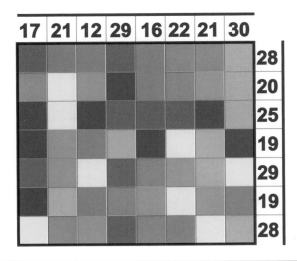

168 Futoshiki 9

Fill in the grid below so that the numbers 1 to 7 appear exactly once in each row and column. Red arrows indicate that a number is greater than its neighbour.
For answer see page 274.

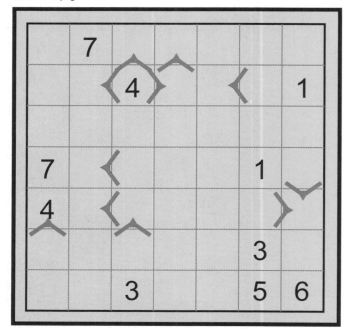

169 Who's Who 3

From the information given, can you match each father to his child? Answer on p302.

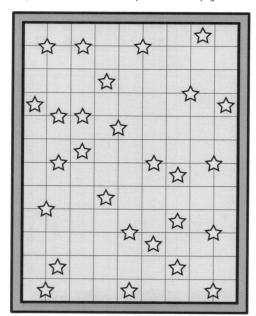

170 Silhouettes 3

Which of the six images fits the silhouette? Answer on page 302.

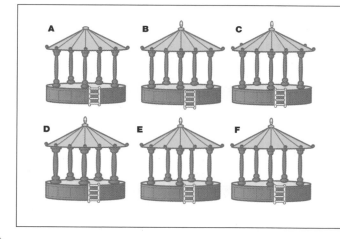

171 Tentai 6

The grid below is divided into a number of shapes. Each shape has a star at its centre, and is made up of one continuous group of cells connected horizontally and/or vertically. The shapes are all symmetrical – they stay the same when rotated by 180 degrees – but may get quite complicated. Where are the shapes? Answer on page 291.

172 Detail Scene 4

The three enlarged squares appear somewhere in the large picture. Can you find them? Answer on page 299.

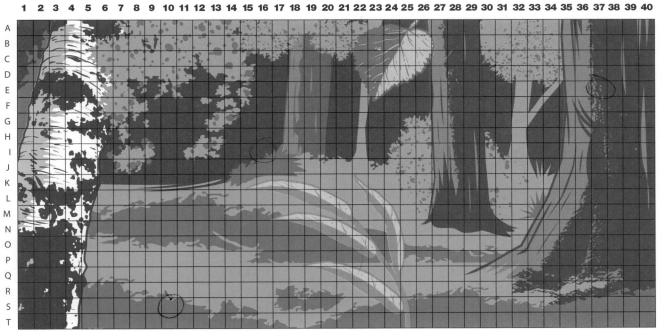

173 Hashiwokakero 4

A number of straight horizontal and vertical bridges connect the islands shown. The number on each island shows how many bridges touch that island. Bridges may not cross each other, and no more than 2 bridges may connect a pair of islands.
Where are the bridges?
Answer on page 297.

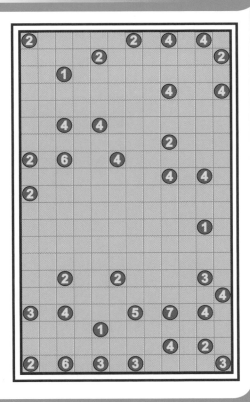

174 Spot the Set

There are four different versions of the picture in the group below, each one reproduced three times. Can you identify the four sets?
Answer on page 304.

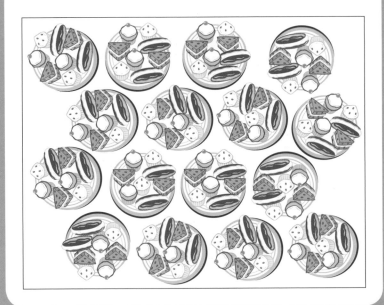

175 Sudoku 10

Fill in the grid below so that the numbers 1–9 appear exactly once in each row, column and 3x3 box. For solution see page 272.

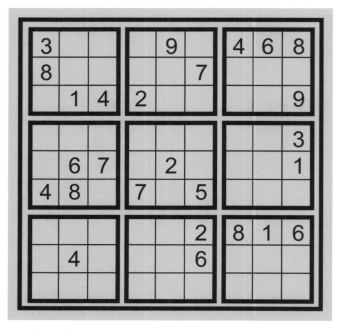

176 Sikaku 8

Divide the grid below into a number of rectangular rooms. Each room must contain exactly one number, equal to the number of cells that make up the room. Answer on page 277.

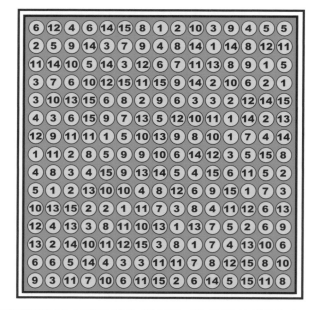

177 Fillomino 8

Each value shown in the grid below is part of a group of cells equal in number to that given value. A '6' is part of a group of six cells, for example. Groups may take any shape, but no two groups of the same size may touch each other horizontally or vertically at any point, and there are no blank cells. Not all groups need have a given value. How are the groups arranged? Answer on page 288.

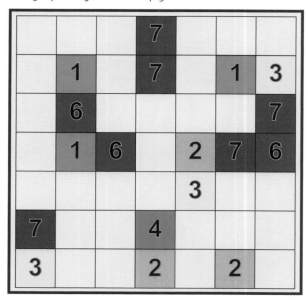

178 Hitori 8

Shade out cells in the grid below so that no number appears more than once in any row or column. Shaded cells cannot touch each other horizontally or vertically, and cannot cut the unshaded cells into two or more groups – the unshaded cells must remain connected horizontally or vertically into one complex branching chain. Which cells are shaded? Answer on page 286.

179 Gokigen Naname 8

Each cell in the grid below contains one diagonal line from corner to corner. The numbered circles show how many lines touch that corner. Fill in the grid so that the lines never form a closed circuit of any size. For answer see page 275.

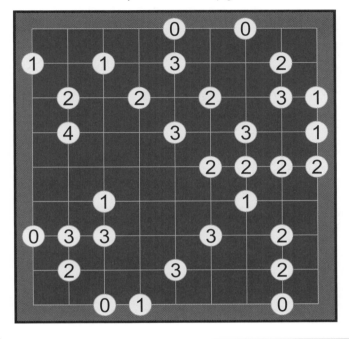

180 Killer Sudoku 2

Fill in the grid below so that the numbers 1–9 appear exactly once in each row, column and 3x3 block, and that the numbers in each dotted room add up to the value in its top right corner. Answer on page 303.

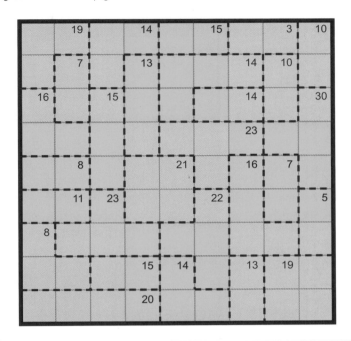

181 Spot the Difference

There are eight differences between the two pictures. Can you find them all?
Answer on p302.

182 Match One 4

Which of the jumbled images is identical to the one presented here? Answer on page 298.

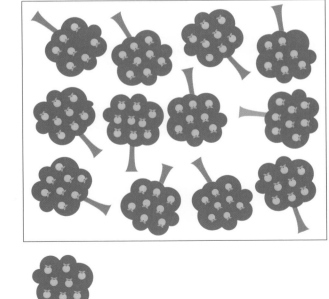

183 Domino placing 8

A set of dominoes containing all possible pairs of numbers from (0,0) to (7,7) is laid out vertically as shown in the blank grid below so that the larger number of each domino is on the top. T he numbers above each column are from the top half of the dominoes in that column.

The numbers below each column are from the bottom half of the dominoes in that column. The numbers to the left of each row are from the respective half-dominoes in that row.

All the numbers are given to you sorted into descending numerical order. How are the dominoes laid out? Answer on page 282.

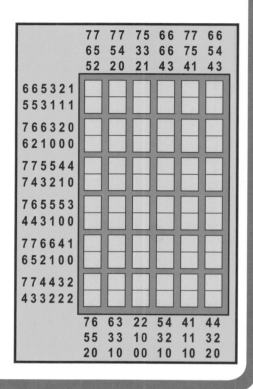

184 Yudoku 4

Fill in the grid below so that the letters s, p, a, r, k, l, i, n and g appear exactly once in each row, column and 3x3 box. Answer on page 301.

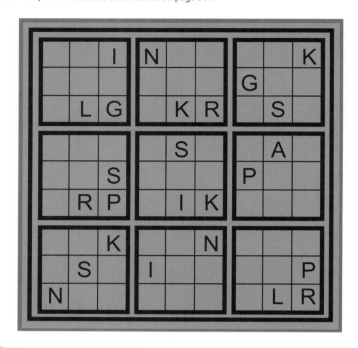

185 Dominoes 8

A full set of dominoes containing all possible pairs of numbers from (0,0) to (9,9) is laid together in one solid rectangle. The dominoes may be placed horizontally or vertically. The numbers in the grid below indicate the value of each half of each domino. How are the dominoes arranged? Answer on page 279.

7	8	9	0	9	3	7	6	9	5	7
2	7	9	5	0	0	3	9	6	0	4
5	1	9	5	8	6	6	4	8	1	9
2	5	1	2	2	1	4	3	5	8	2
3	1	7	5	2	4	8	1	6	8	7
6	1	0	2	7	0	5	3	5	6	2
4	6	9	1	0	7	7	2	8	3	6
5	1	7	2	0	3	3	9	2	1	0
9	3	9	6	7	3	3	4	8	6	4
4	5	4	0	4	4	8	8	8	1	0

186 Slitherlink 8

A number of the intersection lines in the grid below have to be joined together to make one single complete loop. The numbers in the cell indicate how many of that cell's sides form part of the loop. Answer on page 278.

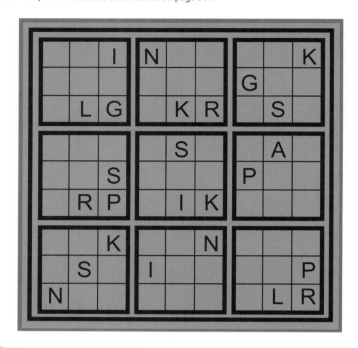

187 Battlehex 5

A number of ships of various sizes are hidden in the hexagonal grid below. The numbers next to each edge indicate how many ship segments are in the rows indicated by the directional arrows. Some ship segments and/or empty water cells have already been filled in. Where are the ships? Answer on page 296.

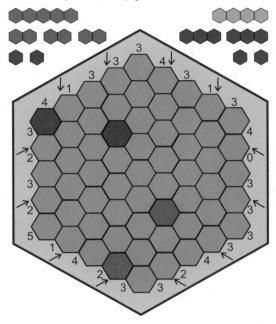

189 Map Colouring 5

RYBu

The rooms of the grid are coloured so that no two rooms of the same colour ever touch. How are the rooms coloured? Answer on page 295.

188 Suiri 4

A group of Glaswegian youths are eating from a fish & chip shop. From the information below, can you tell what kind of fish (2) each boy (1) had with their chips, what extra deep-fried dish (3) they bought, and how much (4) they paid?

1. Morton paid more than the boy who had a plaice supper.
2. The boy who ordered deep-fried bread paid less than the boy who didn't have a sole supper, but who wanted a deep-fried Mars bar.
3. Either Iain ate the sole supper and Alistair had a deep-fried pizza, or Morton ate the sole supper and Iain had the deep-fried pizza.
4. Neal, who got a hunk of deep-fried cheese, paid 50p more than the boy who had a haddock supper, who was either Dougal or Morton. The haddock supper meal cost more than the cod supper meal.
5. Either Dougal or Morton paid £5.50 and has a deep-fried Mars bar.
6. Someone had deep-fried scraps.
7. The amounts paid for the fish suppers were £4.00, £4.50, £5.00, £5.50 and £6.00.
Answer on page 298.

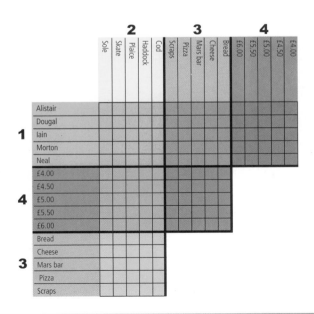

| | | **2** | | | | **3** | | | | | **4** | | | | |
	Sole	Skate	Plaice	Haddock	Cod	Scraps	Pizza	Mars bar	Cheese	Bread	£6.00	£5.50	£5.00	£4.50	£4.00
1 Alistair															
Dougal															
Iain															
Morton															
Neal															
4 £4.00															
£4.50															
£5.00															
£5.50															
£6.00															
3 Bread															
Cheese															
Mars bar															
Pizza															
Scraps															

190 Differences

Each copy of the picture has one flaw that none of the others share. Can you find them all? Answer on page 304.

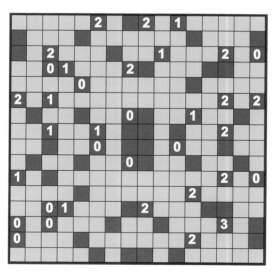

191 Identicals 4

Which pair of images is identical? Answer on page 300.

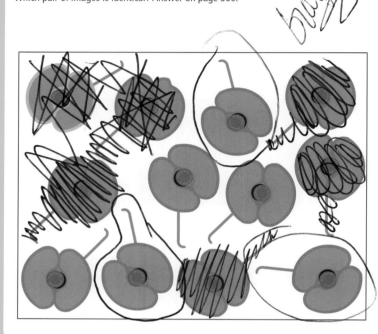

192 Bijutsukan 8

The bright cells and dark cells in the grid below represent corridors and walls respectively. Light sources shine a horizontal and vertical beam of light. A corridor cell becomes illuminated if it is in the same row or column as a light source and there is no wall cell in between them. Place light sources in the corridor cells so that every corridor cell is illuminated, and no light source illuminates another light source. The numbers in some walls tell you how many light sources are touching that wall horizontally or vertically. Answer on page 281.

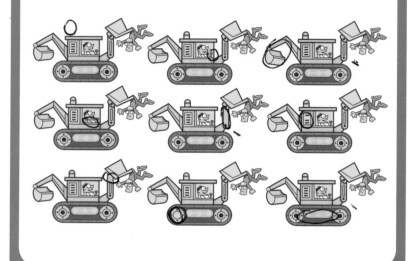

193 Mirror Image 4

Which of the five images below is an identical mirror image of the one above? Answer on page 300.

194 Super Sudoku 2

Fill in the grid below so that the digits 1, 2, 3, 4, 5, 6, 7, 8, 9, a, b, c, d, e, f and g appear exactly once in each row and column. Answer on page 303.

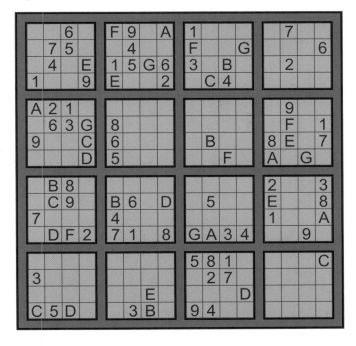

195 Masyu 4

A line passes through some or all of the cells in the grid below in such a way that it forms a single continuous non-intersecting loop. The line always exits a cell by a different side to the one it entered by, and passes through all cells containing a circle. The line travels straight through a cell with a light circle but turns in the previous and/or following cells in its path. The line turns in a cell containing a dark cell, but travels straight through both the previous and following cells in its path. Where is the line? Answer on page 300.

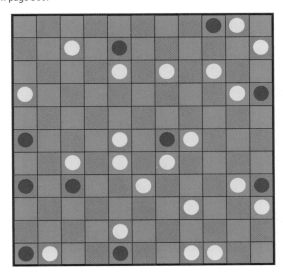

196 Number Link 8

The numbered cells in the grid below indicate the start and end points of single continuous paths. These paths fill the grid completely, and do not branch, cross each other, or touch themselves to form any pool of cells (2x2 or greater). How are the paths arranged? Answer on page 284.

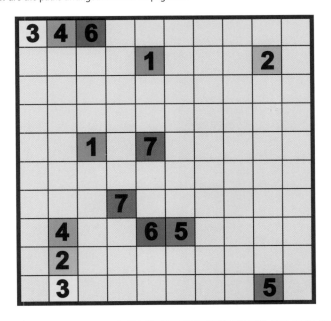

197 Samurai Sudoku 2

Fill in each 9x9 grid below so that the numbers 1–9 appear exactly once in each row, column and 3x3 block. Numbers in overlapping blocks count identically towards both grids. Answer on page 303.

198 Tents 8

The grid below indicates a patch of woodland. Some cells contain grass, and others contain trees. Tents are placed on grass cells so that each tree has one tent next to it horizontally or vertically, although note that tents may be adjacent to more than one tree. No tent may be horizontally, vertically or diagonally adjacent to another tent. The numbers beside each row and column tell you how many tents are in that row or column. Where are the tents? Answer on page 285.

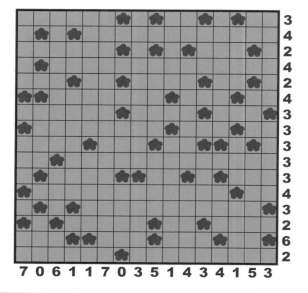

199 Battleships 8

A number of ships of various sizes are hidden in the grid below. The numbers next to each row and column indicate how many ship segments are in that row or column. Some ship segments have already been filled in. Where are the ships? Answer on page 289.

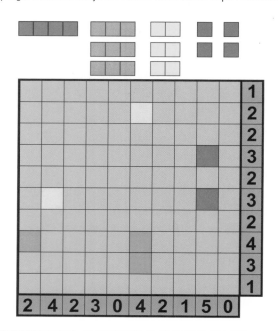

200 Missing Landmarks 6

Which famous landmark is blurred out of this photo? Answer on page 292.

201 Kin-kon-kan 2

In the grid below, some cells contain diagonal mirrors which reflect light on both sides. One mirror is hidden in each room.

The coloured boxes around the edge indicate the start and finish of a coloured beam of light fired into the grid. These beams always travel in a straight line, but are reflected through a 90-degree angle when hitting a mirror. The number in each box shows how many grid cells its beam of light travels through before exiting again.

Where are the mirrors, and how are they placed? For solution see page 273.

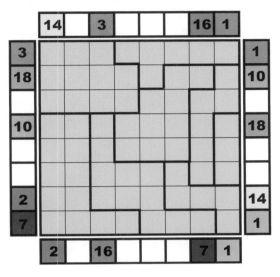

202 Futoshiki 10

Fill in the grid below so that the numbers 1 to 7 appear exactly once in each row and column. Red arrows indicate that a number is greater than its neighbour.

For answer see page 274.

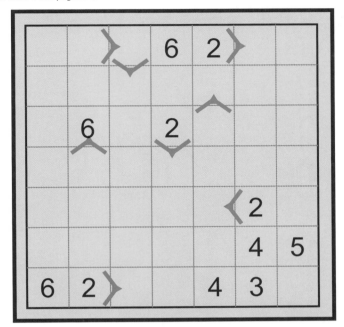

203 Sudoku 11

Fill in the grid below so that the numbers 1–9 appear exactly once in each row, column and 3x3 box. For solution see page 272.

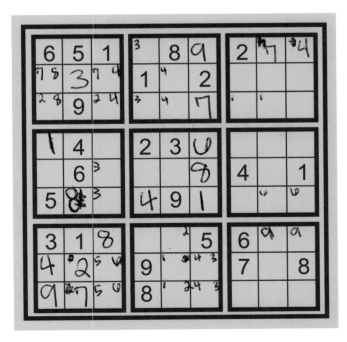

204 Nonogram 6

A number of cells in the grid below are to be shaded. Each row and column may contain one or more continuous lines of shaded cells ('blocks'). The numbers adjacent to the row or column indicate the lengths of the different blocks contained. Blocks are separated from others in the same row or column by at least one empty cell. Where are the shaded cells? A picture will emerge when the cells are shaded correctly. Answer on page 294.

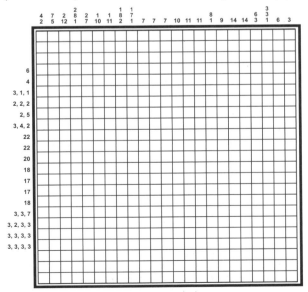

205 Artist's Errors

The artist drawing this scene has made a number of visual, conceptual and logical errors. Can you find them all?
Answer on page 304.

206 Kakuro 6

The empty squares in this grid contain digits from 1 to 9 so that each continuous unbroken line of numbers adds up to the clue value in the filled segment to its left (for horizontal lines) or above it (for vertical lines). No number may be used more than once in any unbroken line. How is the grid filled? Answer on page 293.

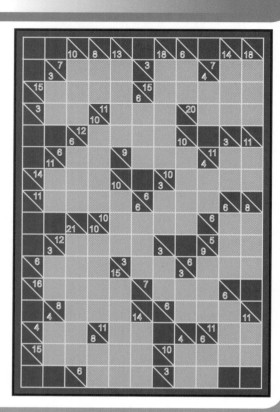

207 Colourminoes 8

In the grid below, each colour has a unique integer value from 0 to 6. The numbers next to each row and column indicate the total value of the cells in that row or column. The values of the cells of the grid correspond in turn to the numbers shown on a half-set of dominoes containing all possible pairs of numbers from (0,0) to (6,6) which has been laid together in one solid rectangle. Dominoes in this rectangle may be placed horizontally or vertically. What number does each colour correspond to, and how are the corresponding dominoes arranged? Answer on page 290.

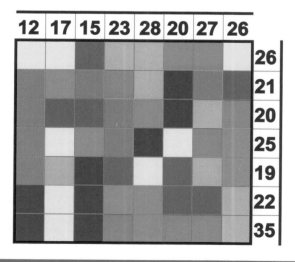

208 Slitherlink 9

A number of the intersection lines in the grid below have to be joined together to make one single complete loop. The numbers in the cell indicate how many of that cell's sides form part of the loop. Answer on page 278.

209 Number Link 9

The numbered cells in the grid below indicate the start and end points of single continuous paths. These paths fill the grid completely, and do not branch, cross each other, or touch themselves to form any pool of cells (2x2 or greater).

How are the paths arranged? Answer on page 284.

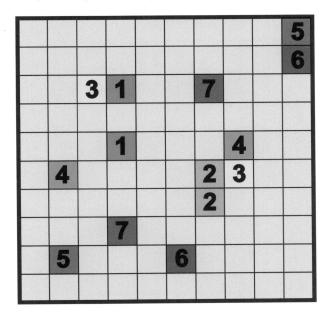

210 Domino placing 9

A set of dominoes containing all possible pairs of numbers from (0,0) to (7,7) is laid out vertically as shown in the blank grid below so that the larger number of each domino is on the top. The numbers above each column are from the top half of the dominoes in that column. The numbers below each column are from the bottom half of the dominoes in that column. The numbers to the left of each row are from the respective half-dominoes in that row. All the numbers are given to you sorted into descending numerical order. How are the dominoes laid out?
 Answer on page 282.

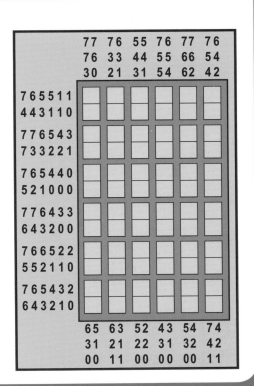

211 Fillomino 9

Each value shown in the grid below is part of a group of cells equal in number to that given value. A '6' is part of a group of six cells, for example. Groups may take any shape, but no two groups of the same size may touch each other horizontally or vertically at any point, and there are no blank cells. Not all groups need have a given value. How are the groups arranged? Answer on page 288.

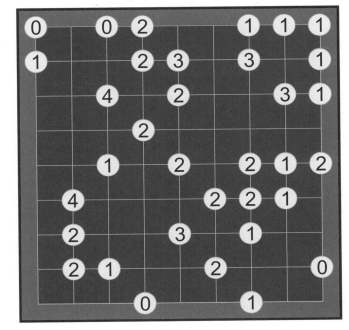

212 Gokigen Naname 9

Each cell in the grid below contains one diagonal line from corner to corner. The numbered circles show how many lines touch that corner. Fill in the grid so that the lines never form a closed circuit of any size. For answer see page 275.

213 Sikaku 9

Divide the grid below into a number of rectangular rooms. Each room must contain exactly one number, equal to the number of cells that make up the room.
Answer on page 277.

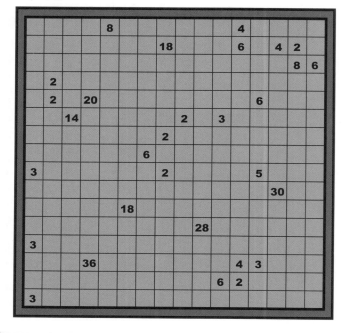

214 Tents 9

The grid below indicates a patch of woodland. Some cells contain grass, and others contain trees. Tents are placed on grass cells so that each tree has one tent next to it horizontally or vertically, although note that tents may be adjacent to more than one tree. No tent may be horizontally, vertically or diagonally adjacent to another tent. The numbers beside each row and column tell you how many tents are in that row or column. Where are the tents? Answer on page 285.

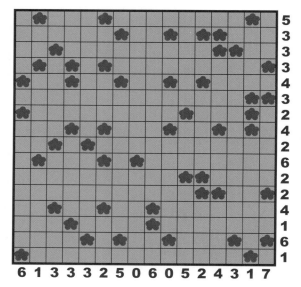

215 Dominoes 9

A full set of dominoes containing all possible pairs of numbers from (0,0) to (9,9) is laid together in one solid rectangle. The dominoes may be placed horizontally or vertically. The numbers in the grid below indicate the value of each half of each domino. How are the dominoes arranged? Answer on page 279.

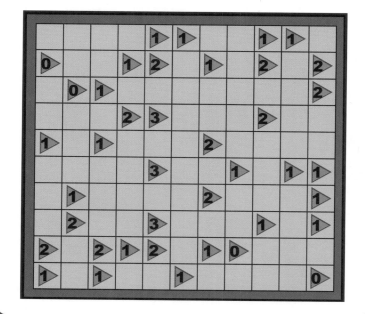

216 Minesweeper 3

The grid below contains a number of bombs hidden in empty squares. Each red flag tells you how many bombs are in the eight cells around it. Where are the bombs?
For answer see page 275.

217 Hitori 9

Shade out cells in the grid below so that no number appears more than once in any row or column. Shaded cells cannot touch each other horizontally or vertically, and cannot cut the unshaded cells into two or more groups – the unshaded cells must remain connected horizontally or vertically into one complex branching chain. Which cells are shaded? Answer on page 286.

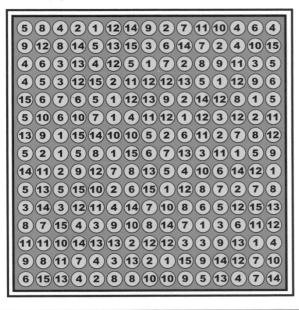

218 Bijutsukan 9

The bright cells and dark cells in the grid below represent corridors and walls respectively. Light sources shine a horizontal and vertical beam of light. A corridor cell becomes illuminated if it is in the same row or column as a light source and there is no wall cell in between them. Place light sources in the corridor cells so that every corridor cell is illuminated, and no light source illuminates another light source. The numbers in some walls tell you how many light sources are touching that wall horizontally or vertically. Answer on page 281.

219 Tentai 7

The grid below is divided into a number of shapes. Each shape has a star at its centre, and is made up of one continuous group of cells connected horizontally and/or vertically. The shapes are all symmetrical – they stay the same when rotated by 180 degrees – but may get quite complicated. Where are the shapes? Answer on page 291.

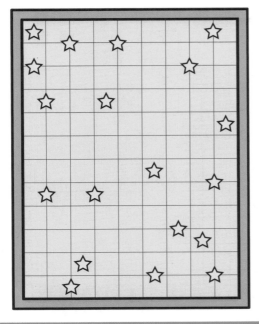

220 Sudoku 12

Fill in the grid below so that the numbers 1–9 appear exactly once in each row, column and 3x3 box. For solution see page 272.

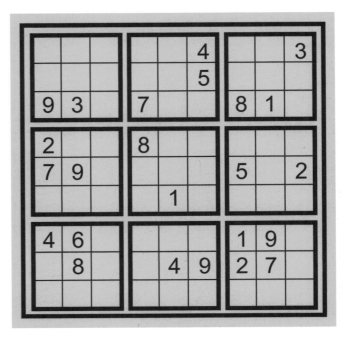

221 Battlehex 6

A number of ships of various sizes are hidden in the hexagonal grid below. The numbers next to each edge indicate how many ship segments are in the rows indicated by the directional arrows. Some ship segments and/or empty water cells have already been filled in. Where are the ships? Answer on page 296.

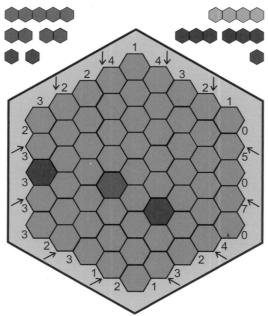

222 Map Colouring 6

The rooms of the grid are coloured so that no two rooms of the same colour ever touch. How are the rooms coloured? Answer on page 295.

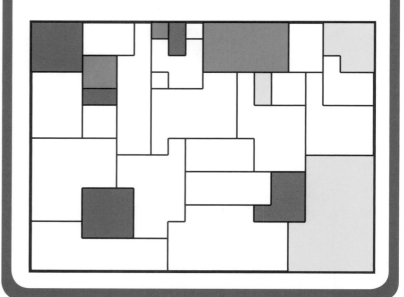

223 Futoshiki 11

Fill in the grid below so that the numbers 1 to 7 appear exactly once in each row and column. Red arrows indicate that a number is greater than its neighbour. For answer see page 274.

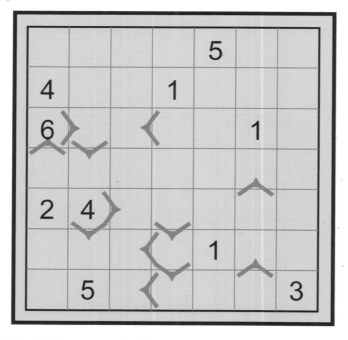

224 Battleships 9

A number of ships of various sizes are hidden in the grid below. The numbers next to each row and column indicate how many ship segments are in that row or column. Some ship segments have already been filled in. Where are the ships? Answer on page 289.

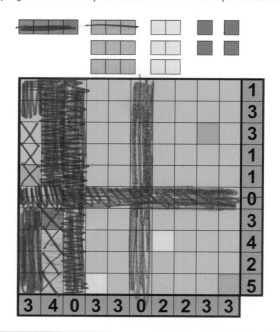

225 Missing Landmarks 7

Which famous landmark is blurred out of this photo? Answer on page 292.

226 Identicals 5

Which pair of images is identical?
Answer on page 299.

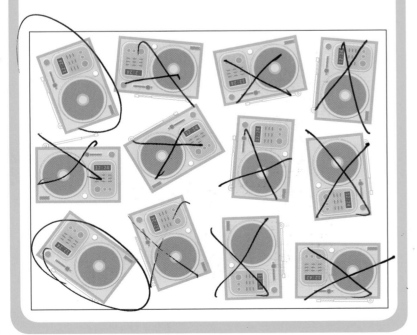

227 Hitori 10

Shade out cells in the grid below so that no number appears more than once in any row or column. Shaded cells cannot touch each other horizontally or vertically, and cannot cut the unshaded cells into two or more groups – the unshaded cells must remain connected horizontally or vertically into one complex branching chain. Which cells are shaded? Answer on page 286.

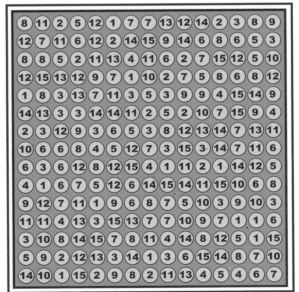

228 Hashiwokakero 5

A number of straight horizontal and vertical bridges connect the islands shown. The number on each island shows how many bridges touch that island. Bridges may not cross each other, and no more than 2 bridges may connect a pair of islands.
Where are the bridges?
Answer on page 297.

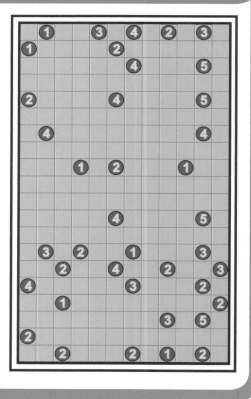

229 Yudoku 5

Fill in the grid below so that the letters s, p, a, r, k, l, i, n and g appear exactly once in each row, column and 3x3 box. Answer on page 301.

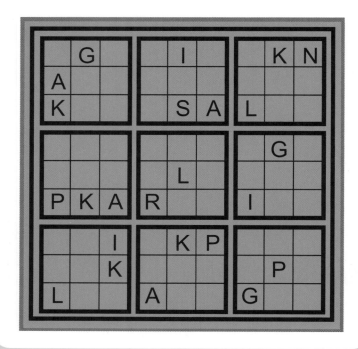

230 Masyu 5

A line passes through some or all of the cells in the grid below in such a way that it forms a single continuous non-intersecting loop. The line always exits a cell by a different side to the one it entered by, and passes through all cells containing a circle. The line travels straight through a cell with a light circle but turns in the previous and/or following cells in its path. The line turns in a cell containing a dark cell, but travels straight through both the previous and following cells in its path. Where is the line?
Answer on page 300.

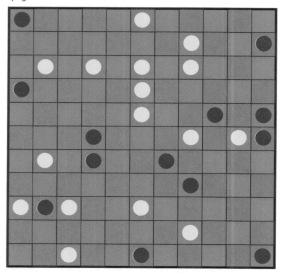

231 Fillomino 10

Each value shown in the grid below is part of a group of cells equal in number to that given value. A '6' is part of a group of six cells, for example. Groups may take any shape, but no two groups of the same size may touch each other horizontally or vertically at any point, and there are no blank cells. Not all groups need have a given value.
How are the groups arranged? Answer on page 288.

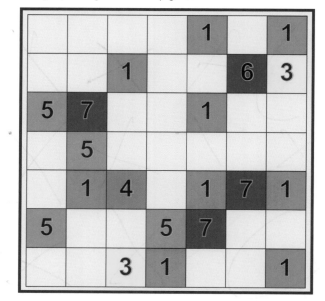

232 Suiri 5

Back in 1939, several former public schoolboys trained to be air-force pilots. None of them made it, because of persistents errors during training. From the information below, can you work out which man (1) went to which school (2), what his nickname was (3), and why he failed training(4)?

1. The man known as Lasher went to Winchester. He was neither Leonard nor Justin.
2. The Shrewsbury man couldn't aim his guns. He was not Adam, who was known as Puffin.
3. The pilot who couldn't navigate went to Harrow.
4. Sebastian was known as Ginger, and he could aim his guns perfectly well.
5. The pilot who kept getting take-off wrong was neither James nor Sebastian.
6. The man known as Toasty did not go to Eton.
7. Leonard couldn't master aerial manoeuvres, and was not known as Loose-Head.
8. One pilot could never land properly.
9. One man went to Rugby.
Answer on page 298.

233 Slitherlink 10

A number of the intersection lines in the grid below have to be joined together to make one single complete loop. The numbers in the cell indicate how many of that cell's sides form part of the loop. Answer on page 278.

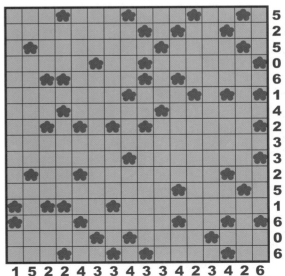

234 Tents 10

The grid below indicates a patch of woodland. Some cells contain grass, and others contain trees. Tents are placed on grass cells so that each tree has one tent next to it horizontally or vertically, although note that tents may be adjacent to more than one tree. No tent may be horizontally, vertically or diagonally adjacent to another tent. The numbers beside each row and column tell you how many tents are in that row or column. Where are the tents? Answer on page 285.

235 Mirror Image 5

Which of the five images below is an identical mirror image of the one above?
Answer on page 300.

A   B   C   D   E

236 Sikaku 10

Divide the grid below into a number of rectangular rooms. Each room must contain exactly one number, equal to the number of cells that make up the room. Answer on page 277.

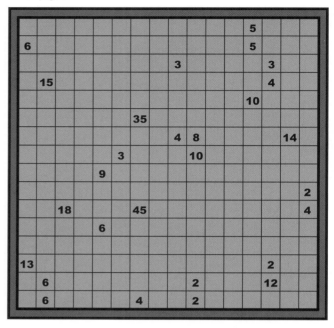

237 Match One 5

Which of the jumbled images is identical to the one presented here? Answer on page 298.

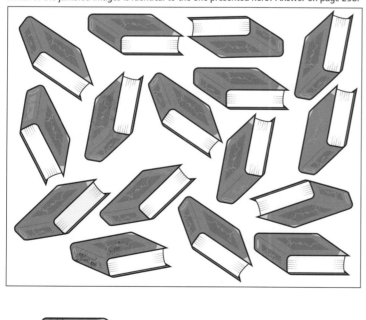

238 Domino placing 10

A set of dominoes containing all possible pairs of numbers from (0,0) to (7,7) is laid out vertically as shown in the blank grid below so that the larger number of each domino is on the top. The numbers above each column are from the top half of the dominoes in that column. The numbers below each column are from the bottom half of the dominoes in that column. The numbers to the left of each row are from the respective half-dominoes in that row.

All the numbers are given to you sorted into descending numerical order. How are the dominoes laid out? Answer on page 282.

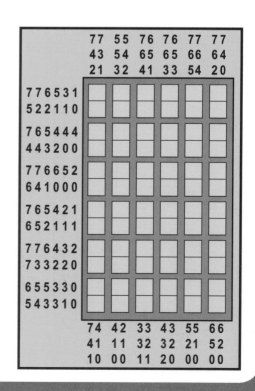

239 Gokigen Naname 10

Each cell in the grid below contains one diagonal line from corner to corner. The numbered circles show how many lines touch that corner. Fill in the grid so that the lines never form a closed circuit of any size. For answer see page 275.

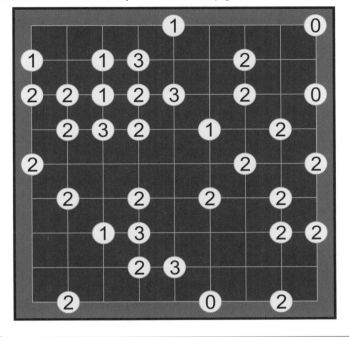

240 Bijutsukan 10

The bright cells and dark cells in the grid below represent corridors and walls respectively. Light sources shine a horizontal and vertical beam of light. A corridor cell becomes illuminated if it is in the same row or column as a light source and there is no wall cell in between them. Place light sources in the corridor cells so that every corridor cell is illuminated, and no light source illuminates another light source. The numbers in some walls tell you how many light sources are touching that wall horizontally or vertically. Answer on page 281.

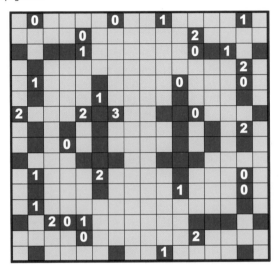

241 Number Link 10

The numbered cells in the grid below indicate the start and end points of single continuous paths. These paths fill the grid completely, and do not branch, cross each other, or touch themselves to form any pool of cells (2x2 or greater).
How are the paths arranged? Answer on page 284.

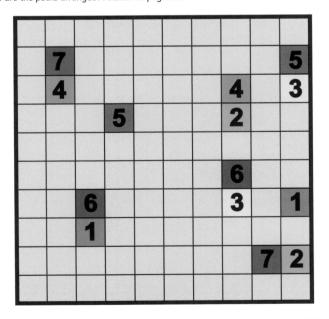

242 Dominoes 10

A full set of dominoes containing all possible pairs of numbers from (0,0) to (9,9) is laid together in one solid rectangle. The dominoes may be placed horizontally or vertically. The numbers in the grid below indicate the value of each half of each domino. How are the dominoes arranged? Answer on page 279.

1	9	3	4	7	5	9	6	5	4	1
8	9	0	9	4	8	0	0	6	6	7
7	9	6	3	6	5	5	5	3	2	0
6	2	8	9	9	6	4	9	0	4	2
5	2	3	0	4	3	4	1	5	7	2
5	4	1	6	8	1	4	8	7	7	1
3	1	7	2	2	6	8	1	0	7	6
3	8	9	1	1	7	3	1	5	2	3
0	9	8	5	5	2	0	8	7	9	0
3	2	2	3	7	4	0	8	6	4	8

243 Colourminoes 9

In the grid below, each colour has a unique integer value from 0 to 6. The numbers next to each row and column indicate the total value of the cells in that row or column. The values of the cells of the grid correspond in turn to the numbers shown on a half-set of dominoes containing all possible pairs of numbers from (0,0) to (6,6) which has been laid together in one solid rectangle. Dominoes in this rectangle may be placed horizontally or vertically. What number does each colour correspond to, and how are the corresponding dominoes arranged? Answer on page 290.

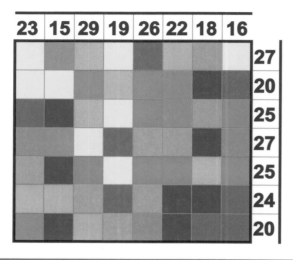

244 Nonogram 7

A number of cells in the grid below are to be shaded. Each row and column may contain one or more continuous lines of shaded cells ('blocks'). The numbers adjacent to the row or column indicate the lengths of the different blocks contained. Blocks are separated from others in the same row or column by at least one empty cell. Where are the shaded cells? A picture will emerge when the cells are shaded correctly. Answer on page 294.

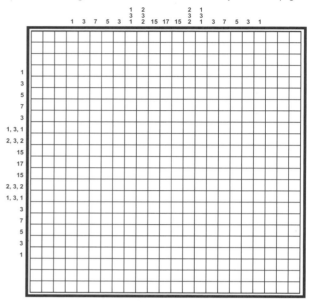

245 Kakuro 7

The empty squares in this grid contain digits from 1 to 9 so that each continuous unbroken line of numbers adds up to the clue value in the filled segment to its left (for horizontal lines) or above it (for vertical lines). No number may be used more than once in any unbroken line. How is the grid filled? Answer on page 293.

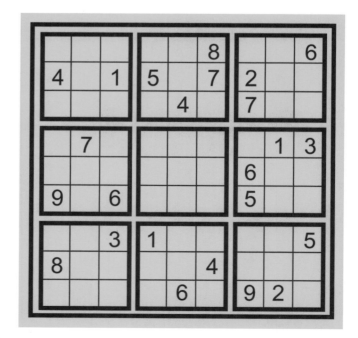

246 Sudoku 13

Fill in the grid below so that the numbers 1–9 appear exactly once in each row, column and 3x3 box. For solution see page 272.

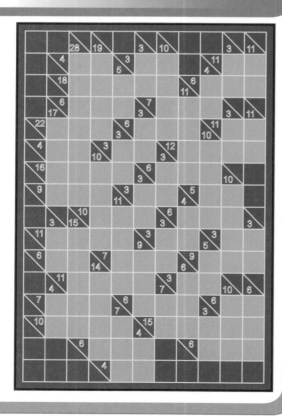

247 Who's Who 4

From the information given, can you match each husband to his wife? Answer on p302.

248 Futoshiki 12

Fill in the grid below so that the numbers 1 to 7 appear exactly once in each row and column. Red arrows indicate that a number is greater than its neighbour. For answer see page 274.

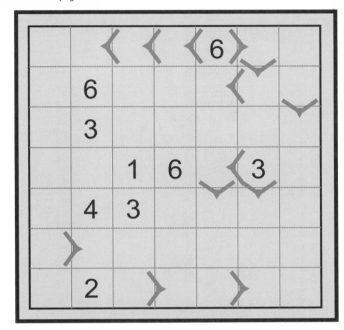

249 Silhouettes 4

Which of the six images fits the silhouette? Answer on page 302.

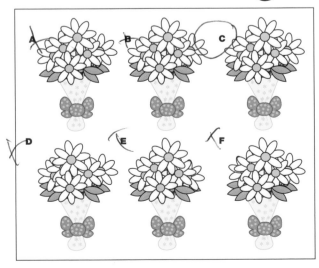

250 Tentai 8

The grid below is divided into a number of shapes. Each shape has a star at its centre, and is made up of one continuous group of cells connected horizontally and/or vertically. The shapes are all symmetrical – they stay the same when rotated by 180 degrees – but may get quite complicated. Where are the shapes? Answer on page 291.

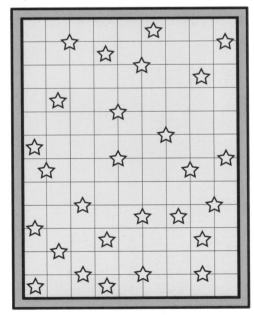

251 Battleships 10

A number of ships of various sizes are hidden in the grid below. The numbers next to each row and column indicate how many ship segments are in that row or column. Some ship segments have already been filled in. Where are the ships? Answer on page 289.

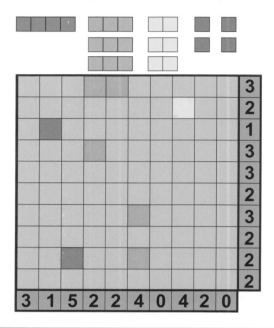

Row totals (top to bottom): 3, 2, 1, 3, 3, 2, 3, 2, 2, 2

Column totals (left to right): 3 1 5 2 2 4 0 4 2 0

252 Slitherlink 11

A number of the intersection lines in the grid below have to be joined together to make one single complete loop. The numbers in the cell indicate how many of that cell's sides form part of the loop. Answer on page 278.

```
.  2  .  .  2  3  .  .  1  .
2  .  .  .  2  .  2  .  .  .
.  2  3  .  3  .  3  2  .  2
.  3  .  .  .  1  .  2  2  .
2  .  .  3  .  .  .  3  2  2
.  1  .  1  1  1  2  .  3  .
.  2  2  .  .  .  .  .  2  1
3  2  2  .  0  3  2  .  .  .
.  .  3  .  .  .  .  2  .  2
.  2  .  .  2  2  .  1  .  .
```

253 Dominoes 11

A full set of dominoes containing all possible pairs of numbers from (0,0) to (9,9) is laid together in one solid rectangle. The dominoes may be placed horizontally or vertically. The numbers in the grid below indicate the value of each half of each domino. How are the dominoes arranged? Answer on page 280.

```
0 0 6 5 7 7 6 5 0 4 5
4 2 6 1 8 5 9 3 7 4 6
3 2 6 0 6 7 9 3 5 7 2
8 1 0 3 3 1 9 0 2 5 5
1 1 2 7 5 0 8 1 9 0 3
1 9 3 9 0 7 7 9 7 7 3
1 8 2 9 2 0 2 2 2 9 1
9 4 2 8 1 6 4 8 8 5 5
5 0 3 1 4 6 4 6 7 9 4
4 4 8 8 8 3 4 3 6 8 6
```

254 Domino placing 11

A set of dominoes containing all possible pairs of numbers from (0,0) to (7,7) is laid out vertically as shown in the blank grid below so that the larger number of each domino is on the top. The numbers above each column are from the top half of the dominoes in that column. The numbers below each column are from the bottom half of the dominoes in that column. The numbers to the left of each row are from the respective half-dominoes in that row.

All the numbers are given to you sorted into descending numerical order. How are the dominoes laid out? Answer on page 282.

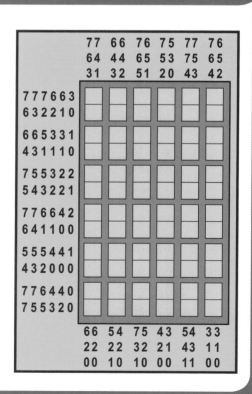

Column tops:
```
77 66 76 75 77 76
64 44 65 53 75 65
31 32 51 20 43 42
```

Row left numbers:
```
777663
632210

665331
431110

755322
543221

776642
641100

555441
432000

776440
755320
```

Column bottoms:
```
66 54 75 43 54 33
22 22 32 21 43 11
00 10 10 00 11 00
```

255 Bijutsukan 11

The bright cells and dark cells in the grid below represent corridors and walls respectively. Light sources shine a horizontal and vertical beam of light. A corridor cell becomes illuminated if it is in the same row or column as a light source and there is no wall cell in between them. Place light sources in the corridor cells so that every corridor cell is illuminated, and no light source illuminates another light source. The numbers in some walls tell you how many light sources are touching that wall horizontally or vertically. Answer on page 281.

256 Hitori 11

Shade out cells in the grid below so that no number appears more than once in any row or column. Shaded cells cannot touch each other horizontally or vertically, and cannot cut the unshaded cells into two or more groups – the unshaded cells must remain connected horizontally or vertically into one complex branching chain. Which cells are shaded? Answer on page 287.

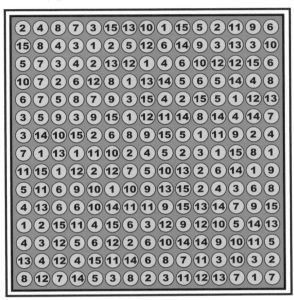

257 Tents 11

The grid below indicates a patch of woodland. Some cells contain grass, and others contain trees. Tents are placed on grass cells so that each tree has one tent next to it horizontally or vertically, although note that tents may be adjacent to more than one tree. No tent may be horizontally, vertically or diagonally adjacent to another tent. The numbers beside each row and column tell you how many tents are in that row or column. Where are the tents? Answer on page 285.

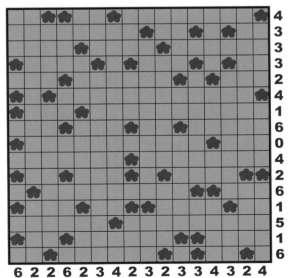

258 Number Link 11

The numbered cells in the grid below indicate the start and end points of single continuous paths. These paths fill the grid completely, and do not branch, cross each other, or touch themselves to form any pool of cells (2x2 or greater).
How are the paths arranged? Answer on page 284.

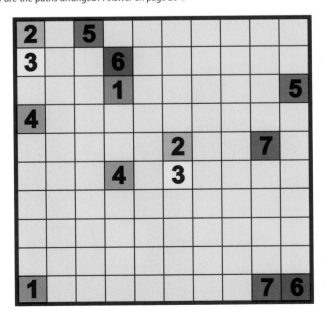

259 Gokigen Naname 11

Each cell in the grid below contains one diagonal line from corner to corner. The numbered circles show how many lines touch that corner. Fill in the grid so that the lines never form a closed circuit of any size. Answer on page 276.

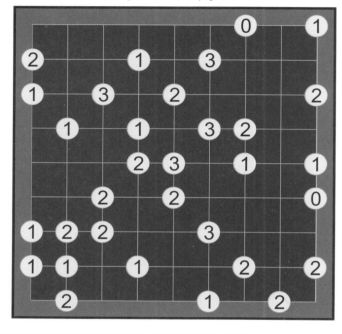

260 Sikaku 11

Divide the grid below into a number of rectangular rooms. Each room must contain exactly one number, equal to the number of cells that make up the room. Answer on page 277.

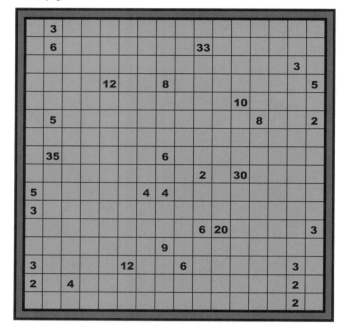

261 Fillomino 11

Each value shown in the grid below is part of a group of cells equal in number to that given value. A '6' is part of a group of six cells, for example. Groups may take any shape, but no two groups of the same size may touch each other horizontally or vertically at any point, and there are no blank cells. Not all groups need have a given value. How are the groups arranged? Answer on page 288.

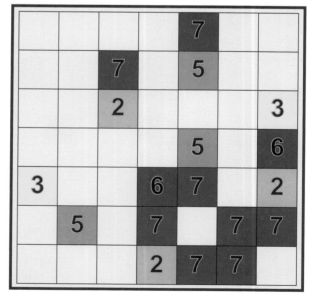

262 Map Colouring 7

The rooms of the grid are coloured so that no two rooms of the same colour ever touch. How are the rooms coloured? Answer on page 295.

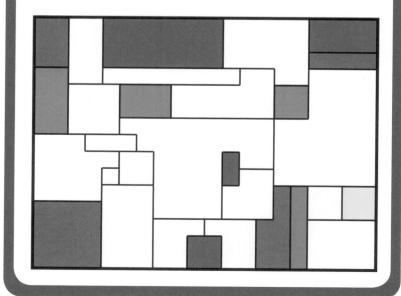

263 Battlehex 7

A number of ships of various sizes are hidden in the hexagonal grid below. The numbers next to each edge indicate how many ship segments are in the rows indicated by the directional arrows. Some ship segments and/or empty water cells have already been filled in. Where are the ships? Answer on page 296.

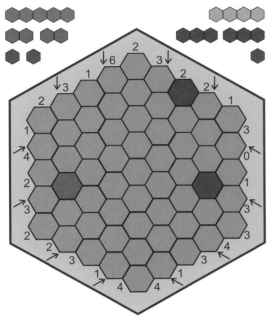

264 Colourminoes 10

In the grid below, each colour has a unique integer value from 0 to 6. The numbers next to each row and column indicate the total value of the cells in that row or column. The values of the cells of the grid correspond in turn to the numbers shown on a half-set of dominoes containing all possible pairs of numbers from (0,0) to (6,6) which has been laid together in one solid rectangle. Dominoes in this rectangle may be placed horizontally or vertically. What number does each colour correspond to, and how are the corresponding dominoes arranged? Answer on page 290.

18	32	12	21	29	23	17	16	
								19
								21
								28
								18
								31
								25
								26

265 Missing Landmarks 8

Which famous landmark is blurred out of this photo? Answer on page 292.

266 Sudoku 14

Fill in the grid below so that the numbers 1–9 appear exactly once in each row, column and 3x3 box. For solution see page 272.

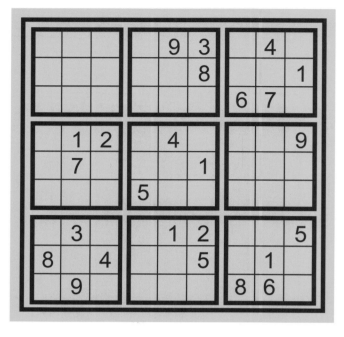

267 Futoshiki 13

Fill in the grid below so that the numbers 1 to 7 appear exactly once in each row and column. Red arrows indicate that a number is greater than its neighbour. For answer see page 274.

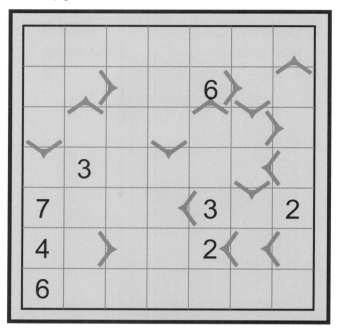

268 Nonogram 8

A number of cells in the grid below are to be shaded. Each row and column may contain one or more continuous lines of shaded cells ('blocks'). The numbers adjacent to the row or column indicate the lengths of the different blocks contained. Blocks are separated from others in the same row or column by at least one empty cell. Where are the shaded cells? A picture will emerge when the cells are shaded correctly. Answer on page 294.

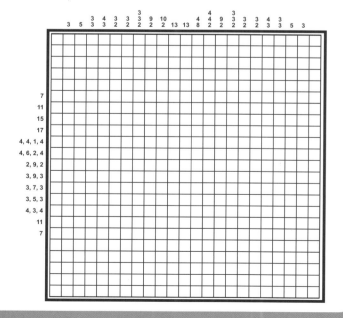

269 Kakuro 8

The empty squares in this grid contain digits from 1 to 9 so that each continuous unbroken line of numbers adds up to the clue value in the filled segment to its left (for horizontal lines) or above it (for vertical lines). No number may be used more than once in any unbroken line. How is the grid filled? Answer on page 293.

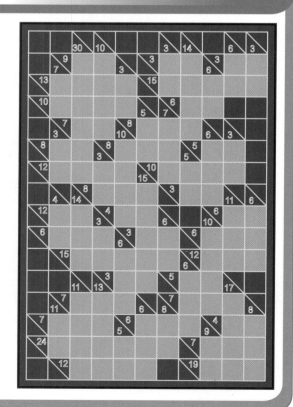

270 Battleships 11

A number of ships of various sizes are hidden in the grid below. The numbers next to each row and column indicate how many ship segments are in that row or column. Some ship segments have already been filled in. Where are the ships? Answer on page 289.

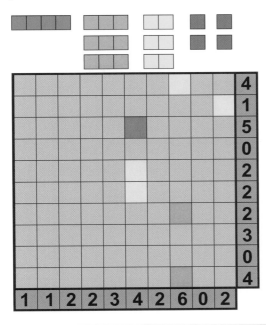

271 Tentai 9

The grid below is divided into a number of shapes. Each shape has a star at its centre, and is made up of one continuous group of cells connected horizontally and/or vertically. The shapes are all symmetrical – they stay the same when rotated by 180 degrees – but may get quite complicated. Where are the shapes? Answer on page 291.

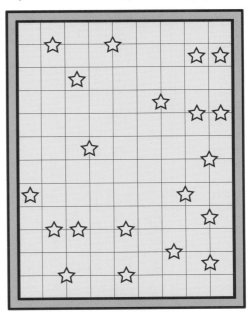

272 Mirror Image 6

Which of the five images below is an identical mirror image of the one above? Answer on page 300.

273 Tents 12

The grid below indicates a patch of woodland. Some cells contain grass, and others contain trees. Tents are placed on grass cells so that each tree has one tent next to it horizontally or vertically, although note that tents may be adjacent to more than one tree. No tent may be horizontally, vertically or diagonally adjacent to another tent. The numbers beside each row and column tell you how many tents are in that row or column. Where are the tents? Answer on page 285.

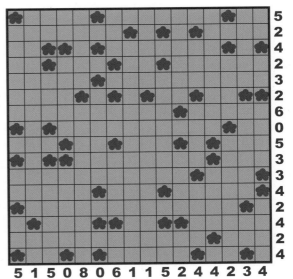

274 Hashiwokakero 6

A number of straight horizontal and vertical bridges connect the islands shown. The number on each island shows how many bridges touch that island. Bridges may not cross each other, and no more than 2 bridges may connect a pair of islands.
Where are the bridges?
Answer on page 297.

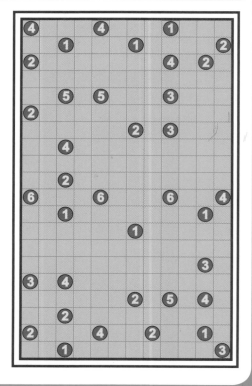

275 Super Sudoku 3

Fill in the grid below so that the digits 1, 2, 3, 4, 5, 6, 7, 8, 9, a, b, c, d, e, f and g appear exactly once in each row and column. Answer on page 303.

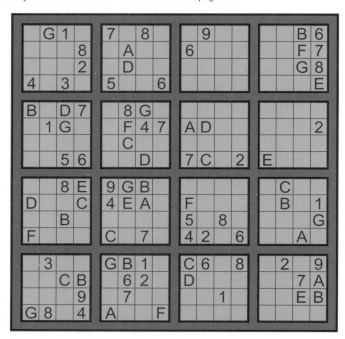

276 Yudoku 6

Fill in the grid below so that the letters s, p, a, r, k, l, i, n and g appear exactly once in each row, column and 3x3 box. Answer on page 301.

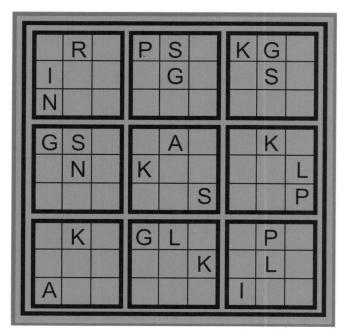

277 Sikaku 12

Divide the grid below into a number of rectangular rooms. Each room must contain exactly one number, equal to the number of cells that make up the room.
Answer on page 277.

278 Differences

Each copy of the picture has one flaw that none of the others share. Can you find them all? Answer on page 304.

279 Bijutsukan 12

The bright cells and dark cells in the grid below represent corridors and walls respectively. Light sources shine a horizontal and vertical beam of light. A corridor cell becomes illuminated if it is in the same row or column as a light source and there is no wall cell in between them. Place light sources in the corridor cells so that every corridor cell is illuminated, and no light source illuminates another light source. The numbers in some walls tell you how many light sources are touching that wall horizontally or vertically. Answer on page 281.

280 Spot the Difference

There are eight differences between the two pictures. Can you find them all? Answer on p302.

281 Spot the Set

There are four different versions of the picture in the group below, each one reproduced three times. Can you identify the four sets? Answer on page 304.

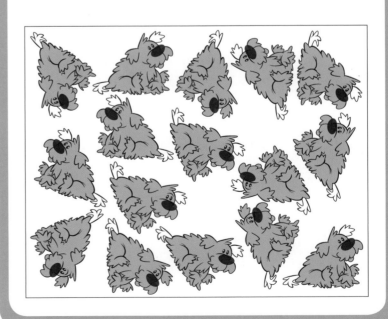

282 Sudoku 15

Fill in the grid below so that the numbers 1–9 appear exactly once in each row, column and 3x3 box. For solution see page 272.

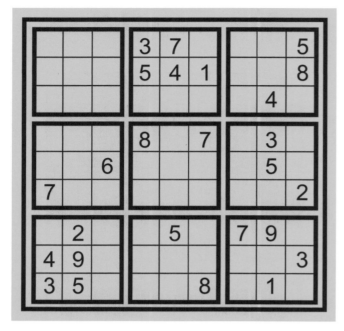

284 Hitori 12

Shade out cells in the grid below so that no number appears more than once in any row or column. Shaded cells cannot touch each other horizontally or vertically, and cannot cut the unshaded cells into two or more groups – the unshaded cells must remain connected horizontally or vertically into one complex branching chain. Which cells are shaded? Answer on page 287.

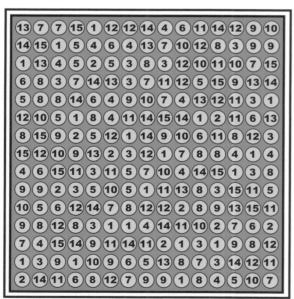

283 Suiri 6

Five people have a pressing reason to shed some pounds. From the information below, can you work out which person (1) has taken up which sport (2) and diet program (3), and for which reason (4)?

1. Stanislav has not taken up swimming.
2. Ludmilla has taken up tennis, but she is not getting ready for a presentation (that person is on a calorie-counting diet).
3. Boris has a wedding coming up.
4. The person who has taken up running is on a low-carb diet, but not to go on holiday or to attend a school reunion.
5. Radka has neither taken up swimming nor is she preparing for a presentation.
6. The person who has taken up cycling has been ordered to get fit by a doctor, but has not gone on a low-fat diet.
7. Vladimir has joined a slimming club diet, but not to get ready for a holiday.
8. Someone is on a glycemic index diet.
9. Someone has taken up squash.
Answer on page 298.

285 Gokigen Naname 12

Each cell in the grid below contains one diagonal line from corner to corner. The numbered circles show how many lines touch that corner. Fill in the grid so that the lines never form a closed circuit of any size. Answer on page 276.

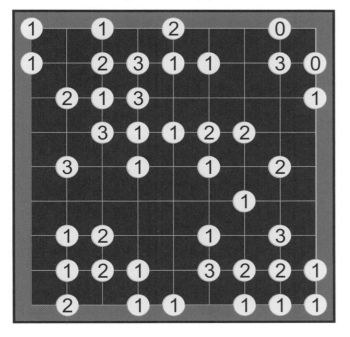

286 Match One 6

Which of the jumbled images is identical to the one presented here? Answer on page 298.

287 Domino placing 12

A set of dominoes containing all possible pairs of numbers from (0,0) to (7,7) is laid out vertically as shown in the blank grid below so that the larger number of each domino is on the top. The numbers above each column are from the top half of the dominoes in that column. The numbers below each column are from the bottom half of the dominoes in that column. The numbers to the left of each row are from the respective half-dominoes in that row.

All the numbers are given to you sorted into descending numerical order. How are the dominoes laid out? Answer on page 282.

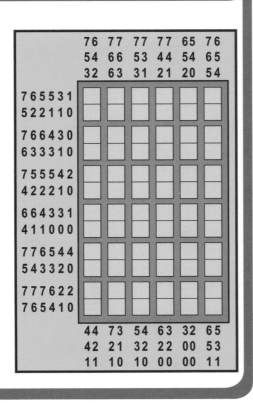

288 Killer Sudoku 3

Fill in the grid below so that the numbers 1–9 appear exactly once in each row, column and 3x3 block, and that the numbers in each dotted room add up to the value in its top right corner. Answer on page 303.

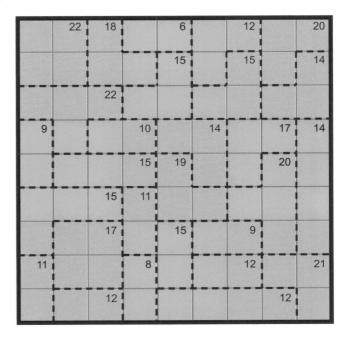

289 Dominoes 12

A full set of dominoes containing all possible pairs of numbers from (0,0) to (9,9) is laid together in one solid rectangle. The dominoes may be placed horizontally or vertically. The numbers in the grid below indicate the value of each half of each domino. How are the dominoes arranged? Answer on page 280.

8	4	2	6	8	4	7	7	3	3	6
5	0	7	6	8	1	6	4	2	5	9
1	9	4	2	8	1	4	7	6	3	1
6	0	0	0	5	3	0	4	9	6	1
0	7	4	2	9	3	5	5	5	6	3
7	3	6	2	1	4	1	4	2	8	2
2	6	3	2	7	4	5	8	8	3	3
2	9	1	1	0	7	5	8	9	9	1
0	8	8	7	9	9	5	7	3	4	0
9	2	5	7	5	6	0	1	8	0	9

290 Samurai Sudoku 3

Fill in each 9x9 grid below so that the numbers 1–9 appear exactly once in each row, column and 3x3 block. Numbers in overlapping blocks count identically towards both grids. Answer on page 303.

291 Masyu 6

A line passes through some or all of the cells in the grid below in such a way that it forms a single continuous non-intersecting loop. The line always exits a cell by a different side to the one it entered by, and passes through all cells containing a circle. The line travels straight through a cell with a light circle but turns in the previous and/or following cells in its path. The line turns in a cell containing a dark cell, but travels straight through both the previous and following cells in its path. Where is the line? Answer on page 300.

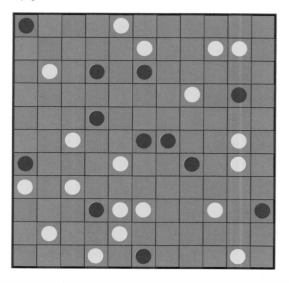

292 Number Link 12

The numbered cells in the grid below indicate the start and end points of single continuous paths. These paths fill the grid completely, and do not branch, cross each other, or touch themselves to form any pool of cells (2x2 or greater).
How are the paths arranged? Answer on page 284.

293 Detail Scene 6

The three enlarged squares appear somewhere in the large picture. Can you find them? Answer on page 299.

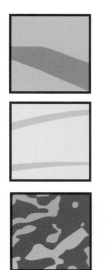

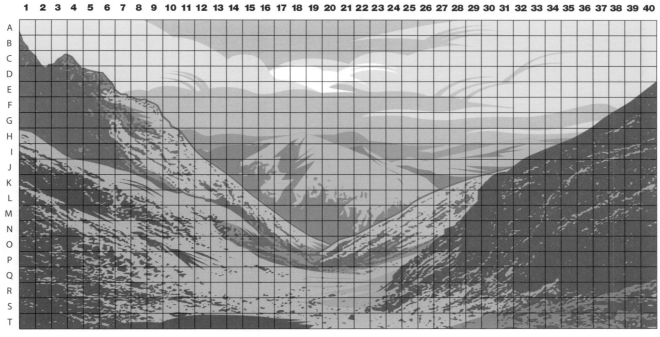

294 Fillomino 12

Each value shown in the grid below is part of a group of cells equal in number to that given value. A '6' is part of a group of six cells, for example. Groups may take any shape, but no two groups of the same size may touch each other horizontally or vertically at any point, and there are no blank cells. Not all groups need have a given value. How are the groups arranged? Answer on page 288.

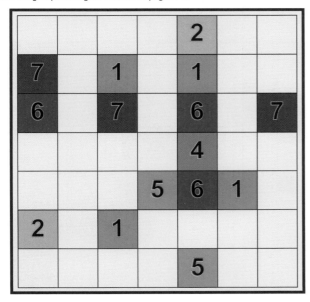

295 Identicals 6

Which pair of images is identical? Answer on page 299.

296 Slitherlink 12

A number of the intersection lines in the grid below have to be joined together to make one single complete loop. The numbers in the cell indicate how many of that cell's sides form part of the loop. Answer on page 278.

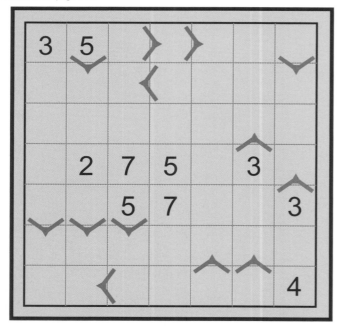

297 Colourminoes 11

In the grid below, each colour has a unique integer value from 0 to 6. The numbers next to each row and column indicate the total value of the cells in that row or column. The values of the cells of the grid correspond in turn to the numbers shown on a half-set of dominoes containing all possible pairs of numbers from (0,0) to (6,6) which has been laid together in one solid rectangle. Dominoes in this rectangle may be placed horizontally or vertically. What number does each colour correspond to, and how are the corresponding dominoes arranged? Answer on page 290.

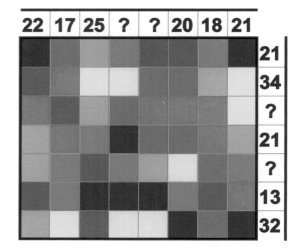

298 Futoshiki 14

Fill in the grid below so that the numbers 1 to 7 appear exactly once in each row and column. Red arrows indicate that a number is greater than its neighbour. For answer see page 274.

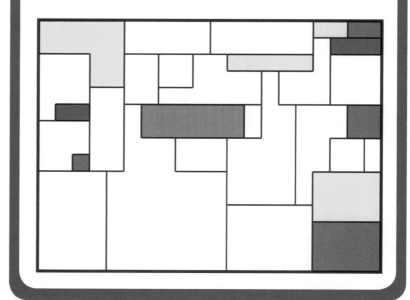

299 Map Colouring 8

The rooms of the grid are coloured so that no two rooms of the same colour ever touch. How are the rooms coloured? Answer on page 295.

300 Missing Landmarks 9

Which famous landmark is blurred out of this photo? Answer on page 292.

301 Sudoku 16

Fill in the grid below so that the numbers 1–9 appear exactly once in each row, column and 3x3 box. For solution see page 272.

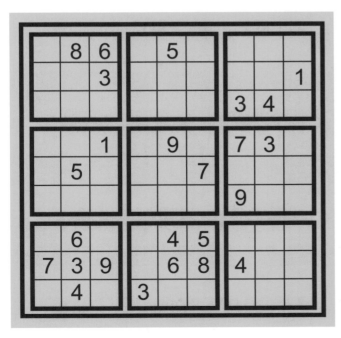

302 Battlehex 8

A number of ships of various sizes are hidden in the hexagonal grid below. The numbers next to each edge indicate how many ship segments are in the rows indicated by the directional arrows. Some ship segments and/or empty water cells have already been filled in. Where are the ships? Answer on page 296.

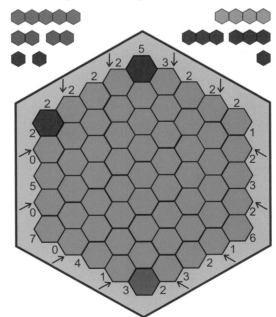

303 Battleships 12

A number of ships of various sizes are hidden in the grid below. The numbers next to each row and column indicate how many ship segments are in that row or column. Some ship segments have already been filled in. Where are the ships? Answer on page 289.

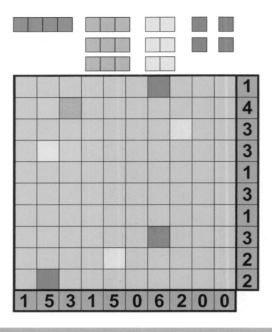

304 Dominoes 13

A full set of dominoes containing all possible pairs of numbers from (0,0) to (9,9) is laid together in one solid rectangle. The dominoes may be placed horizontally or vertically. The numbers in the grid below indicate the value of each half of each domino. How are the dominoes arranged? Answer on page 280.

9	0	4	9	2	1	2	0	5	6	1
5	7	6	1	9	9	6	8	3	4	4
8	4	9	7	8	2	3	4	3	3	2
5	5	6	7	1	1	5	1	1	8	6
8	9	8	7	0	3	6	4	2	0	0
4	1	8	7	9	5	1	1	4	6	7
6	9	2	0	9	7	7	5	4	6	0
8	0	2	0	8	5	3	0	4	3	5
9	1	9	5	8	2	8	3	6	0	6
4	5	3	7	2	7	7	2	2	3	3

305 Minesweeper 4

The grid below contains a number of bombs hidden in empty squares. Each red flag tells you how many bombs are in the eight cells around it. Where are the bombs?
For answer see page 275.

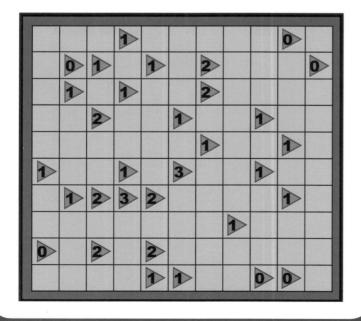

306 Gokigen Naname 13

Each cell in the grid below contains one diagonal line from corner to corner. The numbered circles show how many lines touch that corner. Fill in the grid so that the lines never form a closed circuit of any size. Answer on page 276.

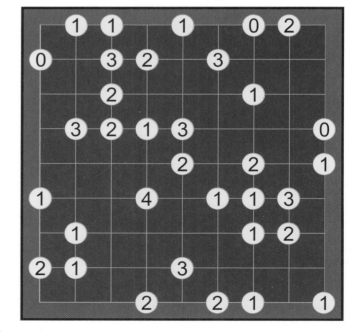

307 Hitori 13

Shade out cells in the grid below so that no number appears more than once in any row or column. Shaded cells cannot touch each other horizontally or vertically, and cannot cut the unshaded cells into two or more groups – the unshaded cells must remain connected horizontally or vertically into one complex branching chain. Which cells are shaded? Answer on page 287.

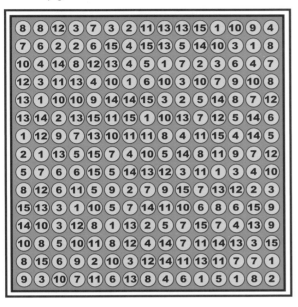

308 Fillomino 13

Each value shown in the grid below is part of a group of cells equal in number to that given value. A '6' is part of a group of six cells, for example. Groups may take any shape, but no two groups of the same size may touch each other horizontally or vertically at any point, and there are no blank cells. Not all groups need have a given value. How are the groups arranged? Answer on page 288.

309 Slitherlink 13

A number of the intersection lines in the grid below have to be joined together to make one single complete loop. The numbers in the cell indicate how many of that cell's sides form part of the loop. Answer on page 278.

310 Tents 13

The grid below indicates a patch of woodland. Some cells contain grass, and others contain trees. Tents are placed on grass cells so that each tree has one tent next to it horizontally or vertically, although note that tents may be adjacent to more than one tree. No tent may be horizontally, vertically or diagonally adjacent to another tent. The numbers beside each row and column tell you how many tents are in that row or column. Where are the tents? Answer on page 285.

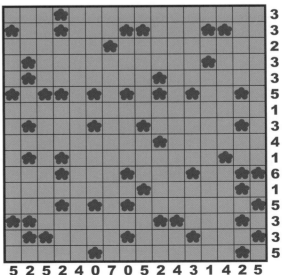

311 Number Link 13

The numbered cells in the grid below indicate the start and end points of single continuous paths. These paths fill the grid completely, and do not branch, cross each other, or touch themselves to form any pool of cells (2x2 or greater).

How are the paths arranged? Answer on page 284.

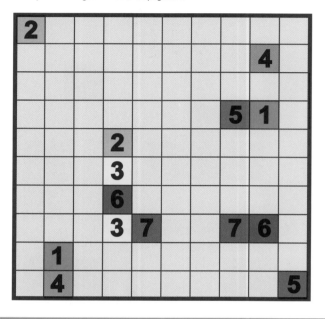

312 Domino placing 13

A set of dominoes containing all possible pairs of numbers from (0,0) to (7,7) is laid out vertically as shown in the blank grid below so that the larger number of each domino is on the top. The numbers above each column are from the top half of the dominoes in that column. The numbers below each column are from the bottom half of the dominoes in that column. The numbers to the left of each row are from the respective half-dominoes in that row.

All the numbers are given to you sorted into descending numerical order. How are the dominoes laid out? Answer on page 282.

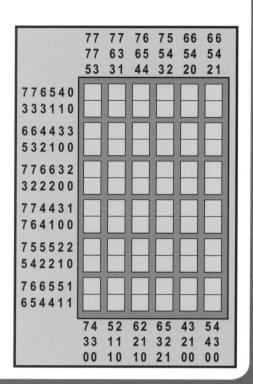

313 Bijutsukan 13

The bright cells and dark cells in the grid below represent corridors and walls respectively. Light sources shine a horizontal and vertical beam of light. A corridor cell becomes illuminated if it is in the same row or column as a light source and there is no wall cell in between them. Place light sources in the corridor cells so that every corridor cell is illuminated, and no light source illuminates another light source. The numbers in some walls tell you how many light sources are touching that wall horizontally or vertically. Answer on page 281.

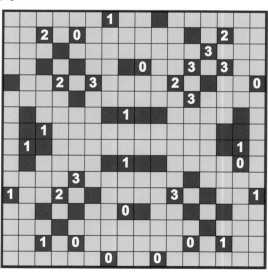

314 Sikaku 13

Divide the grid below into a number of rectangular rooms. Each room must contain exactly one number, equal to the number of cells that make up the room. Answer on page 277.

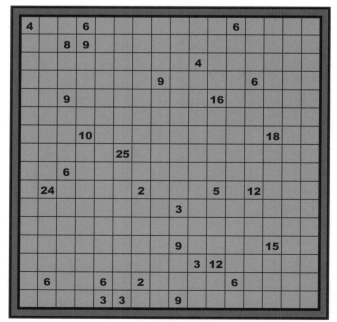

315 Tentai 10

The grid below is divided into a number of shapes. Each shape has a star at its centre, and is made up of one continuous group of cells connected horizontally and/or vertically. The shapes are all symmetrical – they stay the same when rotated by 180 degrees – but may get quite complicated. Where are the shapes? Answer on page 291.

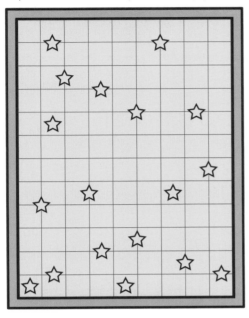

316 Silhouettes 5

Which of the six images fits the silhouette? Answer on page 302.

317 Futoshiki 15

Fill in the grid below so that the numbers 1 to 7 appear exactly once in each row and column. Red arrows indicate that a number is greater than its neighbour. For answer see page 274.

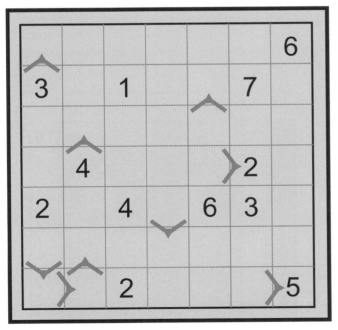

318 Who's Who 5

From the information given, can you match each teacher to his pupil? Answer on p302.

I'm Mr. Grey, my pupil, Jon, has a catapult.

I'm Mr. Williams, my pupil, Wes, is not ink-stained.

I'm Mr. Broad, my pupil is Lloyd.

I am Mr. Kent.

I'm Matt.

319 Artist's Errors

The artist drawing this scene has made a number of visual, conceptual and logical errors. Can you find them all?
Answer on page 304.

320 Nonogram 9

A number of cells in the grid below are to be shaded. Each row and column may contain one or more continuous lines of shaded cells ('blocks'). The numbers adjacent to the row or column indicate the lengths of the different blocks contained. Blocks are separated from others in the same row or column by at least one empty cell. Where are the shaded cells? A picture will emerge when the cells are shaded correctly. Answer on page 294.

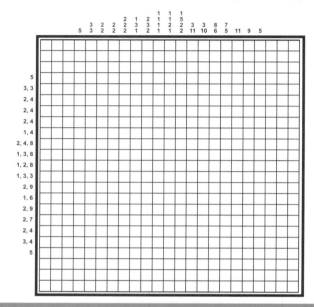

321 Kakuro 9

The empty squares in this grid contain digits from 1 to 9 so that each continuous unbroken line of numbers adds up to the clue value in the filled segment to its left (for horizontal lines) or above it (for vertical lines). No number may be used more than once in any unbroken line. How is the grid filled? Answer on page 293.

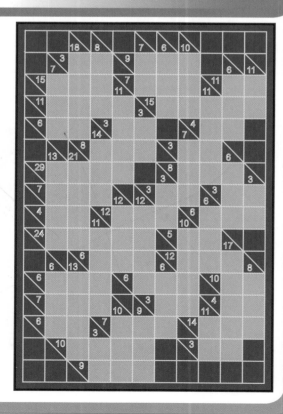

322 Colourminoes 12

In the grid below, each colour has a unique integer value from 0 to 6. The numbers next to each row and column indicate the total value of the cells in that row or column. The values of the cells of the grid correspond in turn to the numbers shown on a half-set of dominoes containing all possible pairs of numbers from (0,0) to (6,6) which has been laid together in one solid rectangle. Dominoes in this rectangle may be placed horizontally or vertically. What number does each colour correspond to, and how are the corresponding dominoes arranged? Answer on page 290.

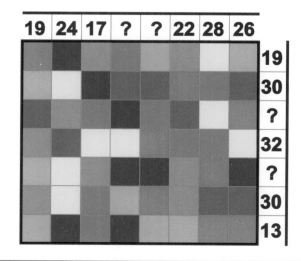

323 Sudoku 17

Fill in the grid below so that the numbers 1–9 appear exactly once in each row, column and 3x3 box. For solution see page 272.

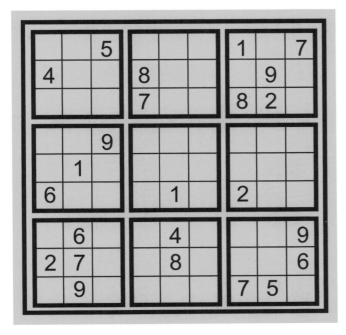

324 Number Link 14

The numbered cells in the grid below indicate the start and end points of single continuous paths. These paths fill the grid completely, and do not branch, cross each other, or touch themselves to form any pool of cells (2x2 or greater).

How are the paths arranged? Answer on page 284.

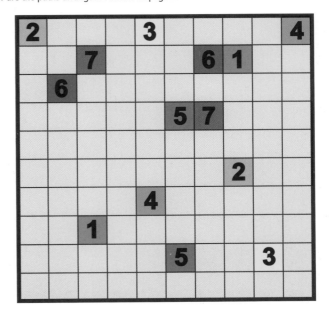

325 Yudoku 7

Fill in the grid below so that the letters s, p, a, r, k, l, i, n and g appear exactly once in each row, column and 3x3 box. Answer on page 301.

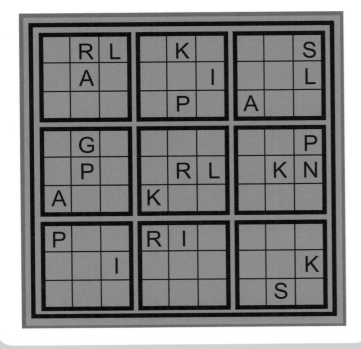

326 Tents 14

The grid below indicates a patch of woodland. Some cells contain grass, and others contain trees. Tents are placed on grass cells so that each tree has one tent next to it horizontally or vertically, although note that tents may be adjacent to more than one tree. No tent may be horizontally, vertically or diagonally adjacent to another tent. The numbers beside each row and column tell you how many tents are in that row or column. Where are the tents? Answer on page 285.

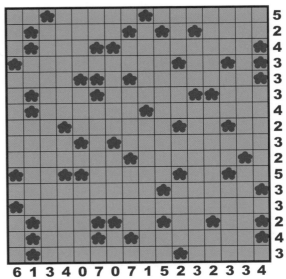

327 Sikaku 14

Divide the grid below into a number of rectangular rooms. Each room must contain exactly one number, equal to the number of cells that make up the room.
Answer on page 277.

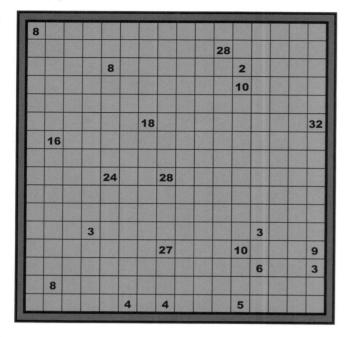

328 Bijutsukan 14

The bright cells and dark cells in the grid below represent corridors and walls respectively. Light sources shine a horizontal and vertical beam of light. A corridor cell becomes illuminated if it is in the same row or column as a light source and there is no wall cell in between them. Place light sources in the corridor cells so that every corridor cell is illuminated, and no light source illuminates another light source. The numbers in some walls tell you how many light sources are touching that wall horizontally or vertically.
Answer on page 281.

329 Identicals 7

Which pair of images is identical? Answer on page 299.

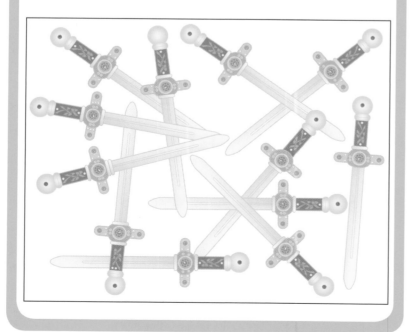

330 Hitori 14

Shade out cells in the grid below so that no number appears more than once in any row or column. Shaded cells cannot touch each other horizontally or vertically, and cannot cut the unshaded cells into two or more groups – the unshaded cells must remain connected horizontally or vertically into one complex branching chain. Which cells are shaded? Answer on page 287.

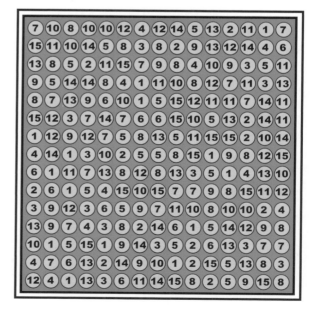

331 Slitherlink 14

A number of the intersection lines in the grid below have to be joined together to make one single complete loop. The numbers in the cell indicate how many of that cell's sides form part of the loop. Answer on page 278.

3	1	2		1	2	3	1	2	
	2	3	2						2
	2	2	2				3		
	2				3		2	1	2
	1	3	1	3			2		
	2	3			2			3	1
	2	2			2		1		
					3	2		3	
		3	3	3		2	1		
	2								3

332 Match One 7

Which of the jumbled images is identical to the one presented here? Answer on page 298.

333 Detail Scene 7

The three enlarged squares appear somewhere in the large picture. Can you find them? Answer on page 299.

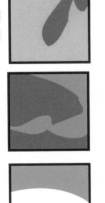

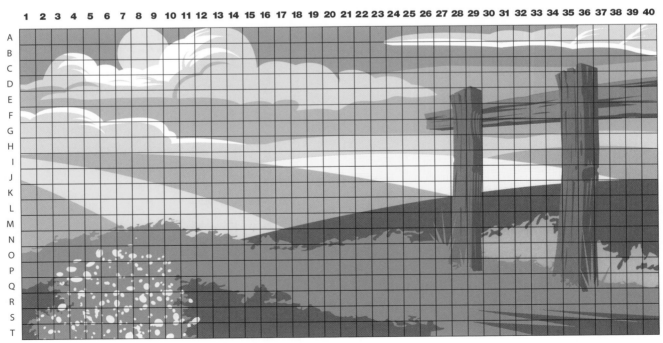

334 Missing Landmarks 10

Which famous landmark is blurred out of this photo? Answer on page 292.

335 Fillomino 14

Each value shown in the grid below is part of a group of cells equal in number to that given value. A '6' is part of a group of six cells, for example. Groups may take any shape, but no two groups of the same size may touch each other horizontally or vertically at any point, and there are no blank cells. Not all groups need have a given value. How are the groups arranged? Answer on page 288.

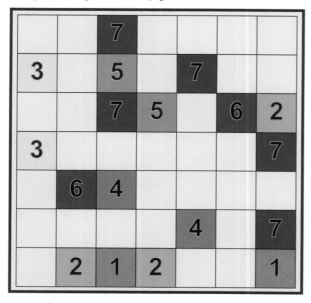

336 Gokigen Naname 14

Each cell in the grid below contains one diagonal line from corner to corner. The numbered circles show how many lines touch that corner. Fill in the grid so that the lines never form a closed circuit of any size. Answer on page 276.

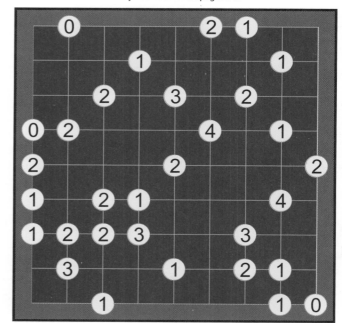

337 Suiri 7

A group of men have bought birthday presents for their wives. From the information given below, can you work out which man (1) is married to which woman (2), what her present is (3), and how long they've been married (4)?

1. It was Dietrich and Birgitta's turn to get married directly before the man who bought the necklace.

2. Ingrid is getting a ring.

3. The man who bought ear-rings has been married 16 years. He is not Volker.

4. Michael bought a camcorder.

5. Roland has been married for 14 years, but not to Anita.

6. Claudia has been married for 5 years.

7. Petra is not getting a necklace or lingerie, and she is not married to Michael.

8. One couple have been married 7 years, another just 3 years.

9. One of the men is named Kurt.

Answer on page 298.

		2					3					4				
		Petra	Ingrid	Claudia	Birgitta	Anita	Ring	Necklace	Lingerie	Ear-rings	Camcorder	16 years	14 years	7 years	5 years	3 years
1	Dietrich	✗	✗	✗	●	✗			✗		✗					
	Kurt				✗		✗	✗			✗					
	Michael	✗	✗		✗		✗				■					
	Roland			■									■			
	Volker				■					✗	✗					
4	3 years		✗		■											
	5 years			■												
	7 years															
	14 years															
	16 years	■			✗	✗										
3	Camcorder															
	Ear-rings			■												
	Lingerie					■										
	Necklace				✗											
	Ring				■											

338 Mirror Image 7

Which of the five images below is an identical mirror image of the one above? Answer on page 300.

A   B   C   D   E

339 Masyu 7

A line passes through some or all of the cells in the grid below in such a way that it forms a single continuous non-intersecting loop. The line always exits a cell by a different side to the one it entered by, and passes through all cells containing a circle. The line travels straight through a cell with a light circle but turns in the previous and/or following cells in its path. The line turns in a cell containing a dark cell, but travels straight through both the previous and following cells in its path. Where is the line? Answer on page 300.

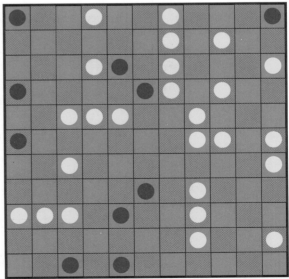

340 Dominoes 14

A full set of dominoes containing all possible pairs of numbers from (0,0) to (9,9) is laid together in one solid rectangle. The dominoes may be placed horizontally or vertically. The numbers in the grid below indicate the value of each half of each domino. How are the dominoes arranged? Answer on page 280.

0	6	7	2	2	5	1	2	7	3	1
5	7	6	0	3	1	3	4	2	9	1
1	9	5	5	7	5	3	7	1	4	1
7	6	4	4	4	9	9	5	0	4	8
0	0	8	5	1	6	6	6	0	6	8
3	1	8	9	9	1	5	3	7	7	8
0	7	8	2	7	3	8	2	4	7	6
0	8	3	1	9	4	0	6	5	9	0
9	2	2	9	4	8	8	2	5	6	3
3	2	4	2	3	5	4	0	6	8	9

341 Hashiwokakero 7

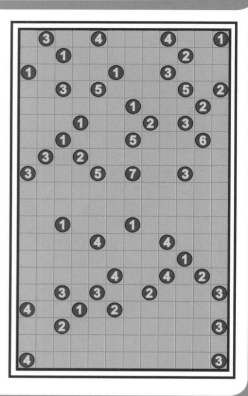

A number of straight horizontal and vertical bridges connect the islands shown. The number on each island shows how many bridges touch that island. Bridges may not cross each other, and no more than 2 bridges may connect a pair of islands.
Where are the bridges? Answer on page 297.

342 Domino placing 14

A set of dominoes containing all possible pairs of numbers from (0,0) to (7,7) is laid out vertically as shown in the blank grid below so that the larger number of each domino is on the top. The numbers above each column are from the top half of the dominoes in that column. The numbers below each column are from the bottom half of the dominoes in that column. The numbers to the left of each row are from the respective half-dominoes in that row. All the numbers are given to you sorted into descending numerical order. How are the dominoes laid out? Answer on page 282.

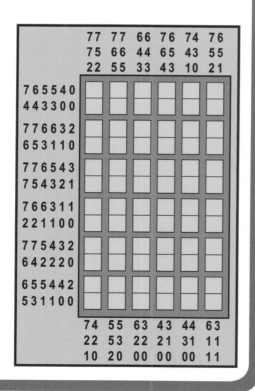

343 Battleships 13

A number of ships of various sizes are hidden in the grid below. The numbers next to each row and column indicate how many ship segments are in that row or column. Some ship segments have already been filled in. Where are the ships? Answer on page 289.

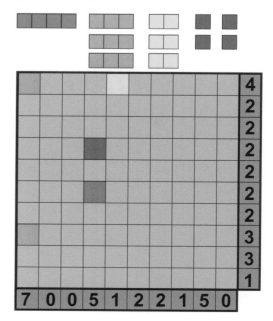

344 Futoshiki 16

Fill in the grid below so that the numbers 1 to 7 appear exactly once in each row and column. Red arrows indicate that a number is greater than its neighbour.
For answer see page 274.

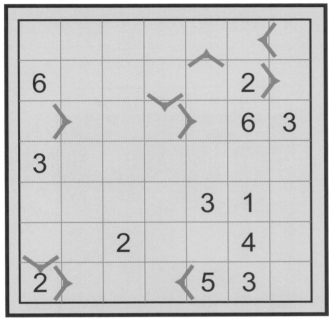

345 Sudoku 18

Fill in the grid below so that the numbers 1–9 appear exactly once in each row, column and 3x3 box. For solution see page 272.

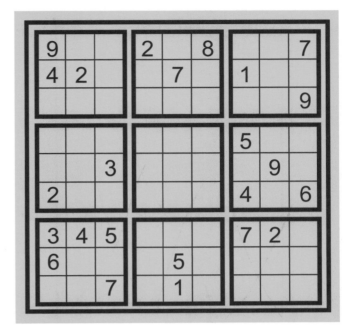

346 Battlehex 9

A number of ships of various sizes are hidden in the hexagonal grid below. The numbers next to each edge indicate how many ship segments are in the rows indicated by the directional arrows. Some ship segments and/or empty water cells have already been filled in. Where are the ships? Answer on page 296.

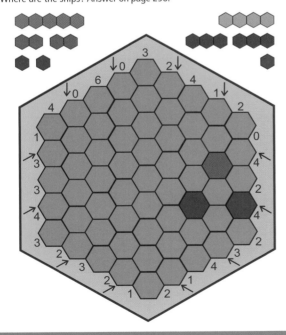

347 Map Colouring 9

The rooms of the grid are coloured so that no two rooms of the same colour ever touch. How are the rooms coloured? Answer on page 295.

348 Tentai 11

The grid below is divided into a number of shapes. Each shape has a star at its centre, and is made up of one continuous group of cells connected horizontally and/or vertically. The shapes are all symmetrical – they stay the same when rotated by 180 degrees – but may get quite complicated. Where are the shapes? Answer on page 291.

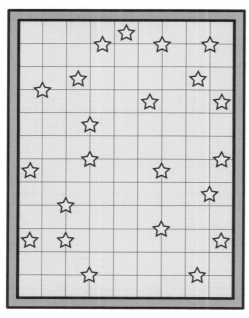

349 Colourminoes 13

In the grid below, each colour has a unique integer value from 0 to 6. The numbers next to each row and column indicate the total value of the cells in that row or column. The values of the cells of the grid correspond in turn to the numbers shown on a half-set of dominoes containing all possible pairs of numbers from (0,0) to (6,6) which has been laid together in one solid rectangle. Dominoes in this rectangle may be placed horizontally or vertically. What number does each colour correspond to, and how are the corresponding dominoes arranged? Answer on page 290.

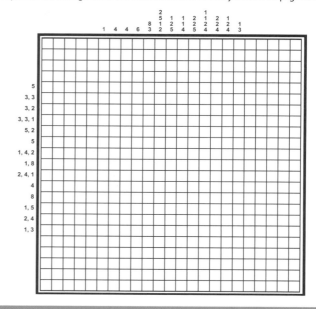

350 Kakuro 10

The empty squares in this grid contain digits from 1 to 9 so that each continuous unbroken line of numbers adds up to the clue value in the filled segment to its left (for horizontal lines) or above it (for vertical lines). No number may be used more than once in any unbroken line. How is the grid filled? Answer on page 293.

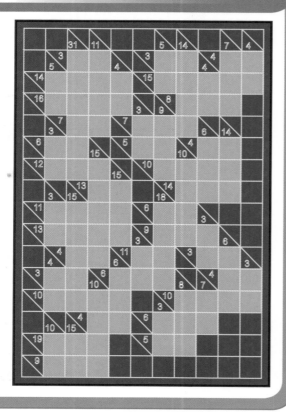

351 Nonogram 10

A number of cells in the grid below are to be shaded. Each row and column may contain one or more continuous lines of shaded cells ('blocks'). The numbers adjacent to the row or column indicate the lengths of the different blocks contained. Blocks are separated from others in the same row or column by at least one empty cell. Where are the shaded cells? A picture will emerge when the cells are shaded correctly. Answer on page 294.

352 Futoshiki 17

Fill in the grid below so that the numbers 1 to 7 appear exactly once in each row and column. Red arrows indicate that a number is greater than its neighbour.
For answer see page 274.

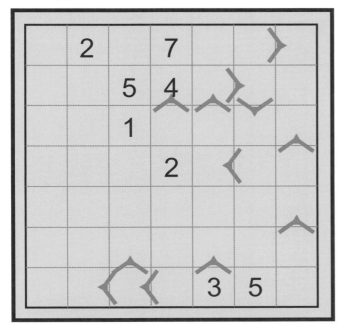

353 Domino placing 15

A set of dominoes containing all possible pairs of numbers from (0,0) to (7,7) is laid out vertically as shown in the blank grid below so that the larger number of each domino is on the top. The numbers above each column are from the top half of the dominoes in that column.
The numbers below each column are from the bottom half of the dominoes in that column.
The numbers to the left of each row are from the respective half-dominoes in that row. All the numbers are given to you sorted into descending numerical order. How are the dominoes laid out?
Answer on page 282.

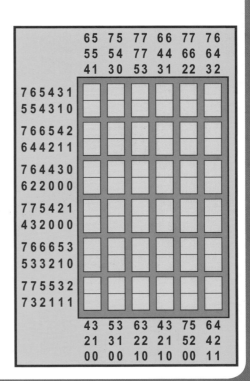

354 Bijutsukan 15

The bright cells and dark cells in the grid below represent corridors and walls respectively. Light sources shine a horizontal and vertical beam of light. A corridor cell becomes illuminated if it is in the same row or column as a light source and there is no wall cell in between them. Place light sources in the corridor cells so that every corridor cell is illuminated, and no light source illuminates another light source. The numbers in some walls tell you how many light sources are touching that wall horizontally or vertically.
Answer on page 281.

355 Number Link 15

The numbered cells in the grid below indicate the start and end points of single continuous paths. These paths fill the grid completely, and do not branch, cross each other, or touch themselves to form any pool of cells (2x2 or greater).
How are the paths arranged? Answer on page 284.

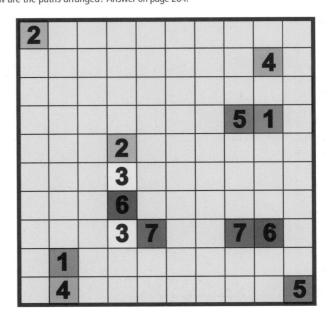

356 Fillomino 15

Each value shown in the grid below is part of a group of cells equal in number to that given value. A '6' is part of a group of six cells, for example. Groups may take any shape, but no two groups of the same size may touch each other horizontally or vertically at any point, and there are no blank cells. Not all groups need have a given value. How are the groups arranged? Answer on page 288.

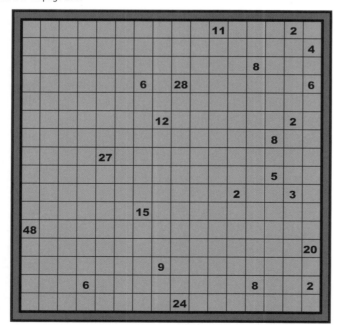

357 Hitori 15

Shade out cells in the grid below so that no number appears more than once in any row or column. Shaded cells cannot touch each other horizontally or vertically, and cannot cut the unshaded cells into two or more groups – the unshaded cells must remain connected horizontally or vertically into one complex branching chain. Which cells are shaded? Answer on page 287.

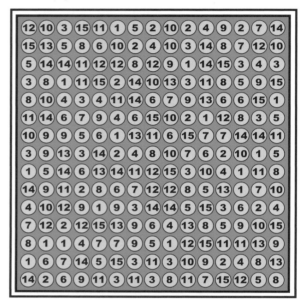

358 Sikaku 15

Divide the grid below into a number of rectangular rooms. Each room must contain exactly one number, equal to the number of cells that make up the room. Answer on page 277.

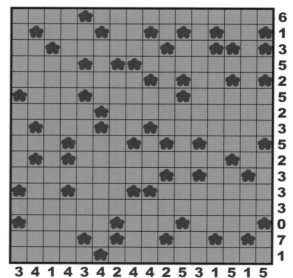

359 Tents 15

The grid below indicates a patch of woodland. Some cells contain grass, and others contain trees. Tents are placed on grass cells so that each tree has one tent next to it horizontally or vertically, although note that tents may be adjacent to more than one tree. No tent may be horizontally, vertically or diagonally adjacent to another tent. The numbers beside each row and column tell you how many tents are in that row or column. Where are the tents? Answer on page 285.

360 Slitherlink 15

A number of the intersection lines in the grid below have to be joined together to make one single complete loop. The numbers in the cell indicate how many of that cell's sides form part of the loop. Answer on page 278.

```
3     2           2 2 3
   3     3 1     2
   2        2            3
   1           3 3       3
3     1     2        1 2
            3 2        2 2
   2 1        2 2 2 1
2              3
      1              0 2
3 3      2 3 3     3 3
```

361 Dominoes 15

A full set of dominoes containing all possible pairs of numbers from (0,0) to (9,9) is laid together in one solid rectangle. The dominoes may be placed horizontally or vertically. The numbers in the grid below indicate the value of each half of each domino. How are the dominoes arranged? Answer on page 280.

7	8	4	7	6	2	0	9	0	4	9
6	8	9	5	7	0	0	3	6	8	8
6	6	1	9	8	4	0	5	8	2	0
1	5	1	9	6	4	5	3	1	1	5
2	7	0	6	6	3	7	6	8	7	5
5	9	1	6	5	5	7	3	6	3	5
0	4	2	8	2	7	4	9	9	9	3
0	1	7	7	0	2	1	1	9	8	3
8	1	3	5	0	9	2	2	2	1	4
2	4	2	4	4	3	3	7	3	8	4

362 Gokigen Naname 15

Each cell in the grid below contains one diagonal line from corner to corner. The numbered circles show how many lines touch that corner. Fill in the grid so that the lines never form a closed circuit of any size. Answer on page 276.

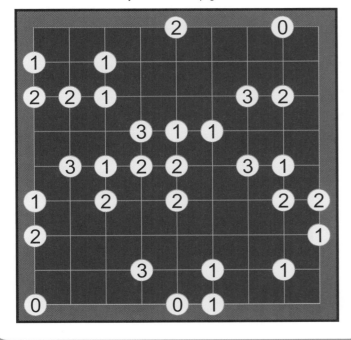

363 Battleships 14

A number of ships of various sizes are hidden in the grid below. The numbers next to each row and column indicate how many ship segments are in that row or column. Some ship segments have already been filled in. Where are the ships? Answer on page 289.

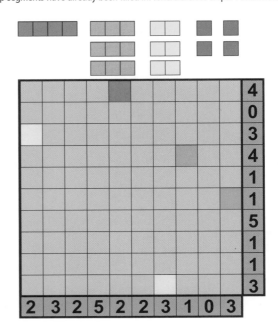

364 Sudoku 19

Fill in the grid below so that the numbers 1–9 appear exactly once in each row, column and 3x3 box. For solution see page 272.

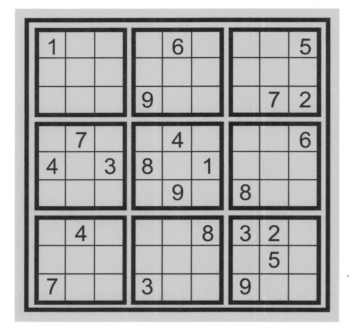

365 Colourminoes 14

In the grid below, each colour has a unique integer value from 0 to 6. The numbers next to each row and column indicate the total value of the cells in that row or column. The values of the cells of the grid correspond in turn to the numbers shown on a half-set of dominoes containing all possible pairs of numbers from (0,0) to (6,6) which has been laid together in one solid rectangle. Dominoes in this rectangle may be placed horizontally or vertically. What number does each colour correspond to, and how are the corresponding dominoes arranged? Answer on page 290.

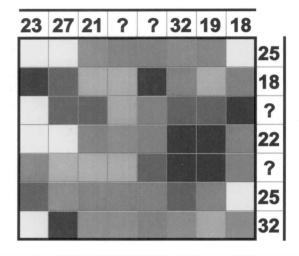

366 Missing Landmarks 11

Which famous landmark is blurred out of this photo?
Answer on page 292.

102

367 Who's Who 6

From the information given, can you match each driver to their car? Answer on p302.

369 Silhouettes 6

Which of the six images fits the silhouette?
Answer on page 302.

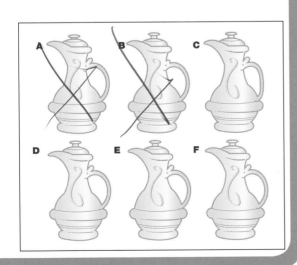

368 Futoshiki 18

Fill in the grid below so that the numbers 1 to 7 appear exactly once in each row and column. Red arrows indicate that a number is greater than its neighbour.
For answer see page 274.

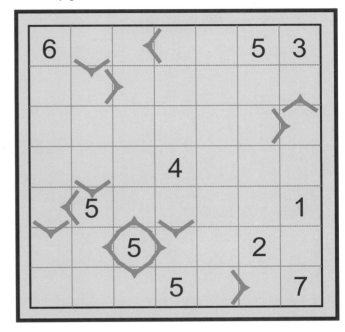

370 Tentai 12

The grid below is divided into a number of shapes. Each shape has a star at its centre, and is made up of one continuous group of cells connected horizontally and/or vertically. The shapes are all symmetrical – they stay the same when rotated by 180 degrees – but may get quite complicated. Where are the shapes? Answer on page 291.

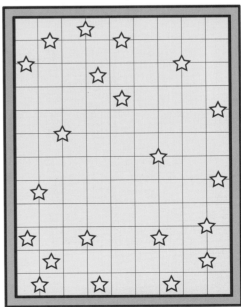

371 Suiri 8

Five drivers are taking cargoes to assorted destinations. From the information below, can you work out which driver (1) is taking which cargo (2) to which city (3) in what sort of vehicle (4)?

1. The silk sheets are not travelling by truck.
2. The 4x4 is being driven to Bahrain.
3. The David Hasselhof albums are being driven by van, but not by Jafar or Iericho.
4. Omar is carrying DVDs, but not to Riyadh.
5. The cargo for Damascus is not being driven by Boutros or Omar.
6. The Riyadh cargo, travelling by ambulance, is not potato flour (which is being driven by Aladdin).
7. Jafar is going to Cairo, but not with cotton.
8. One cargo is going to Medina.
9. One cargo is travelling by car.
Answer on page 298.

		Sheets	Flour	DVDs	Cotton	Albums	Riyadh	Medina	Damascus	Cairo	Bahrain	Van	Truck	Car	Ambulance	4x4
1	Aladdin															
	Boutros															
	Iericho															
	Jafar															
	Omar															
4	4x4															
	Ambulance															
	Car															
	Truck															
	Van															
3	Bahrain															
	Cairo															
	Damascus															
	Medina															
	Riyadh															

372 Gokigen Naname 16

Each cell in the grid below contains one diagonal line from corner to corner. The numbered circles show how many lines touch that corner. Fill in the grid so that the lines never form a closed circuit of any size. Answer on page 276.

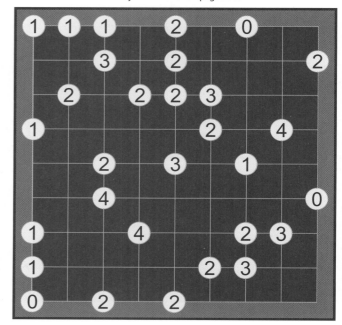

373 Bijutsukan 16

The bright cells and dark cells in the grid below represent corridors and walls respectively. Light sources shine a horizontal and vertical beam of light. A corridor cell becomes illuminated if it is in the same row or column as a light source and there is no wall cell in between them. Place light sources in the corridor cells so that every corridor cell is illuminated, and no light source illuminates another light source. The numbers in some walls tell you how many light sources are touching that wall horizontally or vertically. Answer on page 281.

374 Map Colouring 10

The rooms of the grid are coloured so that no two rooms of the same colour ever touch. How are the rooms coloured? Answer on page 295.

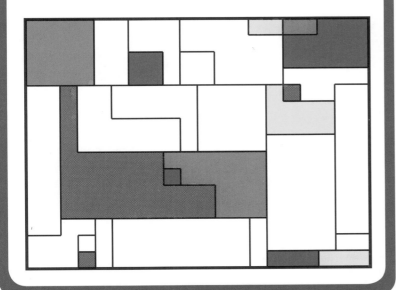

375 Hashiwokakero 8

A number of straight horizontal and vertical bridges connect the islands shown. The number on each island shows how many bridges touch that island. Bridges may not cross each other, and no more than 2 bridges may connect a pair of islands.
Where are the bridges? Answer on page 297.

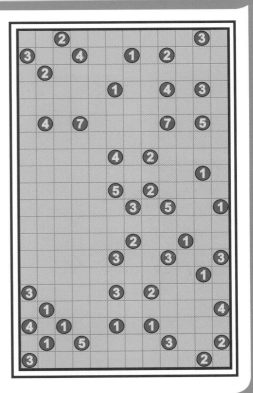

376 Spot the Difference

There are eight differences between the two pictures. Can you find them all? Answer on p302.

377 Domino placing 16

A set of dominoes containing all possible pairs of numbers from (0,0) to (7,7) is laid out vertically as shown in the blank grid below so that the larger number of each domino is on the top. The numbers above each column are from the top half of the dominoes in that column. The numbers below each column are from the bottom half of the dominoes in that column. The numbers to the left of each row are from the respective half-dominoes in that row.

All the numbers are given to you sorted into descending numerical order. How are the dominoes laid out? Answer on page 282.

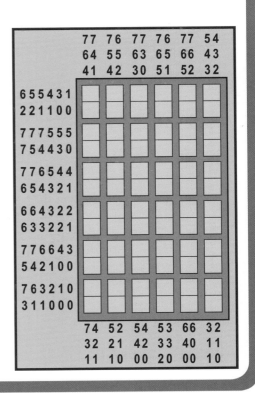

378 Detail Scene 8

The three enlarged squares appear somewhere in the large picture. Can you find them? Answer on page 299.

379 Super Sudoku 4

Fill in the grid below so that the digits 1, 2, 3, 4, 5, 6, 7, 8, 9, a, b, c, d, e, f and g appear exactly once in each row and column. Answer on page 303.

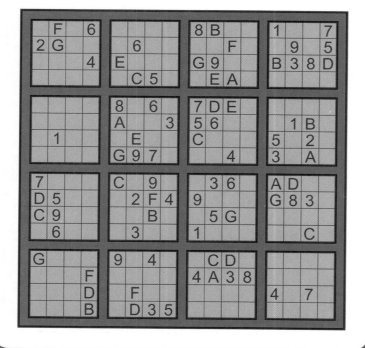

380 Spot the Set

There are four different versions of the picture in the group below, each one reproduced three times. Can you identify the four sets? Answer on page 304.

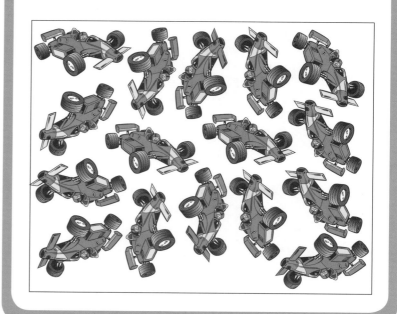

381 Hitori 16

Shade out cells in the grid below so that no number appears more than once in any row or column. Shaded cells cannot touch each other horizontally or vertically, and cannot cut the unshaded cells into two or more groups – the unshaded cells must remain connected horizontally or vertically into one complex branching chain. Which cells are shaded? Answer on page 287.

15	14	8	3	9	5	1	7	9	6	3	10	7	11	14
5	8	15	4	11	13	1	6	14	4	9	14	2	7	10
9	4	13	12	10	8	8	9	1	2	14	12	1	3	15
13	14	9	11	8	14	3	4	10	8	4	1	2	1	5
1	12	7	5	4	1	2	13	8	10	11	12	15	9	4
14	5	4	13	8	12	4	2	2	5	1	3	9	15	11
6	7	12	14	3	2	10	4	3	1	11	6	2	5	15
4	8	10	3	14	7	6	1	9	8	11	13	1	12	
15	9	8	12	7	10	13	14	13	11	11	10	11	4	3
7	3	11	15	15	14	14	12	5	3	10	9	4	1	4
2	10	4	15	14	7	9	5	14	1	13	12	12	6	
1	3	14	2	5	2	12	3	7	9	13	6	11	15	15
10	1	1	8	12	9	9	2	11	7	4	7	7	13	14
11	6	5	7	9	4	13	8	9	12	14	15	14	6	6
3	2	2	1	6	8	4	15	12	7	12	6	10	14	13

382 Differences

Each copy of the picture has one flaw that none of the others share. Can you find them all? Answer on page 304.

383 Dominoes 16

A full set of dominoes containing all possible pairs of numbers from (0,0) to (9,9) is laid together in one solid rectangle. The dominoes may be placed horizontally or vertically. The numbers in the grid below indicate the value of each half of each domino. How are the dominoes arranged? Answer on page 280.

2	9	3	1	5	2	0	1	9	8	2
2	5	5	5	5	8	0	5	9	8	0
1	7	6	1	1	2	3	4	0	9	6
2	7	6	5	0	0	4	0	8	4	7
8	6	1	7	0	8	3	4	4	9	4
2	8	7	6	0	8	9	7	6	2	2
2	4	7	7	4	3	3	3	3	5	9
7	8	1	3	3	5	5	8	6	9	
1	7	4	1	6	0	0	6	9	9	6
1	3	2	6	8	1	9	4	3	7	4

384 Fillomino 16

Each value shown in the grid below is part of a group of cells equal in number to that given value. A '6' is part of a group of six cells, for example. Groups may take any shape, but no two groups of the same size may touch each other horizontally or vertically at any point, and there are no blank cells. Not all groups need have a given value. How are the groups arranged? Answer on page 288.

						2		
			6				7	
7			3			3	1	
		6				3	6	
								4
2			6					
			1				4	1

385 Mirror Image 8

Which of the five images below is an identical mirror image of the one above?
Answer on page 300.

A   B   C   D   E

386 Sikaku 16

Divide the grid below into a number of rectangular rooms. Each room must contain exactly one number, equal to the number of cells that make up the room.
Answer on page 277.

387 Identicals 8

Which pair of images is identical? Answer on page 299.

388 Samurai Sudoku 4

Fill in each 9x9 grid below so that the numbers 1–9 appear exactly once in each row, column and 3x3 block. Numbers in overlapping blocks count identically towards both grids. Answer on page 303.

389 Killer Sudoku 4

Fill in the grid below so that the numbers 1–9 appear exactly once in each row, column and 3x3 block, and that the numbers in each dotted room add up to the value in its top right corner. Answer on page 303.

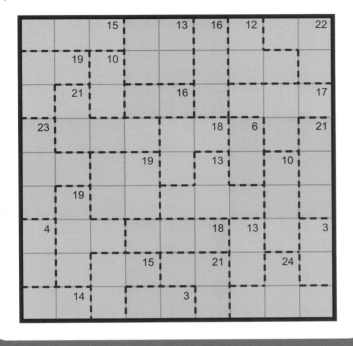

390 Match One 8

Which of the jumbled images is identical to the one presented here? Answer on page 298.

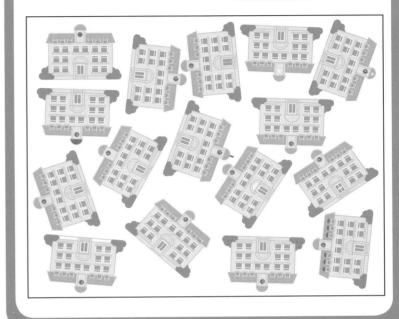

391 Tents 16

The grid below indicates a patch of woodland. Some cells contain grass, and others contain trees. Tents are placed on grass cells so that each tree has one tent next to it horizontally or vertically, although note that tents may be adjacent to more than one tree. No tent may be horizontally, vertically or diagonally adjacent to another tent. The numbers beside each row and column tell you how many tents are in that row or column. Where are the tents? Answer on page 285.

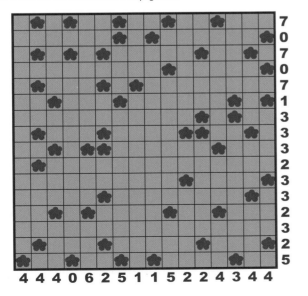

392 Slitherlink 16

A number of the intersection lines in the grid below have to be joined together to make one single complete loop. The numbers in the cell indicate how many of that cell's sides form part of the loop. Answer on page 278.

393 Yudoku 8

Fill in the grid below so that the letters s, p, a, r, k, l, i, n and g appear exactly once in each row, column and 3x3 box. Answer on page 301.

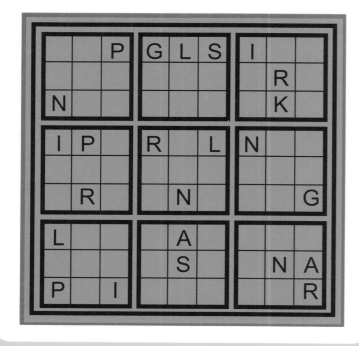

394 Masyu 8

A line passes through some or all of the cells in the grid below in such a way that it forms a single continuous non-intersecting loop. The line always exits a cell by a different side to the one it entered by, and passes through all cells containing a circle. The line travels straight through a cell with a light circle but turns in the previous and/or following cells in its path. The line turns in a cell containing a dark cell, but travels straight through both the previous and following cells in its path. Where is the line? Answer on page 301.

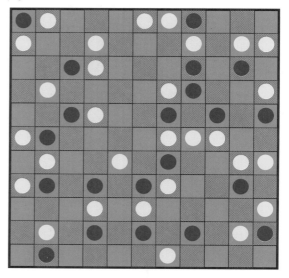

395 Sudoku 20

Fill in the grid below so that the numbers 1–9 appear exactly once in each row, column and 3x3 box. For solution see page 272.

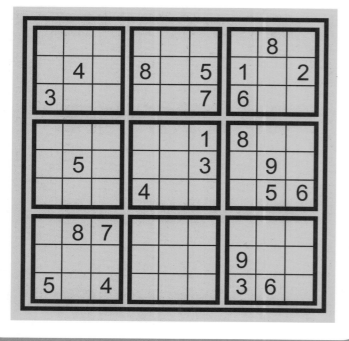

396 Number Link 16

The numbered cells in the grid below indicate the start and end points of single continuous paths. These paths fill the grid completely, and do not branch, cross each other, or touch themselves to form any pool of cells (2x2 or greater). How are the paths arranged? Answer on page 284.

397 Battlehex 10

A number of ships of various sizes are hidden in the hexagonal grid below. The numbers next to each edge indicate how many ship segments are in the rows indicated by the directional arrows. Some ship segments and/or empty water cells have already been filled in. Where are the ships? Answer on page 296.

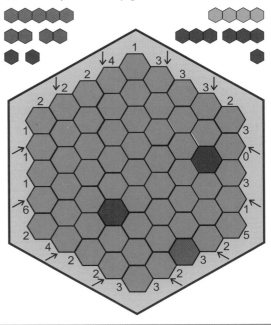

398 Battleships 15

A number of ships of various sizes are hidden in the grid below. The numbers next to each row and column indicate how many ship segments are in that row or column. Some ship segments have already been filled in. Where are the ships? Answer on page 289.

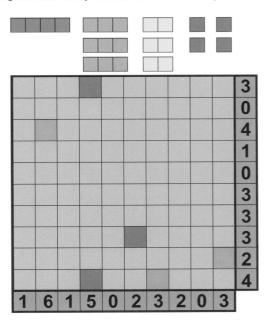

399 Nonogram 11

A number of cells in the grid below are to be shaded. Each row and column may contain one or more continuous lines of shaded cells ('blocks'). The numbers adjacent to the row or column indicate the lengths of the different blocks contained. Blocks are separated from others in the same row or column by at least one empty cell. Where are the shaded cells? A picture will emerge when the cells are shaded correctly. Answer on page 294.

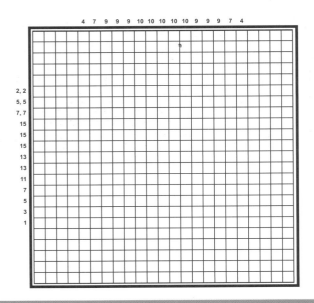

400 Kakuro 11

The empty squares in this grid contain digits from 1 to 9 so that each continuous unbroken line of numbers adds up to the clue value in the filled segment to its left (for horizontal lines) or above it (for vertical lines). No number may be used more than once in any unbroken line. How is the grid filled? Answer on page 293.

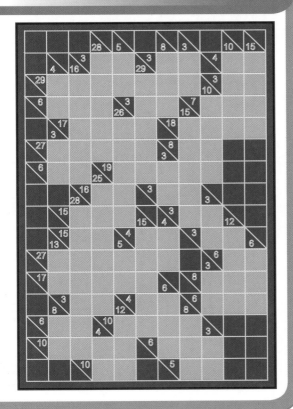

401 Futoshiki 19

Fill in the grid below so that the numbers 1 to 7 appear exactly once in each row and column. Red arrows indicate that a number is greater than its neighbour.
For answer see page 274.

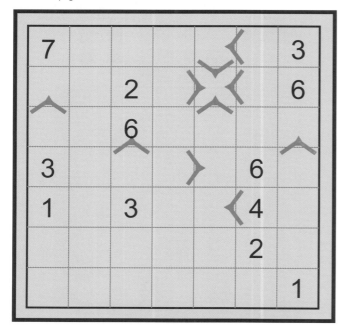

402 Colourminoes 15

In the grid below, each colour has a unique integer value from 0 to 6. The numbers next to each row and column indicate the total value of the cells in that row or column. The values of the cells of the grid correspond in turn to the numbers shown on a half-set of dominoes containing all possible pairs of numbers from (0,0) to (6,6) which has been laid together in one solid rectangle. Dominoes in this rectangle may be placed horizontally or vertically. What number does each colour correspond to, and how are the corresponding dominoes arranged? Answer on page 290.

403 Kin-kon-kan 3

In the grid below, some cells contain diagonal mirrors which reflect light on both sides. One mirror is hidden in each room.

The coloured boxes around the edge indicate the start and finish of a coloured beam of light fired into the grid. These beams always travel in a straight line, but are reflected through a 90-degree angle when hitting a mirror. The number in each box shows how many grid cells its beam of light travels through before exiting again.

Where are the mirrors, and how are they placed? For solution see page 273.

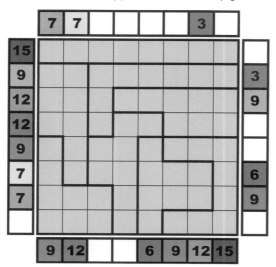

404 Missing Landmarks 12

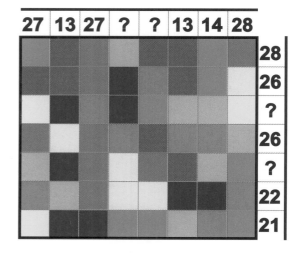

Which famous landmark is blurred out of this photo?
Answer on page 292.

112

405 Sudoku 21

Fill in the grid below so that the numbers 1–9 appear exactly once in each row, column and 3x3 box. For solution see page 272. For solution see page 272.

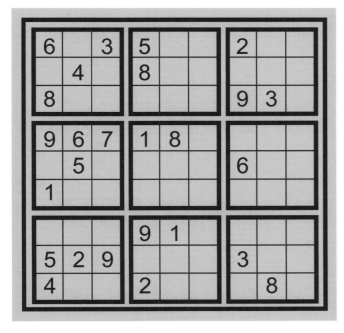

406 Bijutsukan 17

The bright cells and dark cells in the grid below represent corridors and walls respectively. Light sources shine a horizontal and vertical beam of light. A corridor cell becomes illuminated if it is in the same row or column as a light source and there is no wall cell in between them. Place light sources in the corridor cells so that every corridor cell is illuminated, and no light source illuminates another light source. The numbers in some walls tell you how many light sources are touching that wall horizontally or vertically. Answer on page 281.

407 Sikaku 17

Divide the grid below into a number of rectangular rooms. Each room must contain exactly one number, equal to the number of cells that make up the room. Answer on page 277.

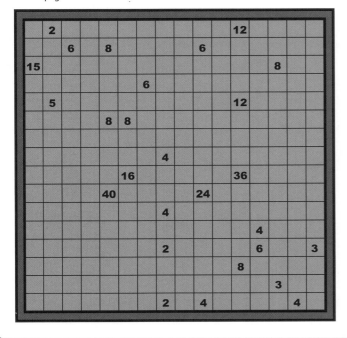

408 Fillomino 17

Each value shown in the grid below is part of a group of cells equal in number to that given value. A '6' is part of a group of six cells, for example. Groups may take any shape, but no two groups of the same size may touch each other horizontally or vertically at any point, and there are no blank cells. Not all groups need have a given value. How are the groups arranged? Answer on page 288.

409 Hitori 17

Shade out cells in the grid below so that no number appears more than once in any row or column. Shaded cells cannot touch each other horizontally or vertically, and cannot cut the unshaded cells into two or more groups – the unshaded cells must remain connected horizontally or vertically into one complex branching chain. Which cells are shaded? Answer on page 287.

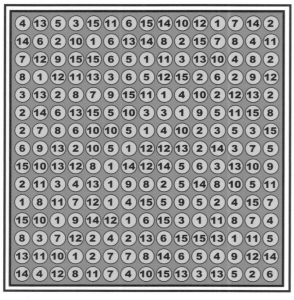

410 Slitherlink 17

A number of the intersection lines in the grid below have to be joined together to make one single complete loop. The numbers in the cell indicate how many of that cell's sides form part of the loop. Answer on page 278.

					2	2	2	
3								
				2	1	2		
	1	3	3		3	2	3	1	3
1	2		2		2			
		2		1		2	1	2
2	1			2		3		
	1	2			0	2		2
1		3		1				
	2	1		3	3	2		3
3		3		2				

411 Number Link 17

The numbered cells in the grid below indicate the start and end points of single continuous paths. These paths fill the grid completely, and do not branch, cross each other, or touch themselves to form any pool of cells (2x2 or greater). How are the paths arranged? Answer on page 284.

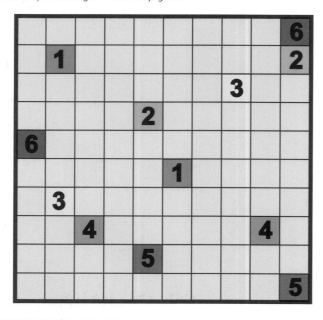

412 Minesweeper 5

The grid below contains a number of bombs hidden in empty squares. Each red flag tells you how many bombs are in the eight cells around it. Where are the bombs? For answer see page 275.

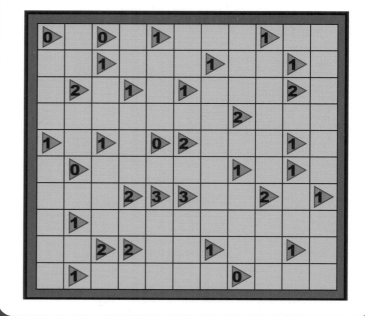

413 Tents 17

The grid below indicates a patch of woodland. Some cells contain grass, and others contain trees. Tents are placed on grass cells so that each tree has one tent next to it horizontally or vertically, although note that tents may be adjacent to more than one tree. No tent may be horizontally, vertically or diagonally adjacent to another tent. The numbers beside each row and column tell you how many tents are in that row or column. Where are the tents? Answer on page 285.

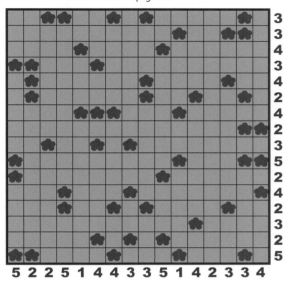

414 Domino placing 17

A set of dominoes containing all possible pairs of numbers from (0,0) to (7,7) is laid out vertically as shown in the blank grid below so that the larger number of each domino is on the top. The numbers above each column are from the top half of the dominoes in that column. The numbers below each column are from the bottom half of the dominoes in that column. The numbers to the left of each row are from the respective half-dominoes in that row. All the numbers are given to you sorted into descending numerical order. How are the dominoes laid out? Answer on page 283.

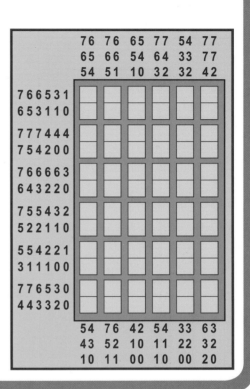

415 Dominoes 17

A full set of dominoes containing all possible pairs of numbers from (0,0) to (9,9) is laid together in one solid rectangle. The dominoes may be placed horizontally or vertically. The numbers in the grid below indicate the value of each half of each domino. How are the dominoes arranged? Answer on page 280.

0	1	0	9	6	5	5	5	3	9	0	3
5	6	0	9	8	0	4	5	7	3	8	
8	0	6	7	1	9	2	5	7	6	8	
6	7	1	1	9	0	7	4	8	4	3	
8	3	4	1	2	2	2	4	6	2	1	
3	9	7	5	6	1	9	5	2	0	8	
5	3	0	4	8	5	1	3	7	8	1	
0	5	4	3	4	9	9	0	4	9	4	
7	7	8	2	2	2	1	2	6	9		
5	2	1	1	6	6	8	6	7	3	6	

416 Gokigen Naname 17

Each cell in the grid below contains one diagonal line from corner to corner. The numbered circles show how many lines touch that corner. Fill in the grid so that the lines never form a closed circuit of any size. Answer on page 276.

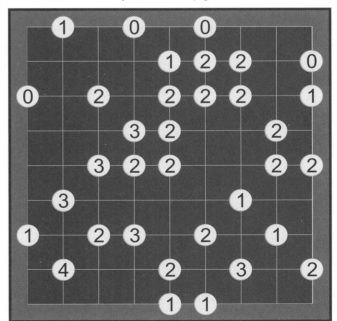

417 Tentai 13

The grid below is divided into a number of shapes. Each shape has a star at its centre, and is made up of one continuous group of cells connected horizontally and/or vertically. The shapes are all symmetrical – they stay the same when rotated by 180 degrees – but may get quite complicated. Where are the shapes? Answer on page 291.

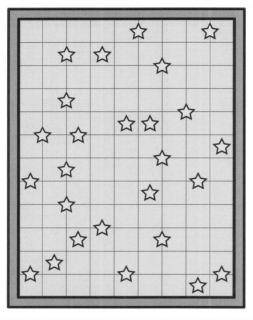

418 Battleships 16

A number of ships of various sizes are hidden in the grid below. The numbers next to each row and column indicate how many ship segments are in that row or column. Some ship segments have already been filled in. Where are the ships? Answer on page 289.

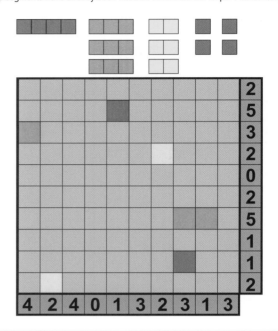

419 Sudoku 22

Fill in the grid below so that the numbers 1–9 appear exactly once in each row, column and 3x3 box. For solution see page 272.

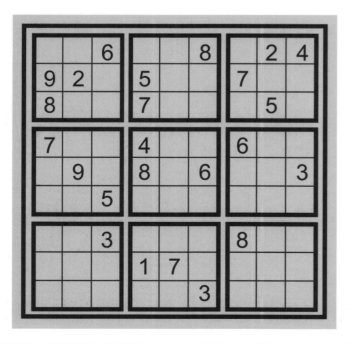

420 Futoshiki 20

Fill in the grid below so that the numbers 1 to 7 appear exactly once in each row and column. Red arrows indicate that a number is greater than its neighbour. For answer see page 274.

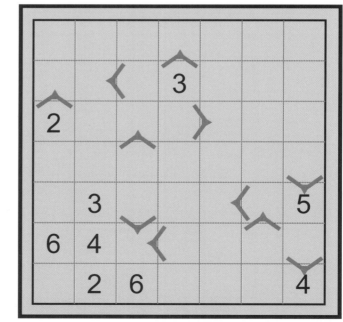

421 Battlehex 11

A number of ships of various sizes are hidden in the hexagonal grid below. The numbers next to each edge indicate how many ship segments are in the rows indicated by the directional arrows. Some ship segments and/or empty water cells have already been filled in. Where are the ships? Answer on page 296.

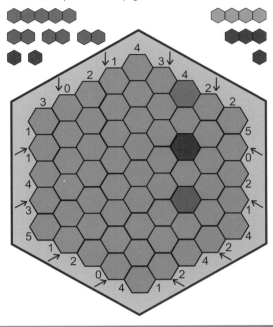

422 Map Colouring 11

The rooms of the grid are coloured so that no two rooms of the same colour ever touch. How are the rooms coloured? Answer on page 295.

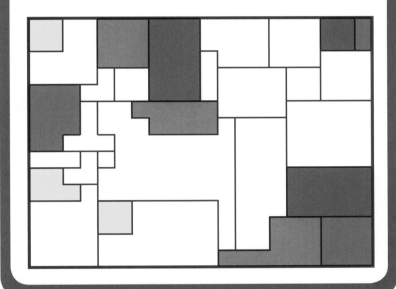

423 Kakuro 12

The empty squares in this grid contain digits from 1 to 9 so that each continuous unbroken line of numbers adds up to the clue value in the filled segment to its left (for horizontal lines) or above it (for vertical lines). No number may be used more than once in any unbroken line. How is the grid filled? Answer on page 293.

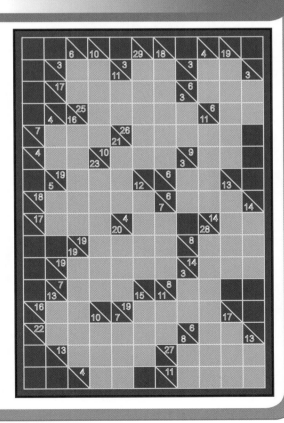

424 Artist's Errors

The artist drawing this scene has made a number of visual, conceptual and logical errors. Can you find them all?
Answer on page 304.

425 Nonogram 12

A number of cells in the grid below are to be shaded. Each row and column may contain one or more continuous lines of shaded cells ('blocks'). The numbers adjacent to the row or column indicate the lengths of the different blocks contained. Blocks are separated from others in the same row or column by at least one empty cell. Where are the shaded cells? A picture will emerge when the cells are shaded correctly. Answer on page 294.

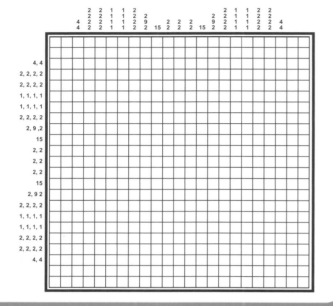

426 Colourminoes 16

In the grid below, each colour has a unique integer value from 0 to 6. The numbers next to each row and column indicate the total value of the cells in that row or column. The values of the cells of the grid correspond in turn to the numbers shown on a half-set of dominoes containing all possible pairs of numbers from (0,0) to (6,6) which has been laid together in one solid rectangle. Dominoes in this rectangle may be placed horizontally or vertically. What number does each colour correspond to, and how are the corresponding dominoes arranged? Answer on page 290.

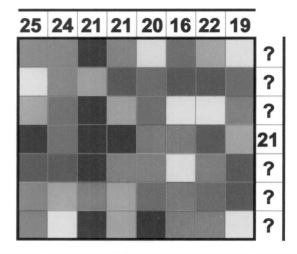

427 Hashiwokakero 9

A number of straight horizontal and vertical bridges connect the islands shown. The number on each island shows how many bridges touch that island. Bridges may not cross each other, and no more than 2 bridges may connect a pair of islands.
Where are the bridges? Answer on page 297.

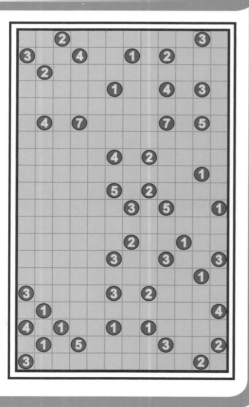

428 Gokigen Naname 18

Each cell in the grid below contains one diagonal line from corner to corner. The numbered circles show how many lines touch that corner. Fill in the grid so that the lines never form a closed circuit of any size. Answer on page 276.

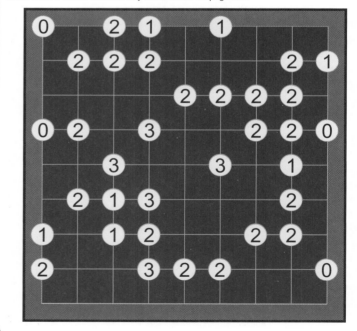

429 **Sikaku 18**

Divide the grid below into a number of rectangular rooms. Each room must contain exactly one number, equal to the number of cells that make up the room.

Answer on page 277.

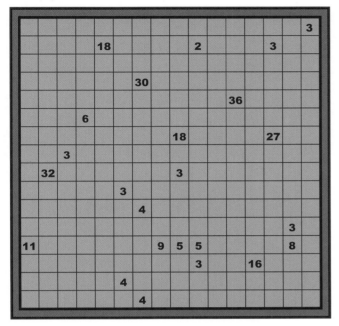

431 **Tents 18**

The grid below indicates a patch of woodland. Some cells contain grass, and others contain trees. Tents are placed on grass cells so that each tree has one tent next to it horizontally or vertically, although note that tents may be adjacent to more than one tree. No tent may be horizontally, vertically or diagonally adjacent to another tent. The numbers beside each row and column tell you how many tents are in that row or column. Where are the tents? Answer on page 285.

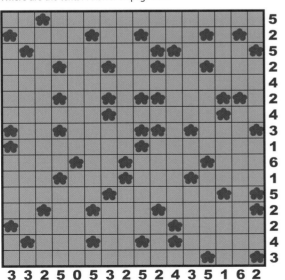

430 **Suiri 9**

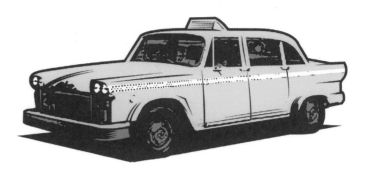

A group of women are travelling around new york by taxi. From the information given below, can you work out where each woman (1) went to (2), to do what (3), and how much she was charged for her ride?

1. Tina paid more for her journey than the woman who went out to get some exercise.
2. Either Lydia or Tina went out for coffee, and paid 5¢ more than the woman who went to meet a friend.
3. The woman going to Central Park paid less than the woman going to Grand Central Station, who was not going shopping.
4. Either Filia went to SoHo and tina went shopping, or Agathi went to SoHo and Filia went shopping.
5. Eleni, who went to Macy's, paid 5¢ more than the woman who went out for coffee.
6. Either Tina or Lydia went sight-seeing and paid 75¢ For the ride.
7. One of the women went to Liberty Island.
8. The fares were 60¢, 65¢, 70¢, 75¢ and 80¢.

Answer on page 298.

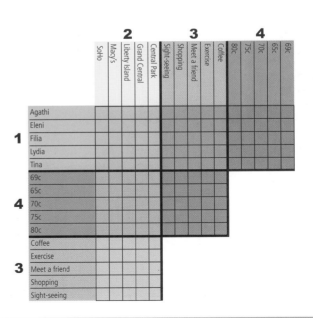

432 Domino placing 18

A set of dominoes containing all possible pairs of numbers from (0,0) to (7,7) is laid out vertically as shown in the blank grid below so that the larger number of each domino is on the top. The numbers above each column are from the top half of the dominoes in that column. The numbers below each column are from the bottom half of the dominoes in that column. The numbers to the left of each row are from the respective half-dominoes in that row.

All the numbers are given to you sorted into descending numerical order. How are the dominoes laid out? Answer on page 282.

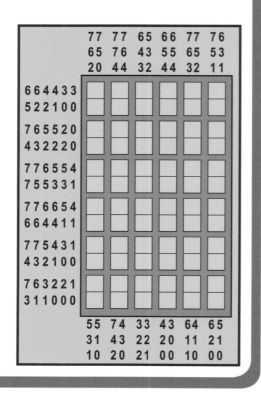

433 Missing Landmarks 13

Which famous landmark is blurred out of this photo? Answer on page 292.

434 Slitherlink 18

A number of the intersection lines in the grid below have to be joined together to make one single complete loop. The numbers in the cell indicate how many of that cell's sides form part of the loop. Answer on page 278.

435 Match one 9

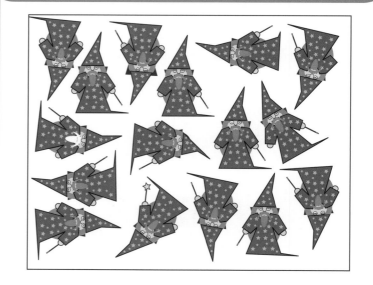

Which of the jumbled images is identical to the one presented here? Answer on page 298.

436 Yudoku 9

Fill in the grid below so that the letters s, p, a, r, k, l, i, n and g appear exactly once in each row, column and 3x3 box. Answer on page 301.

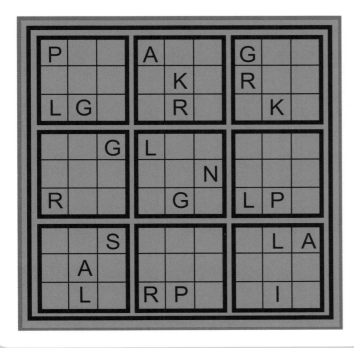

437 Dominoes 18

A full set of dominoes containing all possible pairs of numbers from (0,0) to (9,9) is laid together in one solid rectangle. The dominoes may be placed horizontally or vertically. The numbers in the grid below indicate the value of each half of each domino. How are the dominoes arranged? Answer on page 280.

5	0	6	1	3	4	6	5	6	4	0
7	3	8	9	8	2	2	1	4	9	7
8	3	4	2	1	3	6	6	4	4	2
9	0	8	5	5	8	7	5	1	1	0
5	3	7	2	7	2	9	9	8	0	0
2	3	5	9	7	4	6	2	0	7	7
5	4	3	0	3	4	8	2	4	5	1
2	9	5	9	4	1	6	9	3	1	7
8	8	5	2	7	0	6	6	0	0	1
8	9	6	1	7	3	1	9	3	6	8

438 Bijutsukan 18

The bright cells and dark cells in the grid below represent corridors and walls respectively. Light sources shine a horizontal and vertical beam of light. A corridor cell becomes illuminated if it is in the same row or column as a light source and there is no wall cell in between them. Place light sources in the corridor cells so that every corridor cell is illuminated, and no light source illuminates another light source. The numbers in some walls tell you how many light sources are touching that wall horizontally or vertically. Answer on page 281.

439 Number Link 18

The numbered cells in the grid below indicate the start and end points of single continuous paths. These paths fill the grid completely, and do not branch, cross each other, or touch themselves to form any pool of cells (2x2 or greater).
How are the paths arranged? Answer on page 284.

440 Masyu 9

A line passes through some or all of the cells in the grid below in such a way that it forms a single continuous non-intersecting loop. The line always exits a cell by a different side to the one it entered by, and passes through all cells containing a circle. The line travels straight through a cell with a light circle but turns in the previous and/or following cells in its path. The line turns in a cell containing a dark cell, but travels straight through both the previous and following cells in its path. Where is the line? Answer on page 301.

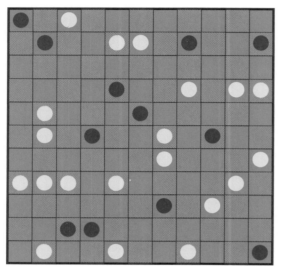

441 Hitori 18

Shade out cells in the grid below so that no number appears more than once in any row or column. Shaded cells cannot touch each other horizontally or vertically, and cannot cut the unshaded cells into two or more groups – the unshaded cells must remain connected horizontally or vertically into one complex branching chain. Which cells are shaded? Answer on page 287.

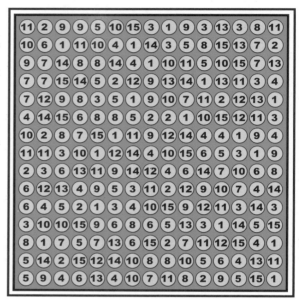

442 Fillomino 18

Each value shown in the grid below is part of a group of cells equal in number to that given value. A '6' is part of a group of six cells, for example. Groups may take any shape, but no two groups of the same size may touch each other horizontally or vertically at any point, and there are no blank cells. Not all groups need have a given value. How are the groups arranged? Answer on page 288.

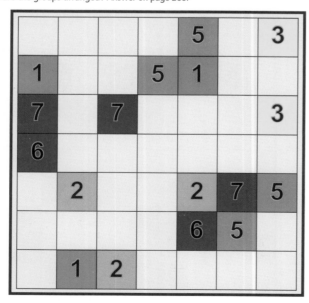

443 Mirror Image 9

Which of the five images below is an identical mirror image of the one above? Answer on page 300.

444 Identicals 9

Which pair of images is identical? Answer on page 299.

445 Battleships 17

A number of ships of various sizes are hidden in the grid below. The numbers next to each row and column indicate how many ship segments are in that row or column. Some ship segments have already been filled in. Where are the ships? Answer on page 289.

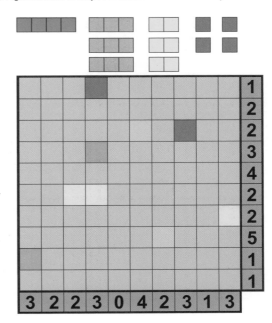

446 Detail Scene 9

The three enlarged squares appear somewhere in the large picture. Can you find them? Answer on page 299.

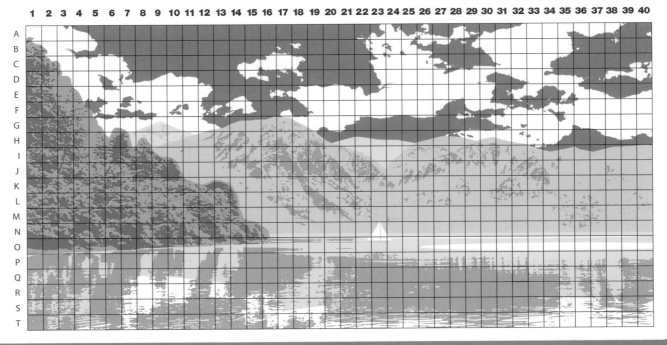

447 Sudoku 23

Fill in the grid below so that the numbers 1–9 appear exactly once in each row, column and 3x3 box.

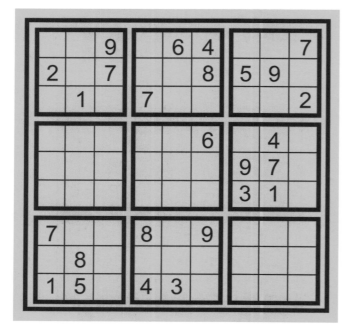

448 Who's Who 7

From the information, can you match each gardener to his prize bloom? Answer on p302.

449 Silhouettes 7

Which of the six images fits the silhouette? Answer on page 302.

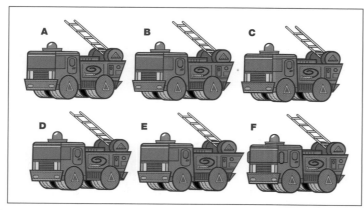

450 Tentai 14

The grid below is divided into a number of shapes. Each shape has a star at its centre, and is made up of one continuous group of cells connected horizontally and/or vertically. The shapes are all symmetrical – they stay the same when rotated by 180 degrees – but may get quite complicated. Where are the shapes? Answer on page 291.

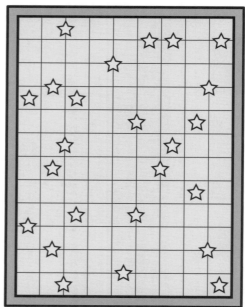

451 Futoshiki 21

Fill in the grid below so that the numbers 1 to 7 appear exactly once in each row and column. Red arrows indicate that a number is greater than its neighbour.
For answer see page 274.

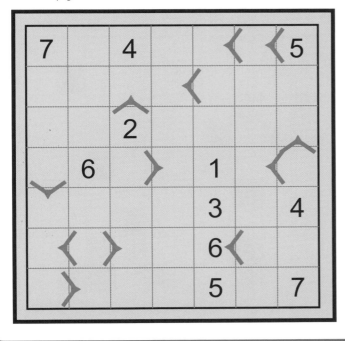

452 Bijutsukan 19

The bright cells and dark cells in the grid below represent corridors and walls respectively. Light sources shine a horizontal and vertical beam of light. A corridor cell becomes illuminated if it is in the same row or column as a light source and there is no wall cell in between them. Place light sources in the corridor cells so that every corridor cell is illuminated, and no light source illuminates another light source. The numbers in some walls tell you how many light sources are touching that wall horizontally or vertically. Answer on page 281.

453 Fillomino 19

Each value shown in the grid below is part of a group of cells equal in number to that given value. A '6' is part of a group of six cells, for example. Groups may take any shape, but no two groups of the same size may touch each other horizontally or vertically at any point, and there are no blank cells. Not all groups need have a given value. How are the groups arranged? Answer on page 288.

454 Gokigen Naname 19

Each cell in the grid below contains one diagonal line from corner to corner. The numbered circles show how many lines touch that corner. Fill in the grid so that the lines never form a closed circuit of any size. Answer on page 276.

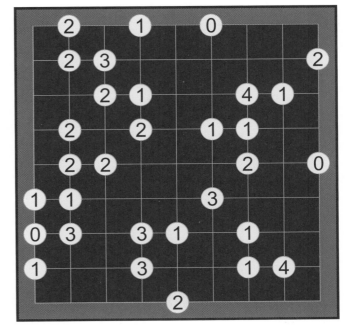

455 Hitori 19

Shade out cells in the grid below so that no number appears more than once in any row or column. Shaded cells cannot touch each other horizontally or vertically, and cannot cut the unshaded cells into two or more groups – the unshaded cells must remain connected horizontally or vertically into one complex branching chain. Which cells are shaded? Answer on page 287.

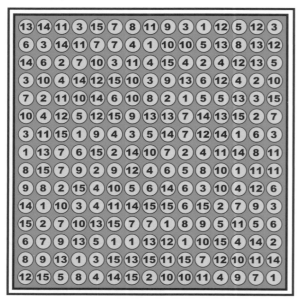

456 Number Link 19

The numbered cells in the grid below indicate the start and end points of single continuous paths. These paths fill the grid completely, and do not branch, cross each other, or touch themselves to form any pool of cells (2x2 or greater).
How are the paths arranged? Answer on page 284.

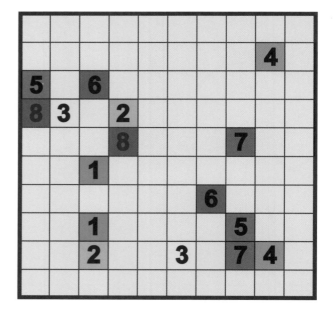

457 Tents 19

The grid below indicates a patch of woodland. Some cells contain grass, and others contain trees. Tents are placed on grass cells so that each tree has one tent next to it horizontally or vertically, although note that tents may be adjacent to more than one tree. No tent may be horizontally, vertically or diagonally adjacent to another tent. The numbers beside each row and column tell you how many tents are in that row or column. Where are the tents? Answer on page 285.

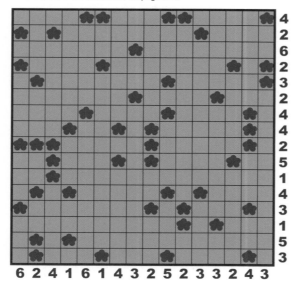

458 Domino placing 19

A set of dominoes containing all possible pairs of numbers from (0,0) to (7,7) is laid out vertically as shown in the blank grid below so that the larger number of each domino is on the top. The numbers above each column are from the top half of the dominoes in that column. The numbers below each column are from the bottom half of the dominoes in that column. The numbers to the left of each row are from the respective half-dominoes in that row. All the numbers are given to you sorted into descending numerical order. How are the dominoes laid out? Answer on page 283.

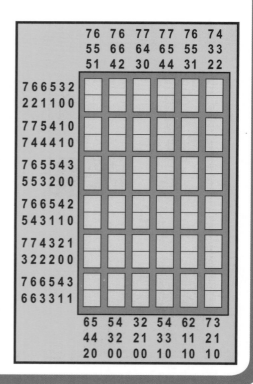

459 Dominoes 19

A full set of dominoes containing all possible pairs of numbers from (0,0) to (9,9) is laid together in one solid rectangle. The dominoes may be placed horizontally or vertically. The numbers in the grid below indicate the value of each half of each domino. How are the dominoes arranged? Answer on page 280.

1	6	7	1	8	2	9	5	5	8	0
8	8	1	3	4	7	6	8	2	2	8
6	1	0	3	0	0	5	7	3	3	5
6	1	0	0	3	0	5	8	7	6	2
9	6	5	9	1	4	2	7	5	9	3
0	1	5	2	1	7	7	8	2	7	9
7	8	0	1	3	4	6	5	3	4	1
2	9	1	2	0	6	0	2	9	9	3
4	8	4	4	4	6	2	5	3	7	—
4	7	8	3	9	9	6	9	5	4	6

460 Slitherlink 19

A number of the intersection lines in the grid below have to be joined together to make one single complete loop. The numbers in the cell indicate how many of that cell's sides form part of the loop. Answer on page 278.

3	3					2	1	2	
1			3	2	3	2	2		
2			2						3
	2				1	3	0	2	2
					2	2			
2		1		2	2				2
2		2	2					1	3
	1	3	2						
2		2		1	3			1	3
3		1	2	2		2	2	3	

461 Sikaku 19

Divide the grid below into a number of rectangular rooms. Each room must contain exactly one number, equal to the number of cells that make up the room. Answer on page 277.

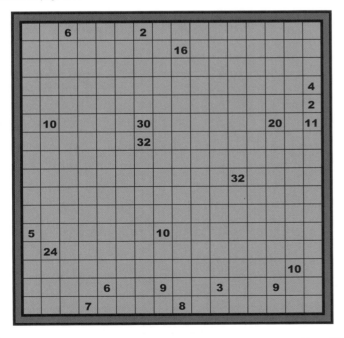

462 Colourminoes 17

In the grid below, each colour has a unique integer value from 0 to 6. The numbers next to each row and column indicate the total value of the cells in that row or column. The values of the cells of the grid correspond in turn to the numbers shown on a half-set of dominoes containing all possible pairs of numbers from (0,0) to (6,6) which has been laid together in one solid rectangle. Dominoes in this rectangle may be placed horizontally or vertically. What number does each colour correspond to, and how are the corresponding dominoes arranged? Answer on page 290.

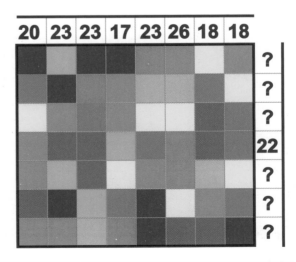

463 Map Colouring 12

The rooms of the grid are coloured so that no two rooms of the same colour ever touch. How are the rooms coloured? Answer on page 295.

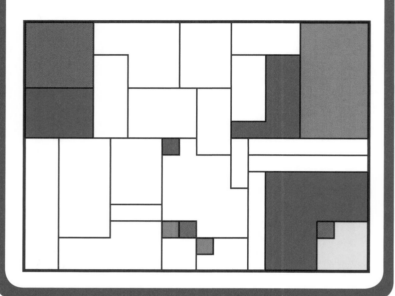

464 Battlehex 12

A number of ships of various sizes are hidden in the hexagonal grid below. The numbers next to each edge indicate how many ship segments are in the rows indicated by the directional arrows. Some ship segments and/or empty water cells have already been filled in. Where are the ships? Answer on page 296.

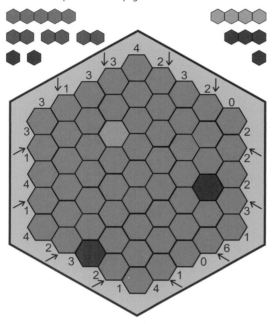

465 Sudoku 24

Fill in the grid below so that the numbers 1–9 appear exactly once in each row, column and 3x3 box. For solution see page 272.

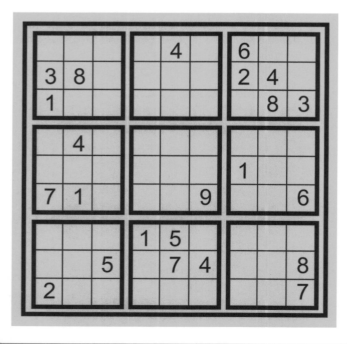

466 Nonogram 13

A number of cells in the grid below are to be shaded. Each row and column may contain one or more continuous lines of shaded cells ('blocks'). The numbers adjacent to the row or column indicate the lengths of the different blocks contained. Blocks are separated from others in the same row or column by at least one empty cell. Where are the shaded cells? A picture will emerge when the cells are shaded correctly. Answer on page 294.

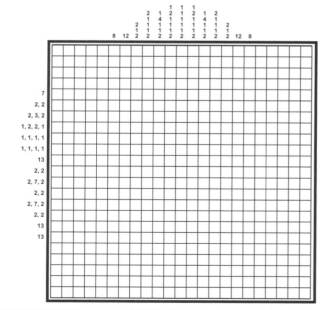

467 Kakuro 13

The empty squares in this grid contain digits from 1 to 9 so that each continuous unbroken line of numbers adds up to the clue value in the filled segment to its left (for horizontal lines) or above it (for vertical lines). No number may be used more than once in any unbroken line. How is the grid filled? Answer on page 293.

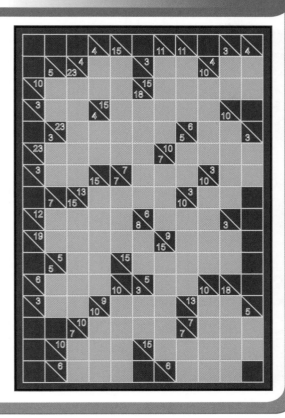

468 Futoshiki 22

Fill in the grid below so that the numbers 1 to 7 appear exactly once in each row and column. Red arrows indicate that a number is greater than its neighbour. For answer see page 274.

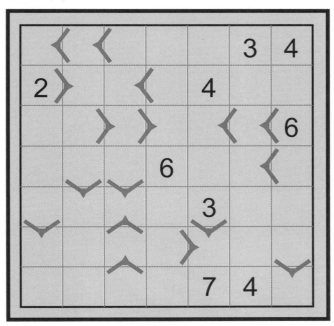

469 Battleships 18

A number of ships of various sizes are hidden in the grid below. The numbers next to each row and column indicate how many ship segments are in that row or column. Some ship segments have already been filled in. Where are the ships? Answer on page 289.

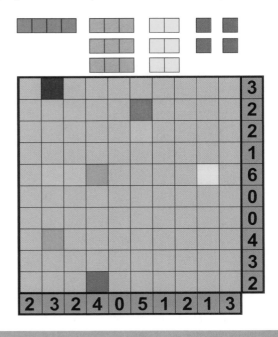

470 Tentai 15

The grid below is divided into a number of shapes. Each shape has a star at its centre, and is made up of one continuous group of cells connected horizontally and/or vertically. The shapes are all symmetrical – they stay the same when rotated by 180 degrees – but may get quite complicated. Where are the shapes? Answer on page 291.

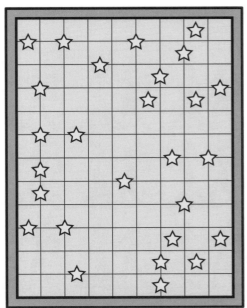

471 Missing Landmarks 14

Which famous landmark is blurred out of this photo? Answer on page 292.

472 Differences

Each copy of the picture has one flaw that none of the others share. Can you find them all? Answer on page 304.

473 Spot the Set

There are four different versions of the picture in the group below, each one reproduced three times. Can you identify the four sets?
Answer on page 304.

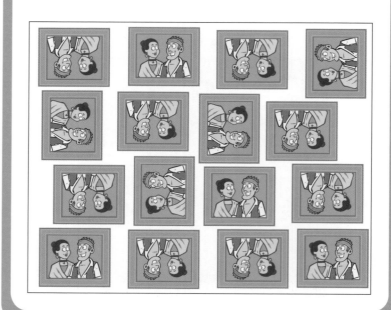

474 Match one 10

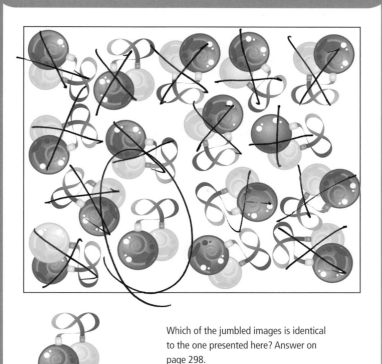

Which of the jumbled images is identical to the one presented here? Answer on page 298.

475 Dominoes 20

A full set of dominoes containing all possible pairs of numbers from (0,0) to (9,9) is laid together in one solid rectangle. The dominoes may be placed horizontally or vertically. The numbers in the grid below indicate the value of each half of each domino. How are the dominoes arranged? Answer on page 280.

4	5	5	1	9	8	8	5	9	1	9
7	6	6	7	3	5	3	8	8	6	9
3	4	0	1	4	8	6	9	3	7	2
5	0	5	5	1	5	7	1	3	0	2
7	6	3	5	9	6	8	4	2	5	8
8	8	0	9	4	7	1	0	2	4	0
7	2	0	4	1	8	2	0	6	4	2
2	3	1	2	7	5	7	9	6	6	9
1	2	1	2	1	3	9	3	0	3	7
4	4	8	6	0	4	0	6	9	3	7

476 Fillomino 20

Each value shown in the grid below is part of a group of cells equal in number to that given value. A '6' is part of a group of six cells, for example. Groups may take any shape, but no two groups of the same size may touch each other horizontally or vertically at any point, and there are no blank cells. Not all groups need have a given value. How are the groups arranged? Answer on page 288.

477 Bijutsukan 20

The bright cells and dark cells in the grid below represent corridors and walls respectively. Light sources shine a horizontal and vertical beam of light. A corridor cell becomes illuminated if it is in the same row or column as a light source and there is no wall cell in between them. Place light sources in the corridor cells so that every corridor cell is illuminated, and no light source illuminates another light source. The numbers in some walls tell you how many light sources are touching that wall horizontally or vertically. Answer on page 281.

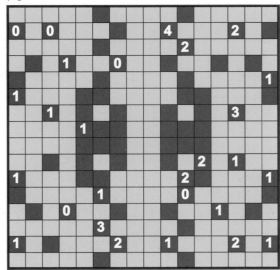

478 Masyu 10

A line passes through some or all of the cells in the grid below in such a way that it forms a single continuous non-intersecting loop. The line always exits a cell by a different side to the one it entered by, and passes through all cells containing a circle. The line travels straight through a cell with a light circle but turns in the previous and/or following cells in its path. The line turns in a cell containing a dark cell, but travels straight through both the previous and following cells in its path. Where is the line? Answer on page 301.

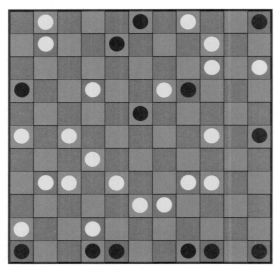

479 Super Sudoku 5

Fill in the grid below so that the digits 1, 2, 3, 4, 5, 6, 7, 8, 9, a, b, c, d, e, f and g appear exactly once in each row and column. Answer on page 303.

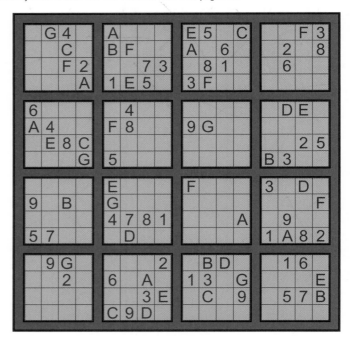

480 Slitherlink 20

A number of the intersection lines in the grid below have to be joined together to make one single complete loop. The numbers in the cell indicate how many of that cell's sides form part of the loop. Answer on page 278.

2	3	2	2	2			2		
						3		3	
			3	3				3	
2	3	2	2			1		3	
		1	2	2					
	2		3		3				
3	2		3		1		2		
	2	2		3					
3		3				2		2	
	2	1	3	1	2	3			

481 Samurai Sudoku 5

Fill in each 9x9 grid below so that the numbers 1–9 appear exactly once in each row, column and 3x3 block. Numbers in overlapping blocks count identically towards both grids. Answer on page 303.

482 Suiri 10

Five ladies have taken exotic holidays. From the information given below, can you work out where each lady (1) has travelled to (2), where she is staying (3), and what she went there for (4)?

1. Tisha went to Mauritius or Indonesia for either the shops or the beach.
2. Morna went on holiday for either the forest or the temple.
3. The Cambodian destination was either a lodge or a resort.
4. The villa was either in Indonesia or Cambodia, and either Adara or Romy went there.
5. The chalet was either near a temple or the shops.
6. Either the hotel or the lodge had a pool.
7. Gina went to either Indonesia or Thailand for either the forest or the shops and stayed in either a chalet or a resort.
8. Romy stayed in either a chalet or a villa, and went for either the pool or the shops.
9. One lady went to Malaysia.

Answer on page 299.

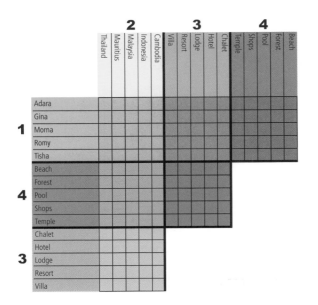

483 Number Link 20

The numbered cells in the grid below indicate the start and end points of single continuous paths. These paths fill the grid completely, and do not branch, cross each other, or touch themselves to form any pool of cells (2x2 or greater).

How are the paths arranged? Answer on page 284.

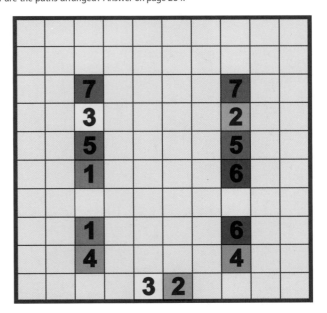

484 Identicals 10

Which pair of images is identical?
Answer on page 299.

485 Detail Scene 10

The three enlarged squares appear somewhere in the large picture. Can you find them? Answer on page 299.

486 Sikaku 20

Divide the grid below into a number of rectangular rooms. Each room must contain exactly one number, equal to the number of cells that make up the room.
Answer on page 277.

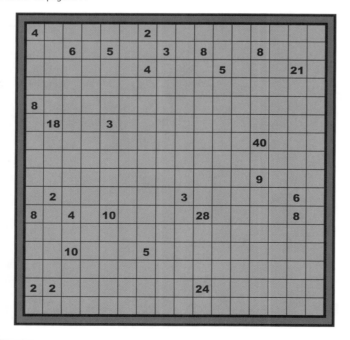

487 Hashiwokakero 10

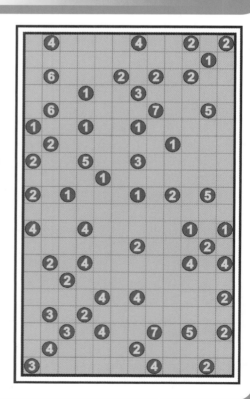

A number of straight horizontal and vertical bridges connect the islands shown. The number on each island shows how many bridges touch that island. Bridges may not cross each other, and no more than 2 bridges may connect a pair of islands.
Where are the bridges?
Answer on page 297.

488 Sudoku 25

Fill in the grid below so that the numbers 1–9 appear exactly once in each row, column and 3x3 box. For solution see page 272.

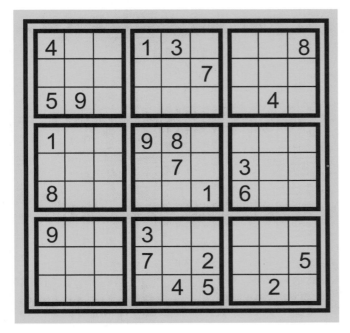

489 Gokigen Naname 20

Each cell in the grid below contains one diagonal line from corner to corner. The numbered circles show how many lines touch that corner. Fill in the grid so that the lines never form a closed circuit of any size. Answer on page 276.

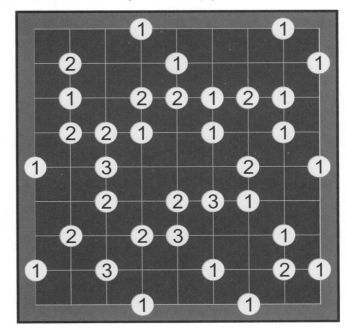

490 Spot the Difference

There are eight differences between the two pictures. Can you find them all? Answer on p302.

491 Tents 20

The grid below indicates a patch of woodland. Some cells contain grass, and others contain trees. Tents are placed on grass cells so that each tree has one tent next to it horizontally or vertically, although note that tents may be adjacent to more than one tree. No tent may be horizontally, vertically or diagonally adjacent to another tent. The numbers beside each row and column tell you how many tents are in that row or column. Where are the tents? Answer on page 285.

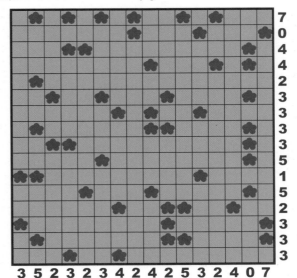

492 Mirror Image 10

Which of the five images below is an identical mirror image of the one above?
Answer on page 300.

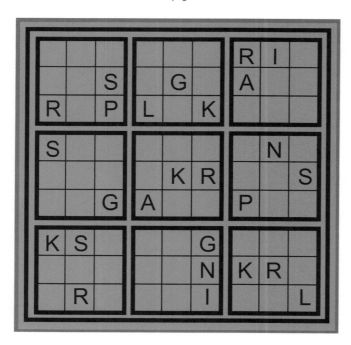

A   B   C   D   E

493 Domino placing 20

A set of dominoes containing all possible pairs of numbers from (0,0) to (7,7) is laid out vertically as shown in the blank grid below so that the larger number of each domino is on the top. The numbers above each column are from the top half of the dominoes in that column. The numbers below each column are from the bottom half of the dominoes in that column. The numbers to the left of each row are from the respective half-dominoes in that row. All the numbers are given to you sorted into descending numerical order. How are the dominoes laid out? Answer on page 283.

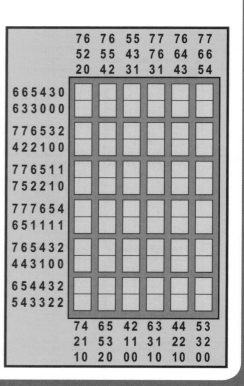

	76	76	55	77	76	77
	52	55	43	76	64	66
	20	42	31	31	43	54

665430
633000

776532
422100

776511
752210

777654
651111

765432
443100

654432
543322

	74	65	42	63	44	53
	21	53	11	31	22	32
	10	20	00	10	10	00

494 Yudoku 10

Fill in the grid below so that the letters s, p, a, r, k, l, i, n and g appear exactly once in each row, column and 3x3 box. Answer on page 301.

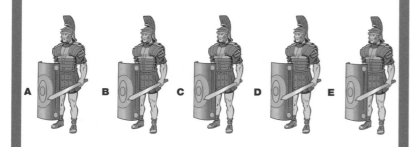

495 Killer Sudoku 5

Fill in the grid below so that the numbers 1–9 appear exactly once in each row, column and 3x3 block, and that the numbers in each dotted room add up to the value in its top right corner. Answer on page 303.

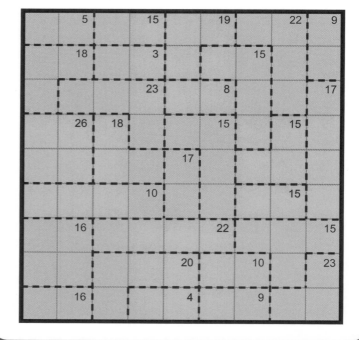

496 Hitori 20

Shade out cells in the grid below so that no number appears more than once in any row or column. Shaded cells cannot touch each other horizontally or vertically, and cannot cut the unshaded cells into two or more groups – the unshaded cells must remain connected horizontally or vertically into one complex branching chain. Which cells are shaded? Answer on page 287.

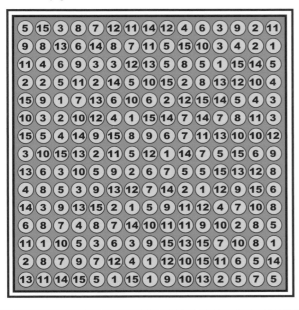

497 Colourminoes 18

In the grid below, each colour has a unique integer value from 0 to 6. The numbers next to each row and column indicate the total value of the cells in that row or column. The values of the cells of the grid correspond in turn to the numbers shown on a half-set of dominoes containing all possible pairs of numbers from (0,0) to (6,6) which has been laid together in one solid rectangle. Dominoes in this rectangle may be placed horizontally or vertically. What number does each colour correspond to, and how are the corresponding dominoes arranged? Answer on page 290.

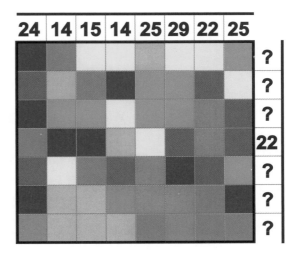

498 Futoshiki 23

Fill in the grid below so that the numbers 1 to 7 appear exactly once in each row and column. Red arrows indicate that a number is greater than its neighbour. For answer see page 274.

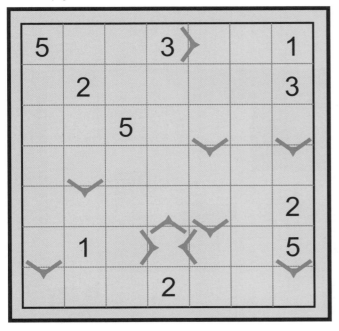

499 Battleships 19

A number of ships of various sizes are hidden in the grid below. The numbers next to each row and column indicate how many ship segments are in that row or column. Some ship segments have already been filled in. Where are the ships? Answer on page 289.

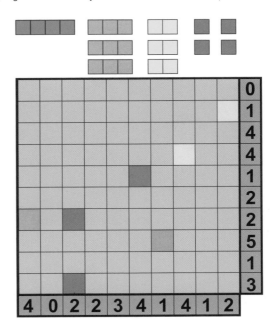

500 Kakuro 14

The empty squares in this grid contain digits from 1 to 9 so that each continuous unbroken line of numbers adds up to the clue value in the filled segment to its left (for horizontal lines) or above it (for vertical lines). No number may be used more than once in any unbroken line. How is the grid filled? Answer on page 293.

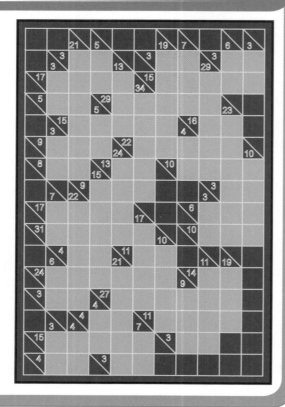

501 Nonogram 14

A number of cells in the grid below are to be shaded. Each row and column may contain one or more continuous lines of shaded cells ('blocks'). The numbers adjacent to the row or column indicate the lengths of the different blocks contained. Blocks are separated from others in the same row or column by at least one empty cell. Where are the shaded cells? A picture will emerge when the cells are shaded correctly. Answer on page 294.

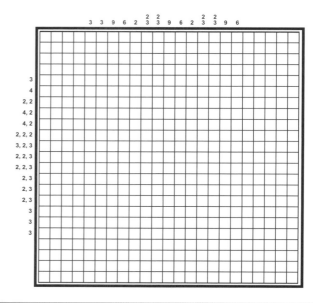

502 Battlehex 13

A number of ships of various sizes are hidden in the hexagonal grid below. The numbers next to each edge indicate how many ship segments are in the rows indicated by the directional arrows. Some ship segments and/or empty water cells have already been filled in. Where are the ships? Answer on page 296.

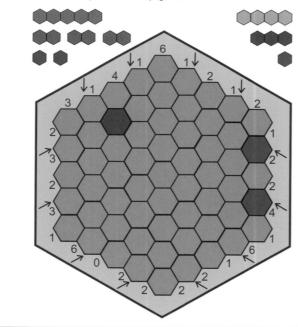

503 Map Colouring 13

The rooms of the grid are coloured so that no two rooms of the same colour ever touch. How are the rooms coloured? Answer on page 295.

504 Sudoku 26

Fill in the grid below so that the numbers 1–9 appear exactly once in each row, column and 3x3 box.

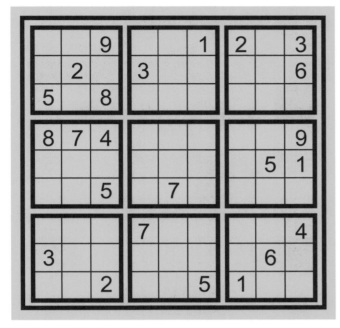

505 Slitherlink 21

A number of the intersection lines in the grid below have to be joined together to make one single complete loop. The numbers in the cell indicate how many of that cell's sides form part of the loop. Answer on page 279.

	3		1				2		
3		2	2		1	3			2
1			2				2		2
2	2		3						3
3			0	2	3	2	3		2
3			1		2		2	1	2
2			2	2	2	2	2	2	
2		2		2	2	2			
2		3						3	
		2			2		3		

506 Missing Landmarks 15

Which famous landmark is blurred out of this photo? Answer on page 292.

507 Domino placing 21

A set of dominoes containing all possible pairs of numbers from (0,0) to (7,7) is laid out vertically as shown in the blank grid below so that the larger number of each domino is on the top. The numbers above each column are from the top half of the dominoes in that column.

The numbers below each column are from the bottom half of the dominoes in that column. The numbers to the left of each row are from the respective half-dominoes in that row.

All the numbers are given to you sorted into descending numerical order. How are the dominoes laid out? Answer on page 283.

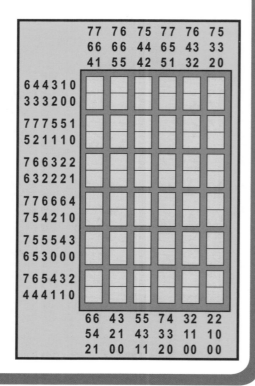

508 Fillomino 21

Each value shown in the grid below is part of a group of cells equal in number to that given value. A '6' is part of a group of six cells, for example. Groups may take any shape, but no two groups of the same size may touch each other horizontally or vertically at any point, and there are no blank cells. Not all groups need have a given value. How are the groups arranged? Answer on page 288.

509 Minesweeper 6

The grid below contains a number of bombs hidden in empty squares. Each red flag tells you how many bombs are in the eight cells around it. Where are the bombs? For answer see page 275.

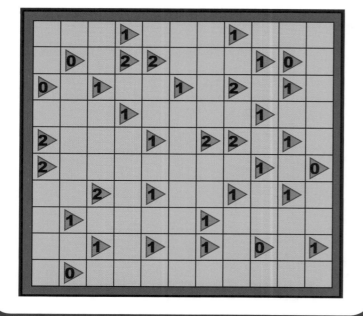

510 Number Link 21

The numbered cells in the grid below indicate the start and end points of single continuous paths. These paths fill the grid completely, and do not branch, cross each other, or touch themselves to form any pool of cells (2x2 or greater). How are the paths arranged? Answer on page 284.

511 Hitori 21

Shade out cells in the grid below so that no number appears more than once in any row or column. Shaded cells cannot touch each other horizontally or vertically, and cannot cut the unshaded cells into two or more groups – the unshaded cells must remain connected horizontally or vertically into one complex branching chain. Which cells are shaded? Answer on page 287.

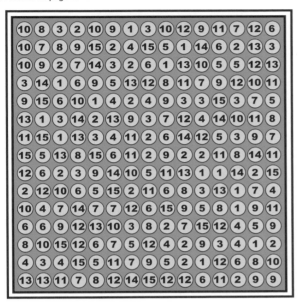

512 Sikaku 21

Divide the grid below into a number of rectangular rooms. Each room must contain exactly one number, equal to the number of cells that make up the room. Answer on page 277.

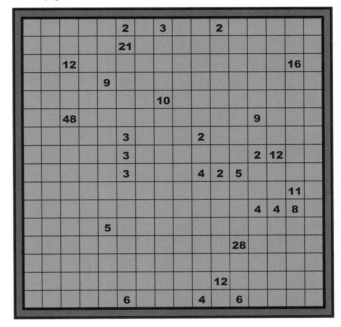

513 Tents 21

The grid below indicates a patch of woodland. Some cells contain grass, and others contain trees. Tents are placed on grass cells so that each tree has one tent next to it horizontally or vertically, although note that tents may be adjacent to more than one tree. No tent may be horizontally, vertically or diagonally adjacent to another tent. The numbers beside each row and column tell you how many tents are in that row or column. Where are the tents? Answer on page 286.

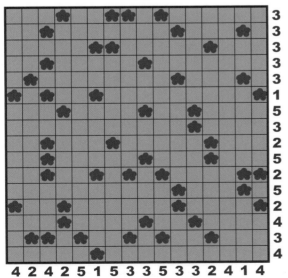

514 Bijutsukan 21

The bright cells and dark cells in the grid below represent corridors and walls respectively. Light sources shine a horizontal and vertical beam of light. A corridor cell becomes illuminated if it is in the same row or column as a light source and there is no wall cell in between them. Place light sources in the corridor cells so that every corridor cell is illuminated, and no light source illuminates another light source. The numbers in some walls tell you how many light sources are touching that wall horizontally or vertically. Answer on page 281.

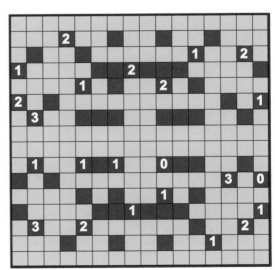

515 Dominoes 21

A full set of dominoes containing all possible pairs of numbers from (0,0) to (9,9) is laid together in one solid rectangle. The dominoes may be placed horizontally or vertically. The numbers in the grid below indicate the value of each half of each domino. How are the dominoes arranged? Answer on page 280.

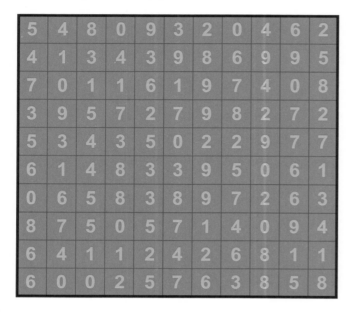

5	4	8	0	9	3	2	0	4	6	2
4	1	3	4	3	9	8	6	9	9	5
7	0	1	1	6	1	9	7	4	0	8
3	9	5	7	2	7	9	8	2	7	2
5	3	4	3	5	0	2	2	9	7	7
6	1	4	8	3	3	9	5	0	6	1
0	6	5	8	3	8	9	7	2	6	3
8	7	5	0	5	7	1	4	0	9	4
6	4	1	1	2	4	2	6	8	1	1
6	0	0	2	5	7	6	3	8	5	8

516 Gokigen Naname 21

Each cell in the grid below contains one diagonal line from corner to corner. The numbered circles show how many lines touch that corner. Fill in the grid so that the lines never form a closed circuit of any size. Answer on page 276.

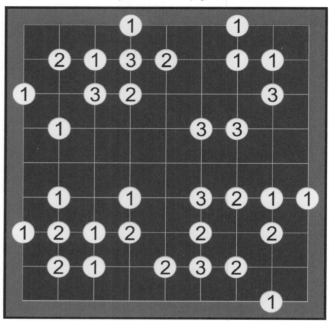

517 Who's Who 8

From the information, can you match each grandparent to their grandchild? Answer on p302.

518 Tentai 16

The grid below is divided into a number of shapes. Each shape has a star at its centre, and is made up of one continuous group of cells connected horizontally and/or vertically. The shapes are all symmetrical – they stay the same when rotated by 180 degrees – but may get quite complicated. Where are the shapes? Answer on page 291.

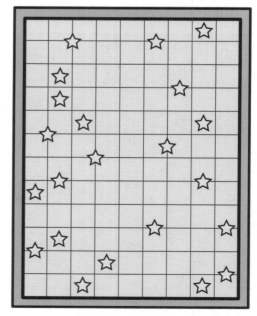

519 Silhouettes 8

Which of the six images fits the silhouette?
Answer on page 302.

520 Futoshiki 24

Fill in the grid below so that the numbers 1 to 7 appear exactly once in each row and column. Red arrows indicate that a number is greater than its neighbour.
For answer see page 274.

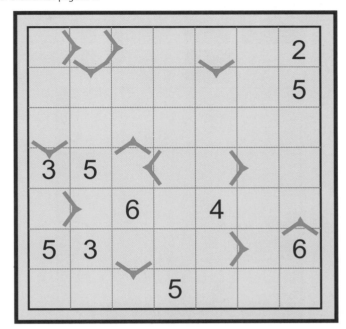

521 Colourminoes 19

In the grid below, each colour has a unique integer value from 0 to 6. The numbers next to each row and column indicate the total value of the cells in that row or column. The values of the cells of the grid correspond in turn to the numbers shown on a half-set of dominoes containing all possible pairs of numbers from (0,0) to (6,6) which has been laid together in one solid rectangle. Dominoes in this rectangle may be placed horizontally or vertically. What number does each colour correspond to, and how are the corresponding dominoes arranged? Answer on page 290.

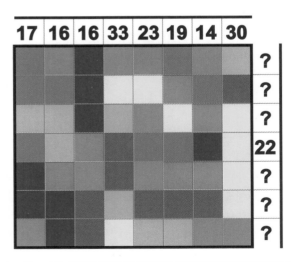

522 Sudoku 27

Fill in the grid below so that the numbers 1–9 appear exactly once in each row, column and 3x3 box. For solution see page 272.

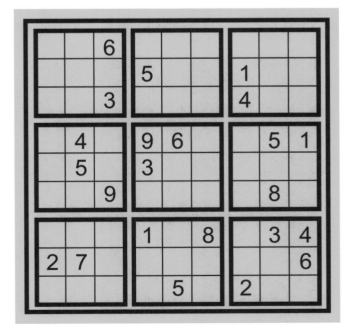

523 Battleships 20

A number of ships of various sizes are hidden in the grid below. The numbers next to each row and column indicate how many ship segments are in that row or column. Some ship segments have already been filled in. Where are the ships? Answer on page 289.

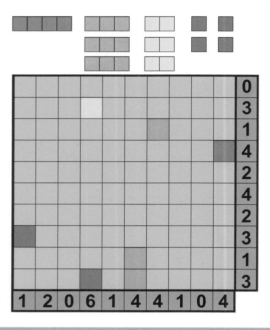

524 Slitherlink 22

A number of the intersection lines in the grid below have to be joined together to make one single complete loop. The numbers in the cell indicate how many of that cell's sides form part of the loop. Answer on page 279.

525 Tents 22

The grid below indicates a patch of woodland. Some cells contain grass, and others contain trees. Tents are placed on grass cells so that each tree has one tent next to it horizontally or vertically, although note that tents may be adjacent to more than one tree. No tent may be horizontally, vertically or diagonally adjacent to another tent. The numbers beside each row and column tell you how many tents are in that row or column. Where are the tents? Answer on page 286.

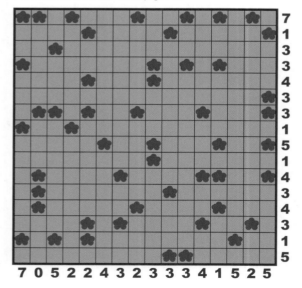

526 Bijutsukan 22

The bright cells and dark cells in the grid below represent corridors and walls respectively. Light sources shine a horizontal and vertical beam of light. A corridor cell becomes illuminated if it is in the same row or column as a light source and there is no wall cell in between them. Place light sources in the corridor cells so that every corridor cell is illuminated, and no light source illuminates another light source. The numbers in some walls tell you how many light sources are touching that wall horizontally or vertically. Answer on page 281.

527 Suiri 11

Five kids are sick. From the information given below, can you work out what illness (2) each child (1) has, what colour that child's pyjamas (3) are, and what treat (4) each one was given as a little pick-me-up?

1. The child in red pyjamas got a book as a treat.
2. The child with measles (not Billie or Frankie) got given a toy.
3. Alexis has mumps. A different child (in green pyjamas) was visited by a friend who had already had his or her disease.
4. Frankie was wearing orange pyjamas, and did not have tonsilitis.
5. Lee had scarlet fever, and was not wearing green pyjamas.
6. The child with chicken pox did not get ice cream.
7. The child in blue pyjamas was neither Robin not Lee.
8. One child wore yellow pyjamas.
9. One child was given jelly.

Answer on page 299.

528 Sikaku 22

Divide the grid below into a number of rectangular rooms. Each room must contain exactly one number, equal to the number of cells that make up the room.

Answer on page 277.

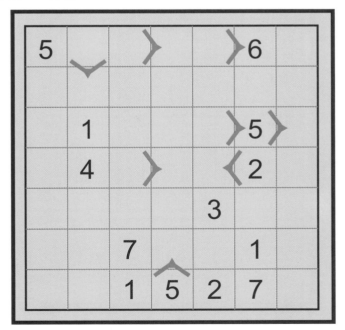

529 Futoshiki 25

Fill in the grid below so that the numbers 1 to 7 appear exactly once in each row and column. Red arrows indicate that a number is greater than its neighbour.

For answer see page 274.

530 Detail Scene 11

The three enlarged squares appear somewhere in the large picture. Can you find them? Answer on page 299.

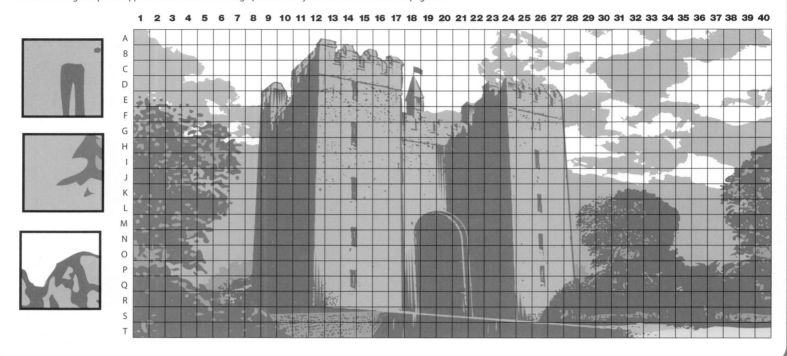

531 Yudoku 11

Fill in the grid below so that the letters s, p, a, r, k, l, i, n and g appear exactly once in each row, column and 3x3 box. Answer on page 301.

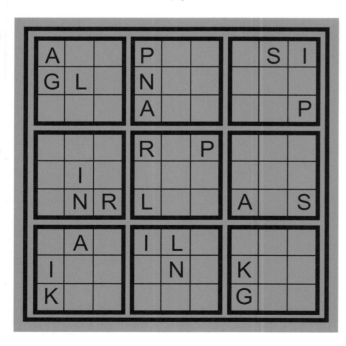

532 Masyu 11

A line passes through some or all of the cells in the grid below in such a way that it forms a single continuous non-intersecting loop. The line always exits a cell by a different side to the one it entered by, and passes through all cells containing a circle. The line travels straight through a cell with a light circle but turns in the previous and/or following cells in its path. The line turns in a cell containing a dark cell, but travels straight through both the previous and following cells in its path. Where is the line? Answer on page 301.

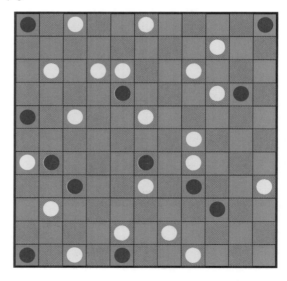

533 Domino placing 22

A set of dominoes containing all possible pairs of numbers from (0,0) to (7,7) is laid out vertically as shown in the blank grid below so that the larger number of each domino is on the top. The numbers above each column are from the top half of the dominoes in that column. The numbers below each column are from the bottom half of the dominoes in that column. The numbers to the left of each row are from the respective half-dominoes in that row. All the numbers are given to you sorted into descending numerical order. How are the dominoes laid out? Answer on page 283.

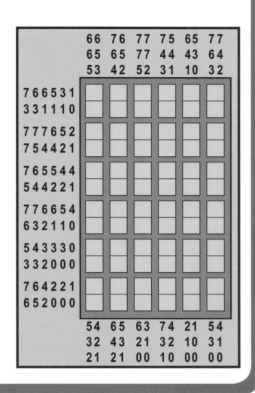

534 Dominoes 22

A full set of dominoes containing all possible pairs of numbers from (0,0) to (9,9) is laid together in one solid rectangle. The dominoes may be placed horizontally or vertically. The numbers in the grid below indicate the value of each half of each domino. How are the dominoes arranged? Answer on page 280.

9	1	8	5	2	8	1	7	4	1	0
5	4	6	8	5	2	3	1	1	2	8
7	5	7	7	0	5	5	6	4	4	3
3	5	7	6	6	0	1	1	5	9	4
2	3	2	0	5	1	8	2	0	0	0
8	9	3	9	7	6	9	1	9	2	6
5	6	6	4	7	5	3	9	2	3	4
8	9	0	0	7	1	4	7	8	3	9
4	4	6	1	2	3	8	8	0	8	4
2	2	6	7	7	9	9	3	6	0	3

535 Gokigen Naname 22

Each cell in the grid below contains one diagonal line from corner to corner. The numbered circles show how many lines touch that corner. Fill in the grid so that the lines never form a closed circuit of any size. Answer on page 276.

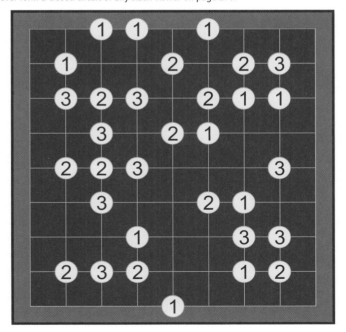

536 Hashiwokakero 11

A number of straight horizontal and vertical bridges connect the islands shown. The number on each island shows how many bridges touch that island. Bridges may not cross each other, and no more than 2 bridges may connect a pair of islands.

Where are the bridges? Answer on page 297.

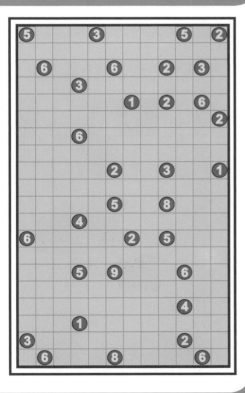

537 Number Link 22

The numbered cells in the grid below indicate the start and end points of single continuous paths. These paths fill the grid completely, and do not branch, cross each other, or touch themselves to form any pool of cells (2x2 or greater).
How are the paths arranged? Answer on page 284.

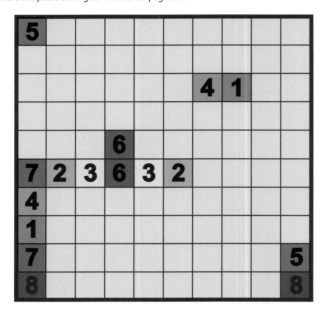

538 Mirror Image 11

Which of the five images below is an identical mirror image of the one above?
Answer on page 300.

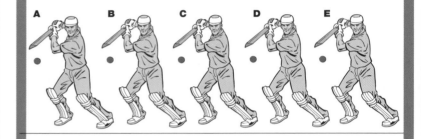

539 Fillomino 22

Each value shown in the grid below is part of a group of cells equal in number to that given value. A '6' is part of a group of six cells, for example. Groups may take any shape, but no two groups of the same size may touch each other horizontally or vertically at any point, and there are no blank cells. Not all groups need have a given value.
How are the groups arranged? Answer on page 288.

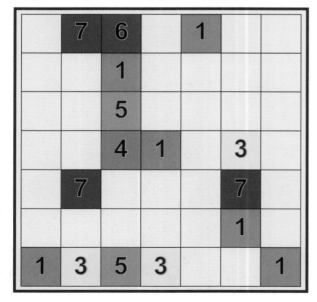

540 Hitori 22

Shade out cells in the grid below so that no number appears more than once in any row or column. Shaded cells cannot touch each other horizontally or vertically, and cannot cut the unshaded cells into two or more groups – the unshaded cells must remain connected horizontally or vertically into one complex branching chain. Which cells are shaded? Answer on page 287.

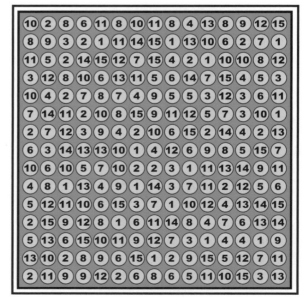

541 Identicals 11

Which pair of images is identical?
Answer on page 300.

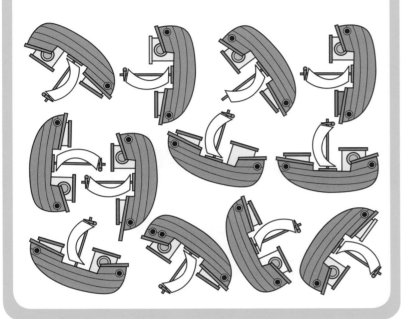

542 Match One 11

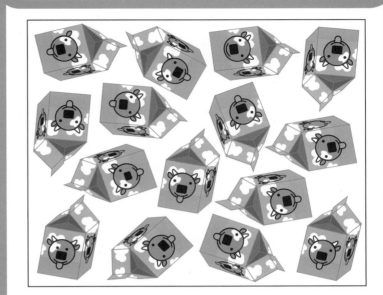

Which of the jumbled images is identical to the one presented here? Answer on page 298.

543 Nonogram 15

A number of cells in the grid below are to be shaded. Each row and column may contain one or more continuous lines of shaded cells ('blocks'). The numbers adjacent to the row or column indicate the lengths of the different blocks contained. Blocks are separated from others in the same row or column by at least one empty cell. Where are the shaded cells? A picture will emerge when the cells are shaded correctly. Answer on page 294.

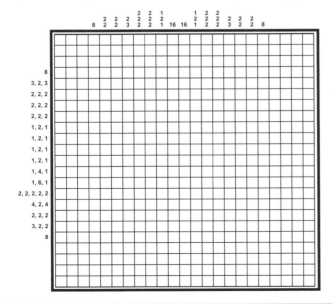

544 Artist's Errors

The artist drawing this scene has made a number of visual, conceptual and logical errors. Can you find them all?
Answer on page 304.

545 Kakuro 15

The empty squares in this grid contain digits from 1 to 9 so that each continuous unbroken line of numbers adds up to the clue value in the filled segment to its left (for horizontal lines) or above it (for vertical lines). No number may be used more than once in any unbroken line. How is the grid filled? Answer on page 293.

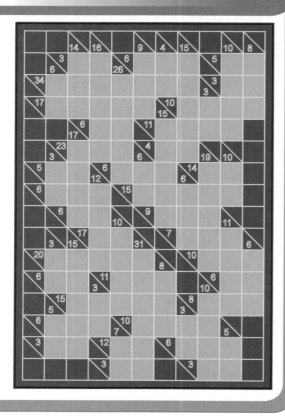

546 Colourminoes 20

In the grid below, each colour has a unique integer value from 0 to 6. The numbers next to each row and column indicate the total value of the cells in that row or column. The values of the cells of the grid correspond in turn to the numbers shown on a half-set of dominoes containing all possible pairs of numbers from (0,0) to (6,6) which has been laid together in one solid rectangle. Dominoes in this rectangle may be placed horizontally or vertically. What number does each colour correspond to, and how are the corresponding dominoes arranged? Answer on page 290.

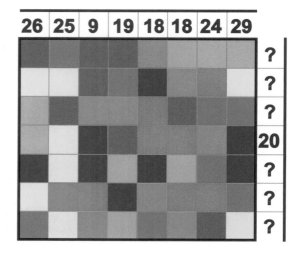

547 Sudoku 28

Fill in the grid below so that the numbers 1–9 appear exactly once in each row, column and 3x3 box. For solution see page 272.

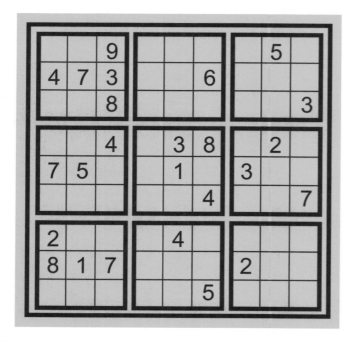

548 Battlehex 14

A number of ships of various sizes are hidden in the hexagonal grid below. The numbers next to each edge indicate how many ship segments are in the rows indicated by the directional arrows. Some ship segments and/or empty water cells have already been filled in. Where are the ships? Answer on page 296.

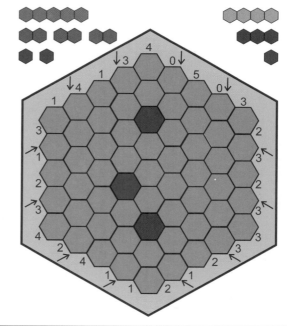

549 Missing Landmarks 16

Which famous landmark is blurred out of this photo?
Answer on page 292.

550 Map colouring 14

The rooms of the grid are coloured so that no two rooms of the same colour ever touch. How are the rooms coloured? Answer on page 295.

551 Tentai 17

The grid below is divided into a number of shapes. Each shape has a star at its centre, and is made up of one continuous group of cells connected horizontally and/or vertically. The shapes are all symmetrical – they stay the same when rotated by 180 degrees – but may get quite complicated. Where are the shapes? Answer on page 291.

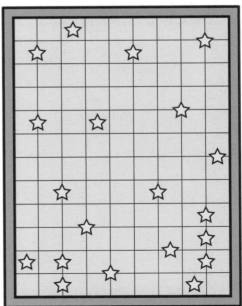

552 Battleships 21

A number of ships of various sizes are hidden in the grid below. The numbers next to each row and column indicate how many ship segments are in that row or column. Some ship segments have already been filled in. Where are the ships? Answer on page 289.

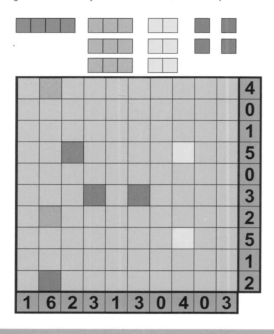

553 Futoshiki 26

Fill in the grid below so that the numbers 1 to 7 appear exactly once in each row and column. Red arrows indicate that a number is greater than its neighbour.
For answer see page 274.

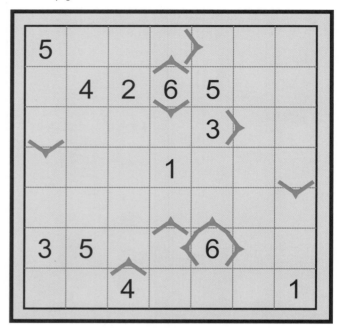

554 Dominoes 23

A full set of dominoes containing all possible pairs of numbers from (0,0) to (9,9) is laid together in one solid rectangle. The dominoes may be placed horizontally or vertically. The numbers in the grid below indicate the value of each half of each domino. How are the dominoes arranged? Answer on page 280.

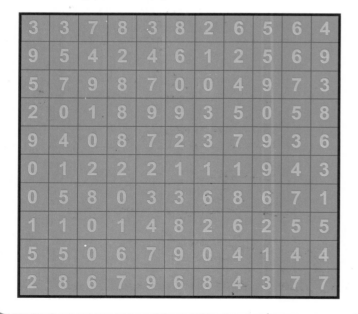

555 Tents 23

The grid below indicates a patch of woodland. Some cells contain grass, and others contain trees. Tents are placed on grass cells so that each tree has one tent next to it horizontally or vertically, although note that tents may be adjacent to more than one tree. No tent may be horizontally, vertically or diagonally adjacent to another tent. The numbers beside each row and column tell you how many tents are in that row or column. Where are the tents? Answer on page 286.

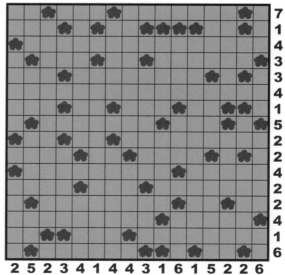

556 Bijutsukan 23

The bright cells and dark cells in the grid below represent corridors and walls respectively. Light sources shine a horizontal and vertical beam of light. A corridor cell becomes illuminated if it is in the same row or column as a light source and there is no wall cell in between them. Place light sources in the corridor cells so that every corridor cell is illuminated, and no light source illuminates another light source. The numbers in some walls tell you how many light sources are touching that wall horizontally or vertically. Answer on page 281.

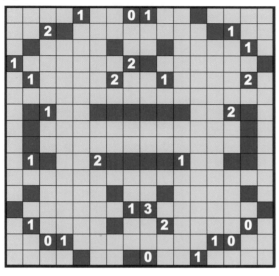

557 Hitori 23

Shade out cells in the grid below so that no number appears more than once in any row or column. Shaded cells cannot touch each other horizontally or vertically, and cannot cut the unshaded cells into two or more groups – the unshaded cells must remain connected horizontally or vertically into one complex branching chain. Which cells are shaded? Answer on page 287.

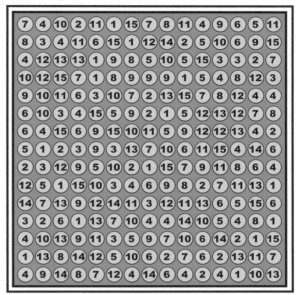

558 Number Link 23

The numbered cells in the grid below indicate the start and end points of single continuous paths. These paths fill the grid completely, and do not branch, cross each other, or touch themselves to form any pool of cells (2x2 or greater).
How are the paths arranged? Answer on page 284.

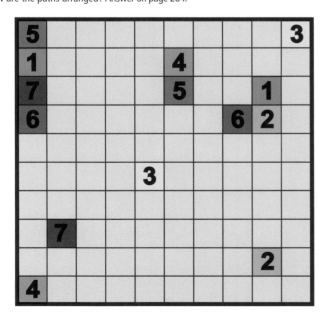

559 Sikaku 23

Divide the grid below into a number of rectangular rooms. Each room must contain exactly one number, equal to the number of cells that make up the room.
Answer on page 277.

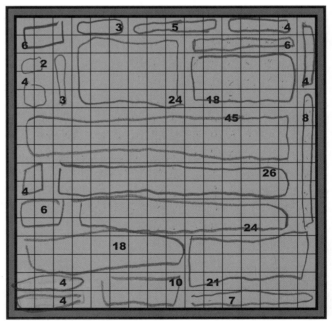

560 Fillomino 23

Each value shown in the grid below is part of a group of cells equal in number to that given value. A '6' is part of a group of six cells, for example. Groups may take any shape, but no two groups of the same size may touch each other horizontally or vertically at any point, and there are no blank cells. Not all groups need have a given value. How are the groups arranged? Answer on page 288.

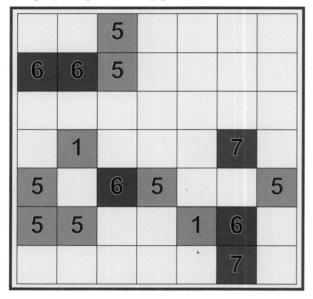

561 Domino placing 23

A set of dominoes containing all possible pairs of numbers from (0,0) to (7,7) is laid out vertically as shown in the blank grid below so that the larger number of each domino is on the top. The numbers above each column are from the top half of the dominoes in that column. The numbers below each column are from the bottom half of the dominoes in that column. The numbers to the left of each row are from the respective half-dominoes in that row. All the numbers are given to you sorted into descending numerical order. How are the dominoes laid out? Answer on page 283.

	76	77	66	77	76	75
	53	76	54	65	54	43
	22	65	41	32	43	10

| 776530 |
| 642110 |
| 777421 |
| 742100 |
| 653321 |
| 432210 |
| 765542 |
| 655320 |
| 776665 |
| 543331 |
| 654443 |
| 211000 |

	54	75	42	66	33	53
	22	43	11	43	22	21
	10	10	00	10	10	00

562 Slitherlink 23

A number of the intersection lines in the grid below have to be joined together to make one single complete loop. The numbers in the cell indicate how many of that cell's sides form part of the loop. Answer on page 279.

```
3   2 1 3 2 3 2 2 3
        3
    2 3   2
2 2             2
    2 2     3     1 2
    2 1             2
2 2 3               3
      2 3 0   2
    2             3
3   3     2 1 3 2
```

563 Gokigen Naname 23

Each cell in the grid below contains one diagonal line from corner to corner. The numbered circles show how many lines touch that corner. Fill in the grid so that the lines never form a closed circuit of any size. Answer on page 276.

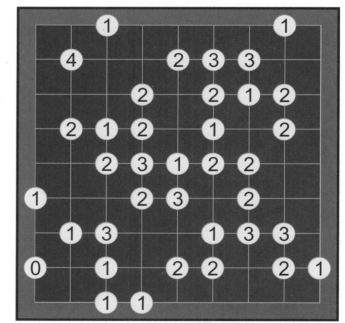

154

564 Sudoku 29

Fill in the grid below so that the numbers 1–9 appear exactly once in each row, column and 3x3 box. Answer on page 272,=.

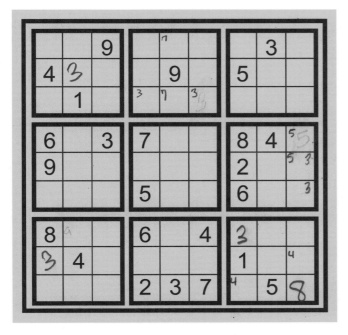

565 Colourminoes 21

In the grid below, each colour has a unique integer value from 0 to 6. The numbers next to each row and column indicate the total value of the cells in that row or column. The values of the cells of the grid correspond in turn to the numbers shown on a half-set of dominoes containing all possible pairs of numbers from (0,0) to (6,6) which has been laid together in one solid rectangle. Dominoes in this rectangle may be placed horizontally or vertically. What number does each colour correspond to, and how are the corresponding dominoes arranged? Answer on page 290.

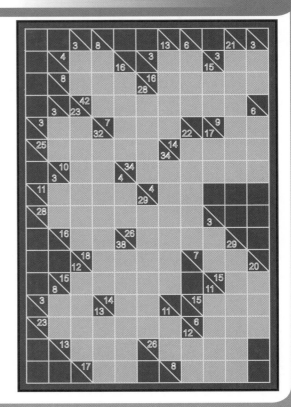

566 Nonogram 16

A number of cells in the grid below are to be shaded. Each row and column may contain one or more continuous lines of shaded cells ('blocks'). The numbers adjacent to the row or column indicate the lengths of the different blocks contained. Blocks are separated from others in the same row or column by at least one empty cell. Where are the shaded cells? A picture will emerge when the cells are shaded correctly. Answer on page 294.

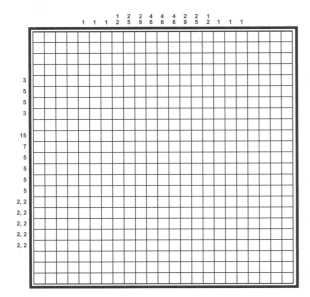

567 Kakuro 16

The empty squares in this grid contain digits from 1 to 9 so that each continuous unbroken line of numbers adds up to the clue value in the filled segment to its left (for horizontal lines) or above it (for vertical lines). No number may be used more than once in any unbroken line. How is the grid filled? Answer on page 293.

568 Who's Who 9

From the information, can you match each boss to his or her secretary? Answer on p302.

I'm Craig and my secretary is called Smith.

I'm Judith, my secretary is called Jones.

I'm Ben, and Brown, my secretary, is an annoyingly nervous man.

I'm Paula, and my secretary is called Green.

My boss's jacket is the same colour as my name.

My boss is female.

569 Futoshiki 27

Fill in the grid below so that the numbers 1 to 7 appear exactly once in each row and column. Red arrows indicate that a number is greater than its neighbour. For answer see page 274.

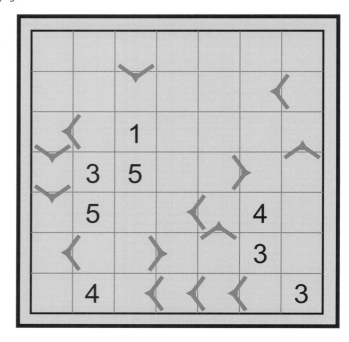

570 Silhouettes 9

Which of the six images fits the silhouette?
Answer on page 302.

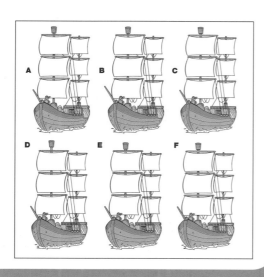

571 Tentai 18

The grid below is divided into a number of shapes. Each shape has a star at its centre, and is made up of one continuous group of cells connected horizontally and/or vertically. The shapes are all symmetrical – they stay the same when rotated by 180 degrees – but may get quite complicated. Where are the shapes? Answer on page 291.

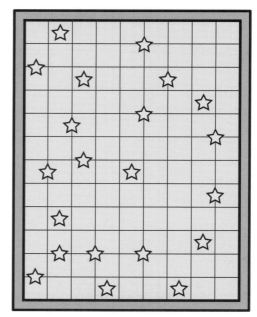

572 Battleships 22

A number of ships of various sizes are hidden in the grid below. The numbers next to each row and column indicate how many ship segments are in that row or column. Some ship segments have already been filled in. Where are the ships? Answer on page 289.

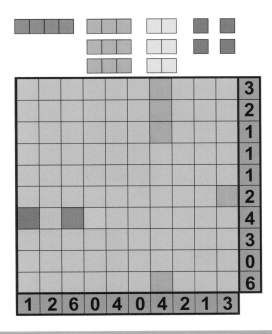

573 Missing Landmarks 17

Which famous landmark is blurred out of this photo? Answer on page 292.

574 Super Sudoku 6

Fill in the grid below so that the digits 1, 2, 3, 4, 5, 6, 7, 8, 9, a, b, c, d, e, f and g appear exactly once in each row and column. Answer on page 303.

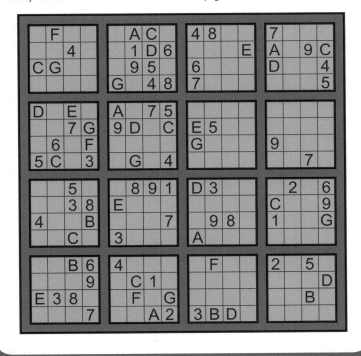

575 Identicals 12

Which pair of images is identical?
Answer on page 300.

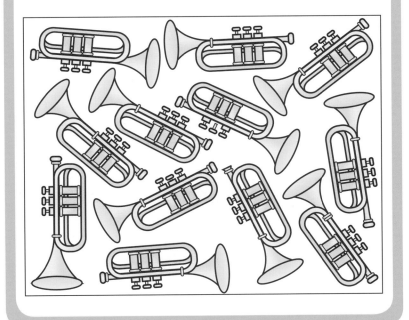

576 Domino placing 24

A set of dominoes containing all possible pairs of numbers from (0,0) to (7,7) is laid out vertically as shown in the blank grid below so that the larger number of each domino is on the top. The numbers above each column are from the top half of the dominoes in that column. The numbers below each column are from the bottom half of the dominoes in that column. The numbers to the left of each row are from the respective half-dominoes in that row.

All the numbers are given to you sorted into descending numerical order. How are the dominoes laid out? Answer on page 283.

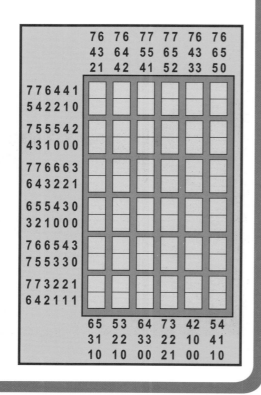

577 Map Colouring 15

The rooms of the grid are coloured so that no two rooms of the same colour ever touch. How are the rooms coloured? Answer on page 295.

578 Detail Scene 12

The three enlarged squares appear somewhere in the large picture. Can you find them? Answer on page 299.

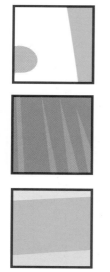
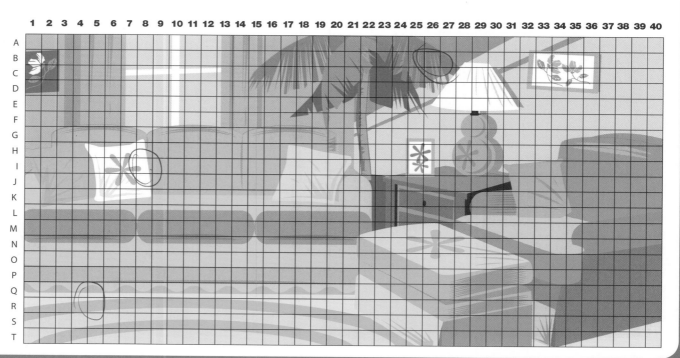

579 Mirror Image 12

Which of the five images below is an identical mirror image of the one above?
Answer on page 300.

A   B   C   D   E

580 Number Link 24

The numbered cells in the grid below indicate the start and end points of single continuous paths. These paths fill the grid completely, and do not branch, cross each other, or touch themselves to form any pool of cells (2x2 or greater).
How are the paths arranged? Answer on page 284.

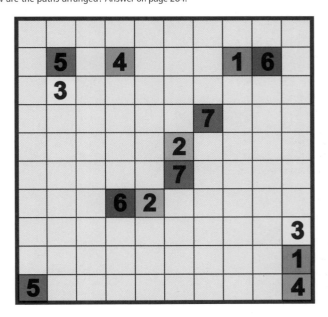

581 Match one 12

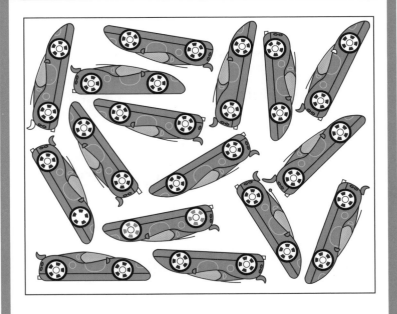

Which of the jumbled images is identical to the one presented here? Answer on page 298.

582 Tents 24

The grid below indicates a patch of woodland. Some cells contain grass, and others contain trees. Tents are placed on grass cells so that each tree has one tent next to it horizontally or vertically, although note that tents may be adjacent to more than one tree. No tent may be horizontally, vertically or diagonally adjacent to another tent. The numbers beside each row and column tell you how many tents are in that row or column. Where are the tents? Answer on page 286.

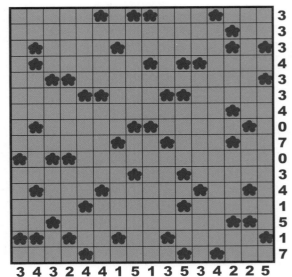

583 Gokigen Naname 24

Each cell in the grid below contains one diagonal line from corner to corner. The numbered circles show how many lines touch that corner. Fill in the grid so that the lines never form a closed circuit of any size. Answer on page 276.

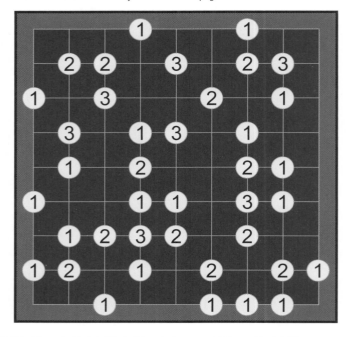

584 Masyu 12

A line passes through some or all of the cells in the grid below in such a way that it forms a single continuous non-intersecting loop. The line always exits a cell by a different side to the one it entered by, and passes through all cells containing a circle. The line travels straight through a cell with a light circle but turns in the previous and/or following cells in its path. The line turns in a cell containing a dark cell, but travels straight through both the previous and following cells in its path. Where is the line? Answer on page 301.

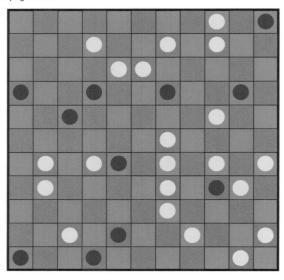

585 Sudoku 30

Fill in the grid below so that the numbers 1–9 appear exactly once in each row, column and 3x3 box. For solution see page 272.

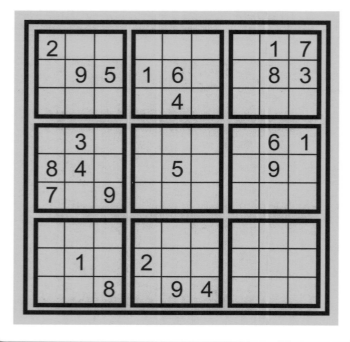

586 Battlehex 15

A number of ships of various sizes are hidden in the hexagonal grid below. The numbers next to each edge indicate how many ship segments are in the rows indicated by the directional arrows. Some ship segments and/or empty water cells have already been filled in. Where are the ships? Answer on page 296.

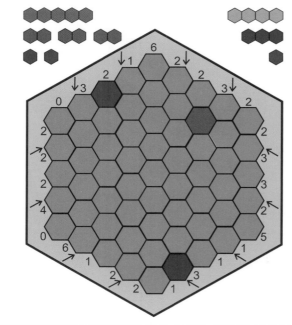

587 Hashiwokakero 12

A number of straight horizontal and vertical bridges connect the islands shown. The number on each island shows how many bridges touch that island. Bridges may not cross each other, and no more than 2 bridges may connect a pair of islands.
Where are the bridges?
Answer on page 297.

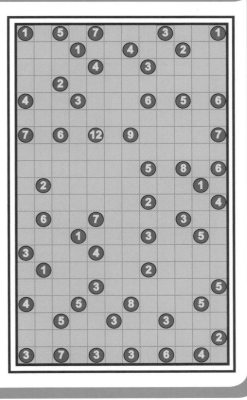

588 Dominoes 24

A full set of dominoes containing all possible pairs of numbers from (0,0) to (9,9) is laid together in one solid rectangle. The dominoes may be placed horizontally or vertically. The numbers in the grid below indicate the value of each half of each domino. How are the dominoes arranged? Answer on page 280.

5	3	7	4	1	0	8	8	4	4	4
7	9	6	5	5	1	8	0	4	6	9
2	2	4	5	8	9	2	2	5	2
7	0	9	4	3	9	6	5	3	6	6
7	3	6	3	7	7	9	9	0	0	5
0	1	6	0	8	3	0	2	1	5	7
1	1	8	9	3	7	8	1	7	0	2
7	7	2	6	4	5	2	6	8	8	2
9	4	5	2	1	1	3	6	3	4
9	3	3	0	6	0	5	8	8	1	9

589 Yudoku 12

Fill in the grid below so that the letters s, p, a, r, k, l, i, n and g appear exactly once in each row, column and 3x3 box. Answer on page 301.

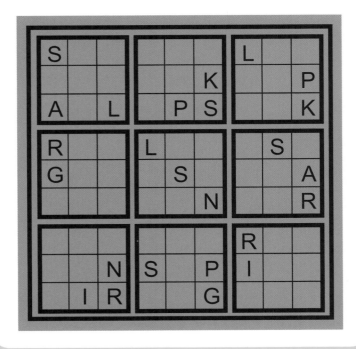

590 Slitherlink 24

A number of the intersection lines in the grid below have to be joined together to make one single complete loop. The numbers in the cell indicate how many of that cell's sides form part of the loop. Answer on page 279.

591 Hitori 24

Shade out cells in the grid below so that no number appears more than once in any row or column. Shaded cells cannot touch each other horizontally or vertically, and cannot cut the unshaded cells into two or more groups – the unshaded cells must remain connected horizontally or vertically into one complex branching chain. Which cells are shaded? Answer on page 287.

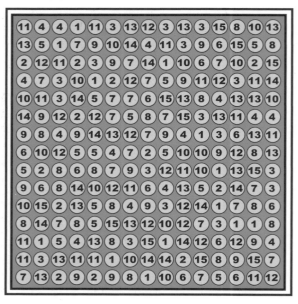

592 Killer Sudoku 6

Fill in the grid below so that the numbers 1–9 appear exactly once in each row, column and 3x3 block, and that the numbers in each dotted room add up to the value in its top right corner. Answer on page 303.

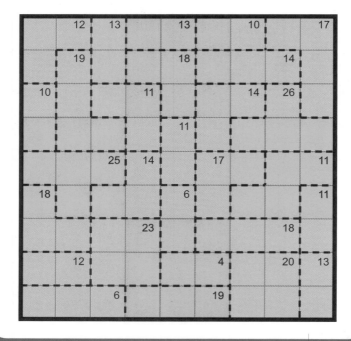

593 Spot the Set

There are four different versions of the picture in the group below, each one reproduced three times. Can you identify the four sets?
Answer on page 304.

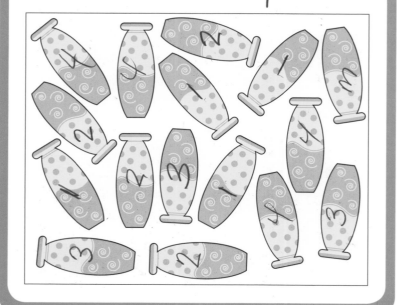

594 Differences

Each copy of the picture has one flaw that none of the others share. Can you find them all?
Answer on page 304.

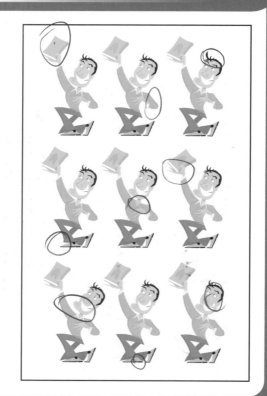

595 Suiri 12

A group of kids take shelter from the rain in a sweet shop. From the information given below, can you work out how many sweets (3) each kid (1) bought, what type they were (2) and what colour his or her raincoat was?

1. Valli wore a black raincoat.
2. The kid in the cyan raincoat – not Gunnar – bought 12 sweets.
3. Hertha bought two more sugar candies than the kid in yellow.
4. Someone bought 6 lollipops.
5. The liquorish lace was not bought by Valli, or by the kids in yellow or white.
6. The kid in magenta bought chocolate.
7. Bjarni bought 10 sweets, which were not toffees.
8. One kid bought 4 sweets, and another one bought 8.
9. One of the kids was called Ragna.

Answer on page 299.

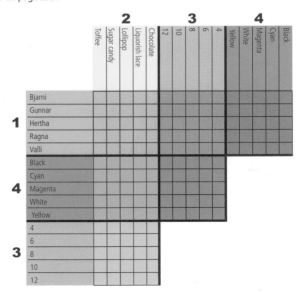

596 Fillomino 24

Each value shown in the grid below is part of a group of cells equal in number to that given value. A '6' is part of a group of six cells, for example. Groups may take any shape, but no two groups of the same size may touch each other horizontally or vertically at any point, and there are no blank cells. Not all groups need have a given value. How are the groups arranged? Answer on page 288.

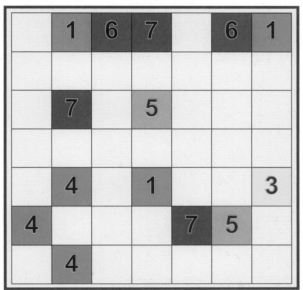

597 Spot the Difference

There are eight differences between the two pictures. Can you find them all? Answer on p302.

598 Sikaku 24

Divide the grid below into a number of rectangular rooms. Each room must contain exactly one number, equal to the number of cells that make up the room.
Answer on page 277.

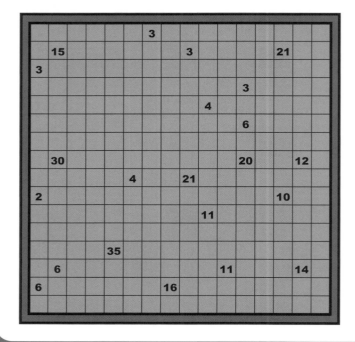

599 Bijutsukan 24

The bright cells and dark cells in the grid below represent corridors and walls respectively. Light sources shine a horizontal and vertical beam of light. A corridor cell becomes illuminated if it is in the same row or column as a light source and there is no wall cell in between them. Place light sources in the corridor cells so that every corridor cell is illuminated, and no light source illuminates another light source. The numbers in some walls tell you how many light sources are touching that wall horizontally or vertically.
Answer on page 281.

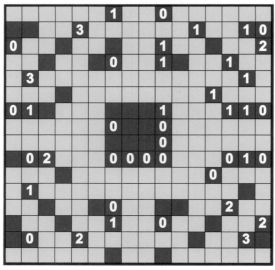

600 Samurai Sudoku 6

Fill in each 9x9 grid below so that the numbers 1–9 appear exactly once in each row, column and 3x3 block. Numbers in overlapping blocks count identically towards both grids. Answer on page 303.

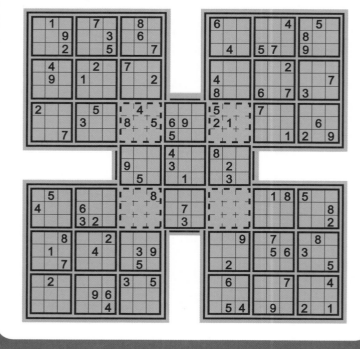

601 Futoshiki 28

Fill in the grid below so that the numbers 1 to 7 appear exactly once in each row and column. Red arrows indicate that a number is greater than its neighbour.
For answer see page 274.

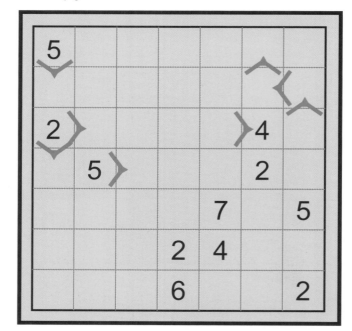

602 Colourminoes 22

In the grid below, each colour has a unique integer value from 0 to 6. The numbers next to each row and column indicate the total value of the cells in that row or column. The values of the cells of the grid correspond in turn to the numbers shown on a half-set of dominoes containing all possible pairs of numbers from (0,0) to (6,6) which has been laid together in one solid rectangle. Dominoes in this rectangle may be placed horizontally or vertically. What number does each colour correspond to, and how are the corresponding dominoes arranged? Answer on page 290.

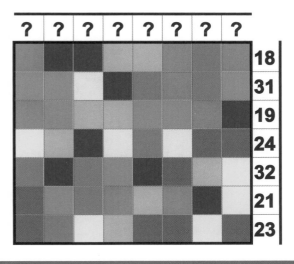

603 Sudoku 31

Fill in the grid below so that the numbers 1–9 appear exactly once in each row, column and 3x3 box. For solution see page 273.

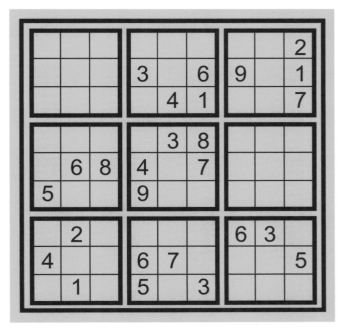

604 Kin-kon-kan 4

In the grid below, some cells contain diagonal mirrors which reflect light on both sides. One mirror is hidden in each room.
The coloured boxes around the edge indicate the start and finish of a coloured beam of light fired into the grid. These beams always travel in a straight line, but are reflected through a 90-degree angle when hitting a mirror. The number in each box shows how many grid cells its beam of light travels through before exiting again.
Where are the mirrors, and how are they placed? For solution see page 273.

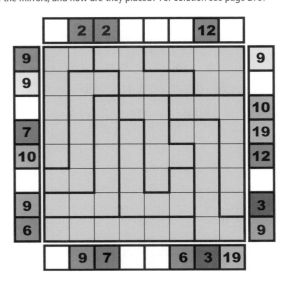

605 Battleships 23

A number of ships of various sizes are hidden in the grid below. The numbers next to each row and column indicate how many ship segments are in that row or column. Some ship segments have already been filled in. Where are the ships? Answer on page 289.

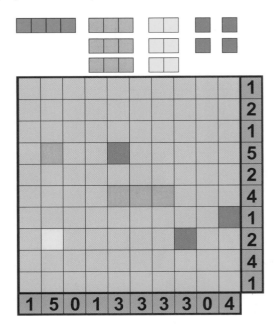

606 Bijutsukan 25

The bright cells and dark cells in the grid below represent corridors and walls respectively. Light sources shine a horizontal and vertical beam of light. A corridor cell becomes illuminated if it is in the same row or column as a light source and there is no wall cell in between them. Place light sources in the corridor cells so that every corridor cell is illuminated, and no light source illuminates another light source. The numbers in some walls tell you how many light sources are touching that wall horizontally or vertically. Answer on page 281.

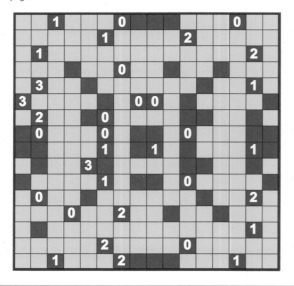

607 Slitherlink 25

A number of the intersection lines in the grid below have to be joined together to make one single complete loop. The numbers in the cell indicate how many of that cell's sides form part of the loop. Answer on page 279.

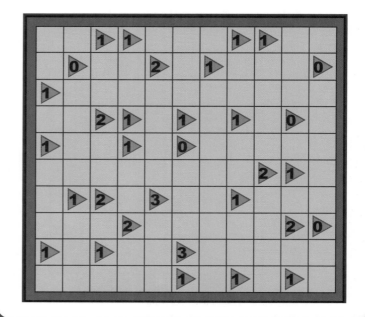

608 Fillomino 25

Each value shown in the grid below is part of a group of cells equal in number to that given value. A '6' is part of a group of six cells, for example. Groups may take any shape, but no two groups of the same size may touch each other horizontally or vertically at any point, and there are no blank cells. Not all groups need have a given value. How are the groups arranged? Answer on page 288.

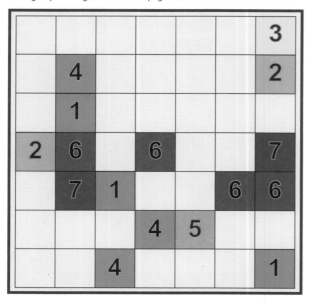

609 Minesweeper 7

The grid below contains a number of bombs hidden in empty squares. Each red flag tells you how many bombs are in the eight cells around it. Where are the bombs? For answer see page 275.

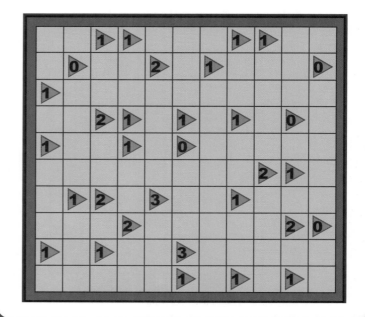

610 Dominoes 25

A set of dominoes containing all possible pairs of numbers from (0,0) to (7,7) is laid out vertically as shown in the blank grid below so that the larger number of each domino is on the top. The numbers above each column are from the top half of the dominoes in that column. The numbers below each column are from the bottom half of the dominoes in that column. The numbers to the left of each row are from the respective half-dominoes in that row. All the numbers are given to you sorted into descending numerical order. How are the dominoes laid out? Answer on page 280.

4	9	8	5	5	5	0	4	7	4	1
0	7	8	3	2	2	1	5	7	8	7
2	9	8	6	0	4	2	2	0	9	9
6	1	6	9	8	3	9	5	4	6	7
5	4	3	6	5	7	0	8	0	5	0
1	4	1	2	5	6	6	6	4	0	1
1	4	7	3	3	1	3	7	0	0	2
3	2	0	9	1	8	5	2	8	8	5
3	4	8	6	3	6	1	2	7	7	9
6	9	8	4	3	9	1	0	3	9	2

611 Tents 25

The grid below indicates a patch of woodland. Some cells contain grass, and others contain trees. Tents are placed on grass cells so that each tree has one tent next to it horizontally or vertically, although note that tents may be adjacent to more than one tree. No tent may be horizontally, vertically or diagonally adjacent to another tent. The numbers beside each row and column tell you how many tents are in that row or column. Where are the tents? Answer on page 286.

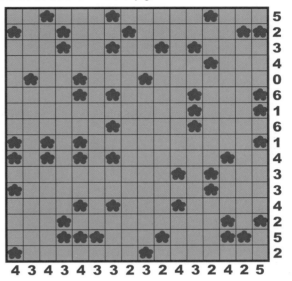

612 Domino placing 25

A set of dominoes containing all possible pairs of numbers from (0,0) to (7,7) is laid out vertically as shown in the blank grid below so that the larger number of each domino is on the top. The numbers above each column are from the top half of the dominoes in that column. The numbers below each column are from the bottom half of the dominoes in that column. The numbers to the left of each row are from the respective half-dominoes in that row. All the numbers are given to you sorted into descending numerical order. How are the dominoes laid out? Answer on page 283.

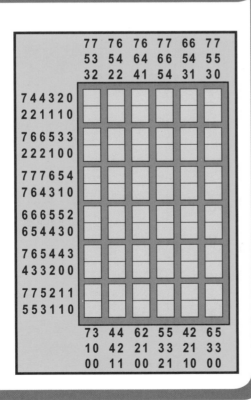

613 Hitori 25

Shade out cells in the grid below so that no number appears more than once in any row or column. Shaded cells cannot touch each other horizontally or vertically, and cannot cut the unshaded cells into two or more groups – the unshaded cells must remain connected horizontally or vertically into one complex branching chain. Which cells are shaded? Answer on page 287.

13	10	12	5	1	1	11	6	7	15	7	13	2	8	3
5	1	6	5	4	9	6	12	15	2	10	13	3	13	14
9	5	2	8	6	5	12	14	11	9	15	6	13	2	7
10	4	15	1	7	11	8	5	7	6	3	1	15	12	14
15	11	3	2	15	5	12	8	14	10	11	9	7	14	1
12	11	9	14	2	4	3	10	5	9	14	7	11	15	13
3	6	4	10	9	12	15	11	13	8	5	2	11	6	5
12	9	12	13	3	10	4	2	6	4	12	6	8	10	15
11	1	2	14	12	13	1	13	9	5	9	10	15	4	9
4	14	5	14	12	7	6	7	9	13	3	15	10	14	2
15	2	3	8	15	1	11	4	8	13	5	6	13	12	
9	13	8	6	14	1	2	7	12	1	4	4	7	10	10
11	6	10	12	11	9	7	15	1	12	2	15	5	7	3
2	5	14	11	5	13	5	4	10	1	9	8	12	10	6
7	14	11	15	8	12	12	3	7	9	6	11	15	13	5

614 Number Link 25

The numbered cells in the grid below indicate the start and end points of single continuous paths. These paths fill the grid completely, and do not branch, cross each other, or touch themselves to form any pool of cells (2x2 or greater).

How are the paths arranged? Answer on page 284.

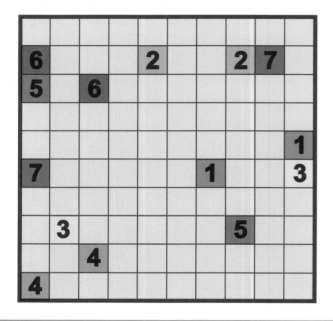

615 Gokigen Naname 25

Each cell in the grid below contains one diagonal line from corner to corner. The numbered circles show how many lines touch that corner. Fill in the grid so that the lines never form a closed circuit of any size. Answer on page 276.

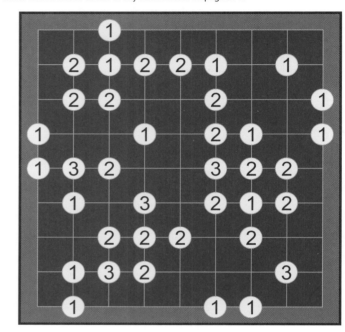

616 Sikaku 25

Divide the grid below into a number of rectangular rooms. Each room must contain exactly one number, equal to the number of cells that make up the room. Answer on page 277.

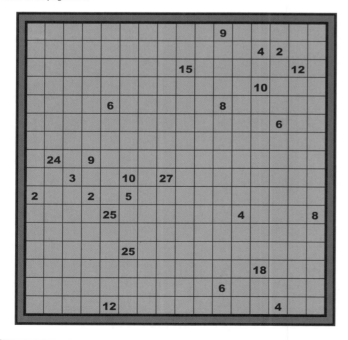

617 Tentai 19

The grid below is divided into a number of shapes. Each shape has a star at its centre, and is made up of one continuous group of cells connected horizontally and/or vertically. The shapes are all symmetrical – they stay the same when rotated by 180 degrees – but may get quite complicated. Where are the shapes? Answer on page 291.

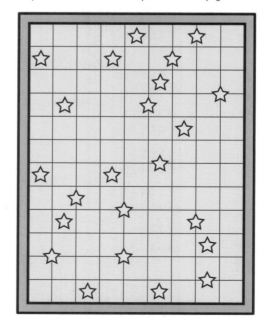

618 Nonogram 17

A number of cells in this grid are to be shaded. Each row and column may contain one or more continuous lines of shaded cells ('blocks'). The numbers adjacent to the row or column indicate the lengths of the different blocks contained. Blocks are separated from others in the same row or column by at least one empty cell. Where are the shaded cells? A picture will emerge when the cells are shaded correctly. Answer on page 294.

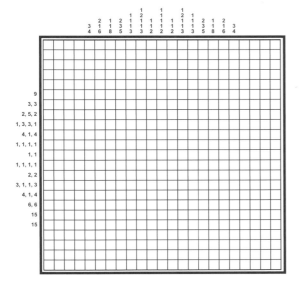

619 Kakuro 17

The empty squares in this grid contain digits from 1 to 9 so that each continuous unbroken line of numbers adds up to the clue value in the filled segment to its left (for horizontal lines) or above it (for vertical lines). No number may be used more than once in any unbroken line. How is the grid filled? Answer on page 293.

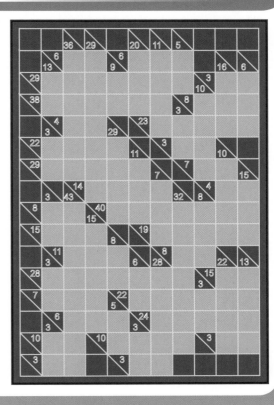

620 Missing Landmarks 18

Which famous landmark is blurred out of this photo?
Answer on page 292.

621 Futoshiki 29

Fill in the grid below so that the numbers 1 to 7 appear exactly once in each row and column. Red arrows indicate that a number is greater than its neighbour.
For answer see page 274.

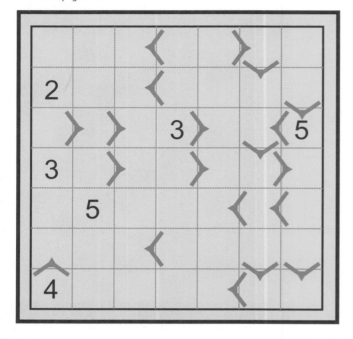

622 Battlehex 16

A number of ships of various sizes are hidden in the hexagonal grid below. The numbers next to each edge indicate how many ship segments are in the rows indicated by the directional arrows. Some ship segments and/or empty water cells have already been filled in. Where are the ships? Answer on page 296.

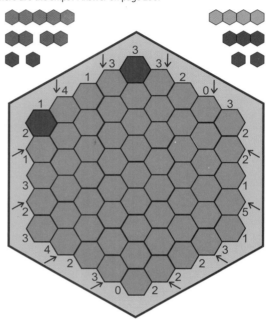

623 Sudoku 32

Fill in the grid below so that the numbers 1–9 appear exactly once in each row, column and 3x3 box. For solution see page 273.

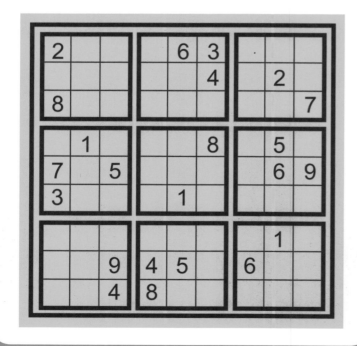

624 Map Colouring 16

The rooms of the grid are coloured so that no two rooms of the same colour ever touch. How are the rooms coloured?
Answer on page 295.

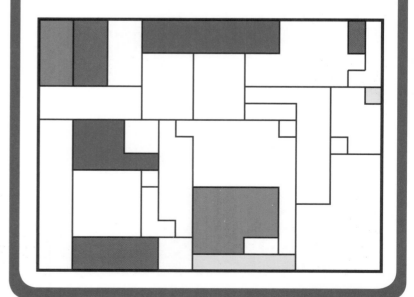

625 Colourminoes 23

In the grid below, each colour has a unique integer value from 0 to 6. The numbers next to each row and column indicate the total value of the cells in that row or column. The values of the cells of the grid correspond in turn to the numbers shown on a half-set of dominoes containing all possible pairs of numbers from (0,0) to (6,6) which has been laid together in one solid rectangle. Dominoes in this rectangle may be placed horizontally or vertically. What number does each colour correspond to, and how are the corresponding dominoes arranged? Answer on page 290.

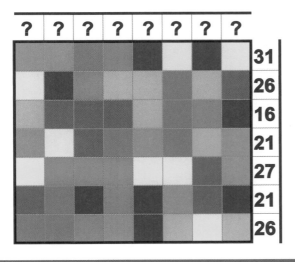

626 Battleships 24

A number of ships of various sizes are hidden in the grid below. The numbers next to each row and column indicate how many ship segments are in that row or column. Some ship segments have already been filled in. Where are the ships? Answer on page 289.

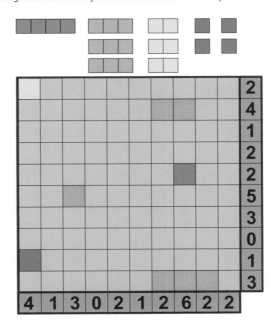

627 Fillomino 26

Each value shown in the grid below is part of a group of cells equal in number to that given value. A '6' is part of a group of six cells, for example. Groups may take any shape, but no two groups of the same size may touch each other horizontally or vertically at any point, and there are no blank cells. Not all groups need have a given value. How are the groups arranged? Answer on page 288.

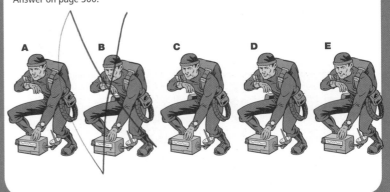

628 Mirror Image 13

Which of the five images below is an identical mirror image of the one above? Answer on page 300.

629 Detail Scene 13

The three enlarged squares appear somewhere in the large picture. Can you find them? Answer on page 299.

630 Yudoku 13

Fill in the grid below so that the letters s, p, a, r, k, l, i, n and g appear exactly once in each row, column and 3x3 box. Answer on page 301.

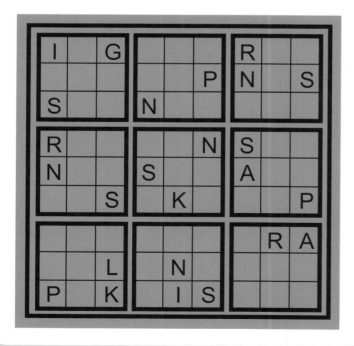

631 Dominoes 26

A full set of dominoes containing all possible pairs of numbers from (0,0) to (9,9) is laid together in one solid rectangle. The dominoes may be placed horizontally or vertically. The numbers in the grid below indicate the value of each half of each domino. How are the dominoes arranged? Answer on page 280.

1	5	3	3	5	8	8	8	4	0	1
1	6	7	4	5	2	3	0	4	3	9
2	4	8	8	1	9	8	5	8	8	6
0	4	6	3	3	7	6	5	9	2	6
0	9	4	4	3	7	9	9	6	6	7
0	1	4	5	3	2	5	5	3	0	9
4	6	0	8	7	9	0	5	7	2	8
1	5	6	6	2	1	6	9	9	0	1
0	7	1	1	4	8	3	3	2	7
2	7	7	2	5	2	2	4	0	9	7

632 Bijutsukan 26

The bright cells and dark cells in the grid below represent corridors and walls respectively. Light sources shine a horizontal and vertical beam of light. A corridor cell becomes illuminated if it is in the same row or column as a light source and there is no wall cell in between them. Place light sources in the corridor cells so that every corridor cell is illuminated, and no light source illuminates another light source. The numbers in some walls tell you how many light sources are touching that wall horizontally or vertically. Answer on page 281.

633 Sikaku 26

Divide the grid below into a number of rectangular rooms. Each room must contain exactly one number, equal to the number of cells that make up the room. Answer on page 277.

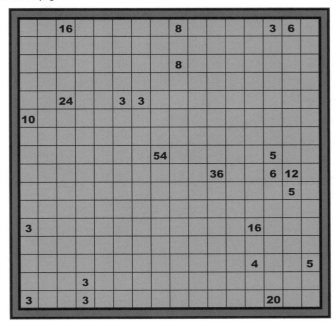

634 Match One 13

Which of the jumbled images is identical to the one presented here? Answer on page 298.

635 Slitherlink 26

A number of the intersection lines in the grid below have to be joined together to make one single complete loop. The numbers in the cell indicate how many of that cell's sides form part of the loop. Answer on page 279.

636 Suiri 13

Five women meet regularly at knitting circle. From the information given below, can you work out what each woman (1) is knitting (2), and what she prefers to drink (3) and eat (4)?

1. Lecia likes butter biscuits, but doesn't drink soup.
2. The lady who is knitting a shawl likes to drink orange juice.
3. The lady who likes ginger snaps is knitting a sweater. She is neither Kay nor Nessa.
4. The lady who is knitting a scarf likes to drink soup. This is not Gertie, who likes digestives.
5. Kay drinks water. She does not like choc chip cookies.
6. The lady who eats garibaldi biscuits is not knitting socks.
7. The lady who likes coffee is not Ida or Lecia.
8. One lady drinks tea.
9. One lady is knitting a bib.
Answer on page 299.

637 Tents 26

The grid below indicates a patch of woodland. Some cells contain grass, and others contain trees. Tents are placed on grass cells so that each tree has one tent next to it horizontally or vertically, although note that tents may be adjacent to more than one tree. No tent may be horizontally, vertically or diagonally adjacent to another tent. The numbers beside each row and column tell you how many tents are in that row or column. Where are the tents? Answer on page 286.

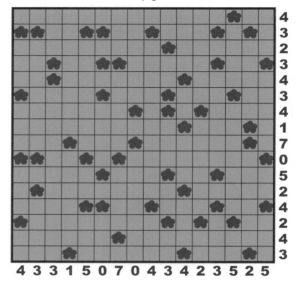

638 Masyu 13

A line passes through some or all of the cells in the grid below in such a way that it forms a single continuous non-intersecting loop. The line always exits a cell by a different side to the one it entered by, and passes through all cells containing a circle. The line travels straight through a cell with a light circle but turns in the previous and/or following cells in its path. The line turns in a cell containing a dark cell, but travels straight through both the previous and following cells in its path. Where is the line? Answer on page 301.

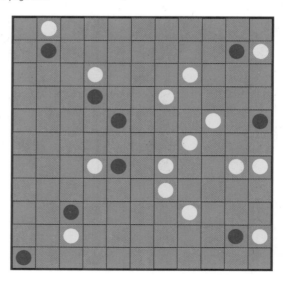

639 Hitori 26

Shade out cells in the grid below so that no number appears more than once in any row or column. Shaded cells cannot touch each other horizontally or vertically, and cannot cut the unshaded cells into two or more groups – the unshaded cells must remain connected horizontally or vertically into one complex branching chain. Which cells are shaded? Answer on page 287.

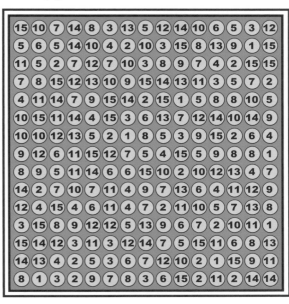

640 Gokigen Naname 26

Each cell in the grid below contains one diagonal line from corner to corner. The numbered circles show how many lines touch that corner. Fill in the grid so that the lines never form a closed circuit of any size. Answer on page 276.

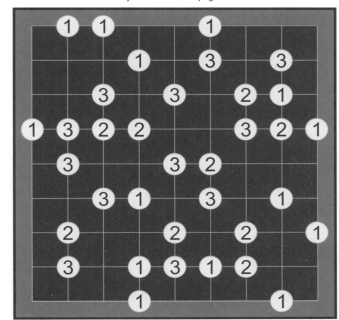

641 Number Link 26

The numbered cells in the grid below indicate the start and end points of single continuous paths. These paths fill the grid completely, and do not branch, cross each other, or touch themselves to form any pool of cells (2x2 or greater).
How are the paths arranged? Answer on page 284.

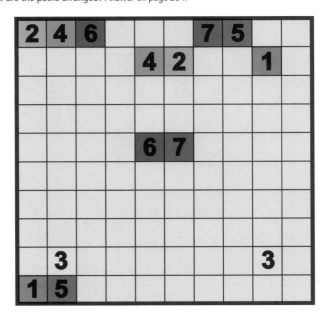

642 Domino placing 26

A set of dominoes containing all possible pairs of numbers from (0,0) to (7,7) is laid out vertically as shown in the blank grid below so that the larger number of each domino is on the top. The numbers above each column are from the top half of the dominoes in that column. The numbers below each column are from the bottom half of the dominoes in that column. The numbers to the left of each row are from the respective half-dominoes in that row.

All the numbers are given to you sorted into descending numerical order. How are the dominoes laid out? Answer on page 283.

	77	76	65	77	77	75
	66	54	55	65	66	44
	20	21	42	33	33	41
766431 531111						
777522 652110						
664433 643200						
754320 532100						
776555 743220						
766541 443200						
	76	10	54	53	64	43
	54	00	22	33	32	21
	10	00	21	21	10	10

175

643 Identicals 13

Which pair of images is identical?
Answer on page 300.

644 Hashiwokakero 13

A number of straight horizontal and vertical bridges connect the islands shown. The number on each island shows how many bridges touch that island. Bridges may not cross each other, and no more than 2 bridges may connect a pair of islands.
Where are the bridges?
Answer on page 297.

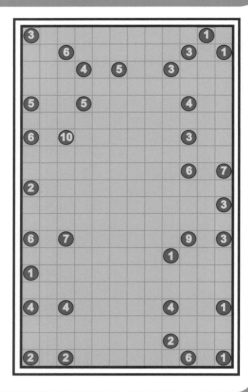

645 Futoshiki 30

Fill in the grid below so that the numbers 1 to 7 appear exactly once in each row and column. Red arrows indicate that a number is greater than its neighbour.
For answer see page 274.

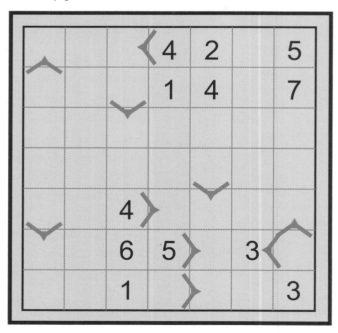

646 Who's Who 10

From the information given, can you match each waiter to his cocktail? Answer on p302.

647 Sudoku 33

Fill in the grid below so that the numbers 1–9 appear exactly once in each row, column and 3x3 box. For solution see page 273.

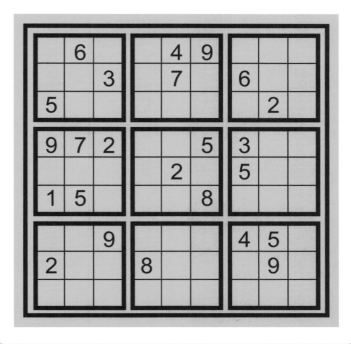

648 Silhouettes 10

Which of the six images fits the silhouette? Answer on page 302.

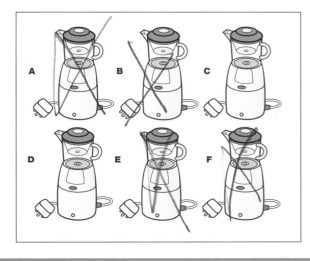

649 Tentai 20

The grid below is divided into a number of shapes. Each shape has a star at its centre, and is made up of one continuous group of cells connected horizontally and/or vertically. The shapes are all symmetrical – they stay the same when rotated by 180 degrees – but may get quite complicated. Where are the shapes? Answer on page 291.

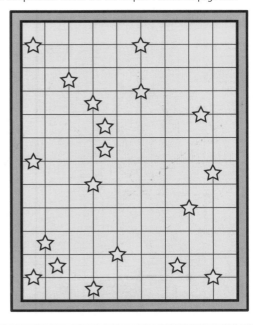

650 Nonogram 18

A number of cells in the grid below are to be shaded. Each row and column may contain one or more continuous lines of shaded cells ('blocks'). The numbers adjacent to the row or column indicate the lengths of the different blocks contained. Blocks are separated from others in the same row or column by at least one empty cell. Where are the shaded cells? A picture will emerge when the cells are shaded correctly. Answer on page 295.

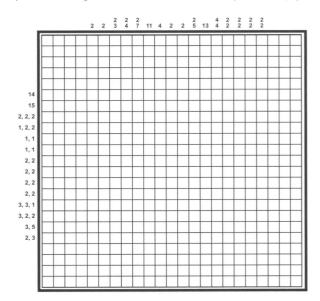

651 Missing Landmarks 19

Which famous landmark is blurred out of this photo? Answer on page 292.

652 Kakuro 18

The empty squares in this grid contain digits from 1 to 9 so that each continuous unbroken line of numbers adds up to the clue value in the filled segment to its left (for horizontal lines) or above it (for vertical lines). No number may be used more than once in any unbroken line. How is the grid filled? Answer on page 293.

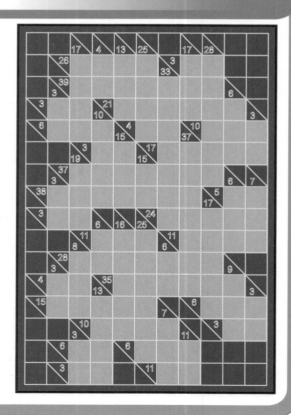

653 Artist's Errors

The artist drawing this scene has made a number of visual, conceptual and logical errors. Can you find them all?
Answer on page 304.

654 Colourminoes 24

In the grid below, each colour has a unique integer value from 0 to 6. The numbers next to each row and column indicate the total value of the cells in that row or column. The values of the cells of the grid correspond in turn to the numbers shown on a half-set of dominoes containing all possible pairs of numbers from (0,0) to (6,6) which has been laid together in one solid rectangle. Dominoes in this rectangle may be placed horizontally or vertically. What number does each colour correspond to, and how are the corresponding dominoes arranged? Answer on page 290.

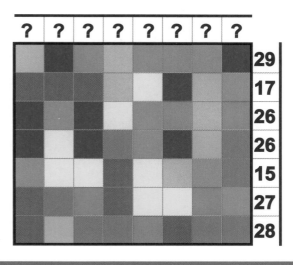

655 Slitherlink 27

A number of the intersection lines in the grid below have to be joined together to make one single complete loop. The numbers in the cell indicate how many of that cell's sides form part of the loop. Answer on page 279.

1	2		3	2	3		2	
2	1	1	3				3		3
2		2					0	
	2						2	
	0	1		3			1	
3					1			
2	2			2	2	3	2	
2		0						
	3		1			3		
		3	1	2		2		

656 Gokigen Naname 27

Each cell in the grid below contains one diagonal line from corner to corner. The numbered circles show how many lines touch that corner. Fill in the grid so that the lines never form a closed circuit of any size. Answer on page 276.

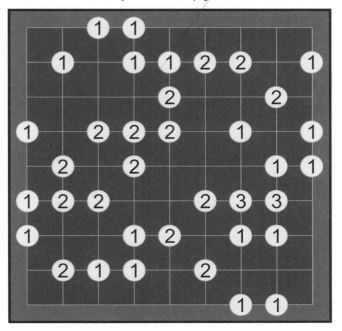

657 Number Link 27

The numbered cells in the grid below indicate the start and end points of single continuous paths. These paths fill the grid completely, and do not branch, cross each other, or touch themselves to form any pool of cells (2x2 or greater). How are the paths arranged? Answer on page 284.

658 Domino placing 27

A set of dominoes containing all possible pairs of numbers from (0,0) to (7,7) is laid out vertically as shown in the blank grid below so that the larger number of each domino is on the top. The numbers above each column are from the top half of the dominoes in that column. The numbers below each column are from the bottom half of the dominoes in that column. The numbers to the left of each row are from the respective half-dominoes in that row.

All the numbers are given to you sorted into descending numerical order. How are the dominoes laid out? Answer on page 283.

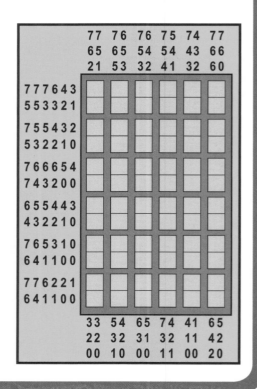

659 Dominoes 27

A full set of dominoes containing all possible pairs of numbers from (0,0) to (9,9) is laid together in one solid rectangle. The dominoes may be placed horizontally or vertically. The numbers in the grid below indicate the value of each half of each domino. How are the dominoes arranged? Answer on page 280.

8	7	4	0	2	9	3	6	8	2	0
3	0	0	1	8	6	9	2	0	6	6
9	3	5	2	3	8	8	3	3	7	7
0	2	1	1	3	9	8	3	7	0	4
1	9	1	7	3	4	1	1	1	1	7
4	5	9	0	6	8	6	3	5	4	7
2	6	6	6	2	8	2	7	5	7	8
2	5	9	4	8	5	0	2	5	7	9
4	3	1	6	0	5	8	0	1	9	5
9	9	7	4	4	2	5	6	4	4	5

660 Tents 27

The grid below indicates a patch of woodland. Some cells contain grass, and others contain trees. Tents are placed on grass cells so that each tree has one tent next to it horizontally or vertically, although note that tents may be adjacent to more than one tree. No tent may be horizontally, vertically or diagonally adjacent to another tent. The numbers beside each row and column tell you how many tents are in that row or column. Where are the tents? Answer on page 286.

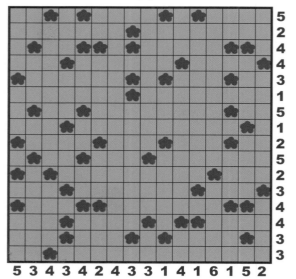

661 Battleships 25

A number of ships of various sizes are hidden in the grid below. The numbers next to each row and column indicate how many ship segments are in that row or column. Some ship segments have already been filled in. Where are the ships? Answer on page 289.

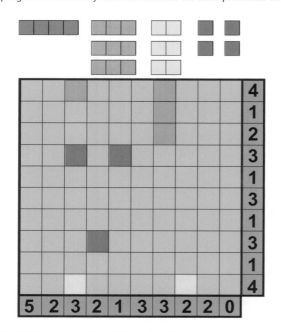

662 Hitori 27

Shade out cells in the grid below so that no number appears more than once in any row or column. Shaded cells cannot touch each other horizontally or vertically, and cannot cut the unshaded cells into two or more groups – the unshaded cells must remain connected horizontally or vertically into one complex branching chain. Which cells are shaded? Answer on page 287.

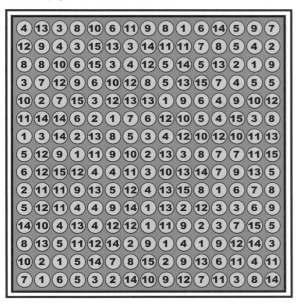

663 Sikaku 27

Divide the grid below into a number of rectangular rooms. Each room must contain exactly one number, equal to the number of cells that make up the room. Answer on page 277.

664 Fillomino 27

Each value shown in the grid below is part of a group of cells equal in number to that given value. A '6' is part of a group of six cells, for example. Groups may take any shape, but no two groups of the same size may touch each other horizontally or vertically at any point, and there are no blank cells. Not all groups need have a given value. How are the groups arranged? Answer on page 288.

665 Bijutsukan 27

The bright cells and dark cells in the grid below represent corridors and walls respectively. Light sources shine a horizontal and vertical beam of light. A corridor cell becomes illuminated if it is in the same row or column as a light source and there is no wall cell in between them. Place light sources in the corridor cells so that every corridor cell is illuminated, and no light source illuminates another light source. The numbers in some walls tell you how many light sources are touching that wall horizontally or vertically. Answer on page 281.

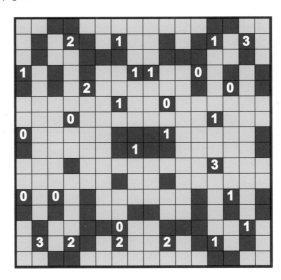

666 Battlehex 17

A number of ships of various sizes are hidden in the hexagonal grid below. The numbers next to each edge indicate how many ship segments are in the rows indicated by the directional arrows. Some ship segments and/or empty water cells have already been filled in. Where are the ships? Answer on page 296.

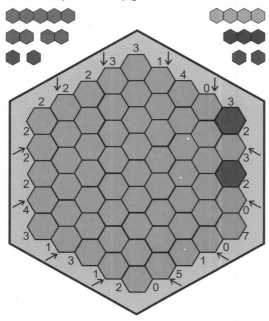

667 Sudoku 34

Fill in the grid below so that the numbers 1–9 appear exactly once in each row, column and 3x3 box. For solution see page 273.

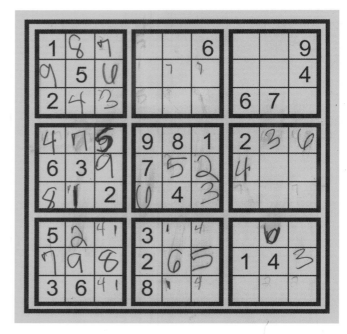

668 Map Colouring 17

The rooms of the grid are coloured so that no two rooms of the same colour ever touch. How are the rooms coloured? Answer on page 295.

669 Futoshiki 31

Fill in the grid below so that the numbers 1 to 7 appear exactly once in each row and column. Red arrows indicate that a number is greater than its neighbour. For answer see page 274.

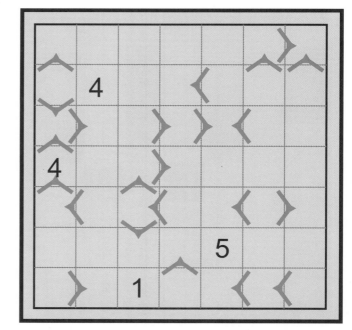

670 Tentai 21

The grid below is divided into a number of shapes. Each shape has a star at its centre, and is made up of one continuous group of cells connected horizontally and/or vertically. The shapes are all symmetrical – they stay the same when rotated by 180 degrees – but may get quite complicated. Where are the shapes? Answer on page 291.

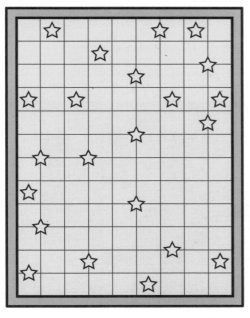

671 Dominoes 28

A full set of dominoes containing all possible pairs of numbers from (0,0) to (9,9) is laid together in one solid rectangle. The dominoes may be placed horizontally or vertically. The numbers in the grid below indicate the value of each half of each domino. How are the dominoes arranged? Answer on page 280.

2	3	2	5	6	6	2	7	5	7	9
9	0	1	8	1	5	0	8	2	0	6
3	0	6	8	8	0	5	7	4	0	3
1	7	9	3	9	6	0	3	0	2	6
1	9	4	1	0	7	4	4	4	4	4
3	5	5	7	3	7	6	2	8	2	2
8	5	1	5	6	8	4	7	7	9	9
9	9	8	1	4	7	3	6	1	3	8
2	5	5	7	4	4	1	3	8	3	0
2	1	5	9	9	0	1	6	8	2	6

672 Missing Landmarks 20

Which famous landmark is blurred out of this photo? Answer on page 292.

673 Gokigen Naname 28

Each cell in the grid below contains one diagonal line from corner to corner. The numbered circles show how many lines touch that corner. Fill in the grid so that the lines never form a closed circuit of any size. Answer on page 276.

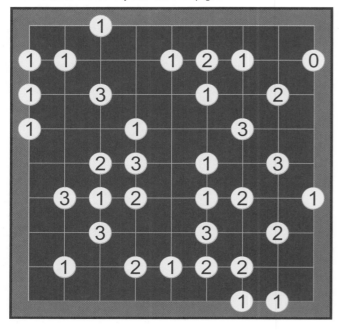

674 Colourminoes 25

In the grid below, each colour has a unique integer value from 0 to 6. The numbers next to each row and column indicate the total value of the cells in that row or column. The values of the cells of the grid correspond in turn to the numbers shown on a half-set of dominoes containing all possible pairs of numbers from (0,0) to (6,6) which has been laid together in one solid rectangle. Dominoes in this rectangle may be placed horizontally or vertically. What number does each colour correspond to, and how are the corresponding dominoes arranged? Answer on page 290.

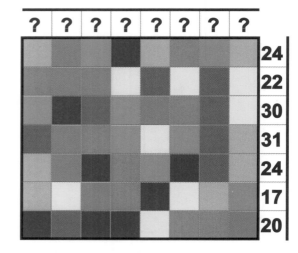

675 Differences

Each copy of the picture has one flaw that none of the others share. Can you find them all? Answer on page 304.

676 Spot the Set

There are four different versions of the picture in the group below, each one reproduced three times. Can you identify the four sets? Answer on page 304.

677 Sikaku 28

Divide the grid below into a number of rectangular rooms. Each room must contain exactly one number, equal to the number of cells that make up the room.
Answer on page 277.

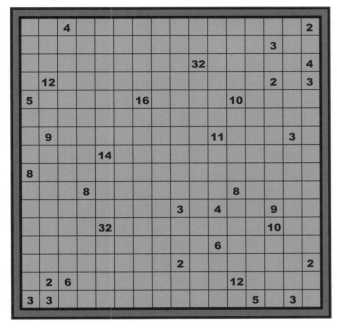

678 Domino placing 28

A set of dominoes containing all possible pairs of numbers from (0,0) to (7,7) is laid out vertically as shown in the blank grid below so that the larger number of each domino is on the top. The numbers above each column are from the top half of the dominoes in that column. The numbers below each column are from the bottom half of the dominoes in that column. The numbers to the left of each row are from the respective half-dominoes in that row. All the numbers are given to you sorted into descending numerical order. How are the dominoes laid out?
Answer on page 283.

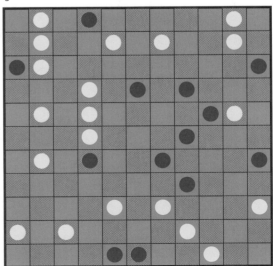

679 Yudoku 14

Fill in the grid below so that the letters s, p, a, r, k, l, i, n and g appear exactly once in each row, column and 3x3 box. Answer on page 301.

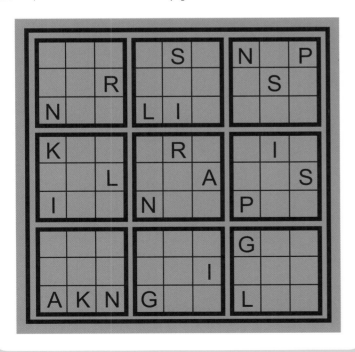

680 Masyu 14

A line passes through some or all of the cells in the grid below in such a way that it forms a single continuous non-intersecting loop. The line always exits a cell by a different side to the one it entered by, and passes through all cells containing a circle. The line travels straight through a cell with a light circle but turns in the previous and/or following cells in its path. The line turns in a cell containing a dark cell, but travels straight through both the previous and following cells in its path. Where is the line?
Answer on page 301.

681 Hitori 28

Shade out cells in the grid below so that no number appears more than once in any row or column. Shaded cells cannot touch each other horizontally or vertically, and cannot cut the unshaded cells into two or more groups – the unshaded cells must remain connected horizontally or vertically into one complex branching chain. Which cells are shaded? Answer on page 287.

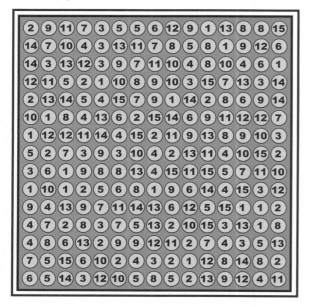

682 Identicals 14

Which pair of images is identical?
Answer on page 300.

683 Fillomino 28

Each value shown in the grid below is part of a group of cells equal in number to that given value. A '6' is part of a group of six cells, for example. Groups may take any shape, but no two groups of the same size may touch each other horizontally or vertically at any point, and there are no blank cells. Not all groups need have a given value. How are the groups arranged? Answer on page 288.

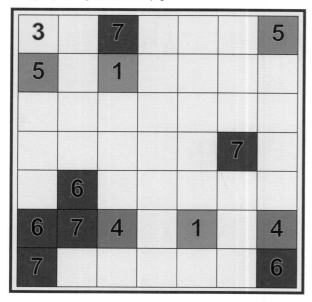

684 Samurai Sudoku 7

Fill in each 9x9 grid below so that the numbers 1–9 appear exactly once in each row, column and 3x3 block. Numbers in overlapping blocks count identically towards both grids. Answer on page 303.

685 Detail Scene 14

The three enlarged squares appear somewhere in the large picture. Can you find them? Answer on page 299.

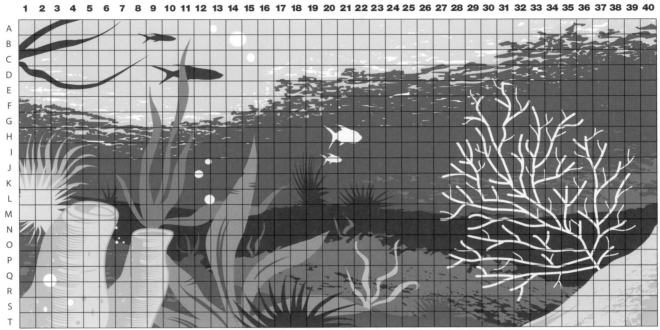

686 Sudoku 35

Fill in the grid below so that the numbers 1–9 appear exactly once in each row, column and 3x3 box. For solution see page 273.

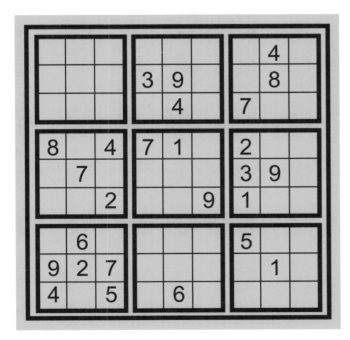

687 Spot the Difference

There are eight differences between the two pictures. Can you find them all? Answer on p302.

688 Hashiwokakero 14

A number of straight horizontal and vertical bridges connect the islands shown. The number on each island shows how many bridges touch that island. Bridges may not cross each other, and no more than 2 bridges may connect a pair of islands.
Where are the bridges?
Answer on page 297.

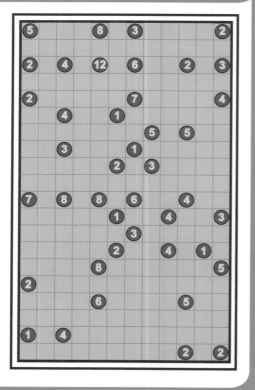

689 Killer Sudoku 7

Fill in the grid below so that the numbers 1–9 appear exactly once in each row, column and 3x3 block, and that the numbers in each dotted room add up to the value in its top right corner. Answer on page 303.

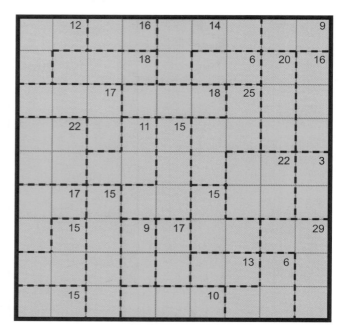

690 Match One 14

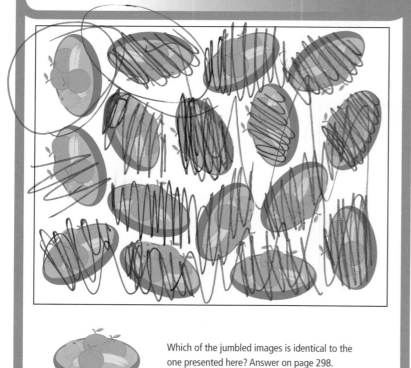

Which of the jumbled images is identical to the one presented here? Answer on page 298.

691 Super sudoku 7

Fill in the grid below so that the digits 1, 2, 3, 4, 5, 6, 7, 8, 9, a, b, c, d, e, f and g appear exactly once in each row and column. Answer on page 303.

692 Suiri 14

It's Mother's Day. Given the information below, can you work out what type (2) and colour (3) of flower each mother (1) is getting from her son (4)?

1. Antoinette is getting blue flowers.
2. Serge is giving his mother yellow flowers. They are not chrysanthemums.
3. Sabine is not Didier's mother, and she is not getting red flowers.
4. Laurent is buying roses for his mother. They are neither pink nor white.
5. Maxine is Vincent's mother. She is not getting the orchids, which are red.
6. Didier's mother is not Dominique.
7. Estelle is getting carnations, which are not pink.
8. One woman is receiving lilies.
9. One woman has a son called Bastien.
Answer on page 299.

693 Tents 28

The grid below indicates a patch of woodland. Some cells contain grass, and others contain trees. Tents are placed on grass cells so that each tree has one tent next to it horizontally or vertically, although note that tents may be adjacent to more than one tree. No tent may be horizontally, vertically or diagonally adjacent to another tent. The numbers beside each row and column tell you how many tents are in that row or column. Where are the tents? Answer on page 286.

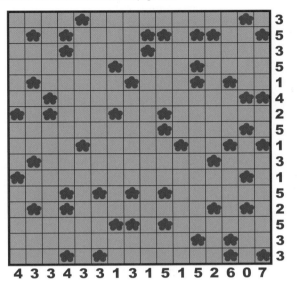

694 Bijutsukan 28

The bright cells and dark cells in the grid below represent corridors and walls respectively. Light sources shine a horizontal and vertical beam of light. A corridor cell becomes illuminated if it is in the same row or column as a light source and there is no wall cell in between them. Place light sources in the corridor cells so that every corridor cell is illuminated, and no light source illuminates another light source. The numbers in some walls tell you how many light sources are touching that wall horizontally or vertically. Answer on page 281.

189

695 Slitherlink 28

A number of the intersection lines in the grid below have to be joined together to make one single complete loop. The numbers in the cell indicate how many of that cell's sides form part of the loop. Answer on page 279.

3		3	1			2	2	3	
			2		1			0	
3			2		2				3
	1	2		2			2		
1	2		3					3	3
	3	2			3				
							2	2	
							3	1	
	3	1			3	1			3
	1		3	2				2	

696 Number Link 28

The numbered cells in the grid below indicate the start and end points of single continuous paths. These paths fill the grid completely, and do not branch, cross each other, or touch themselves to form any pool of cells (2x2 or greater).
How are the paths arranged? Answer on page 284.

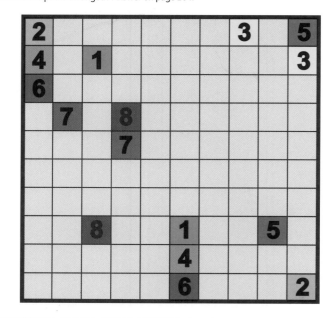

697 Mirror Image 14

Which of the five images below is an identical mirror image of the one above? Answer on page 300.

698 Battleships 26

A number of ships of various sizes are hidden in the grid below. The numbers next to each row and column indicate how many ship segments are in that row or column. Some ship segments have already been filled in. Where are the ships? Answer on page 289.

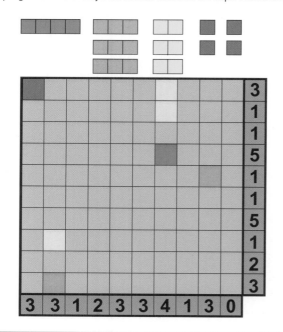

699 Kakuro 19

The empty squares in this grid contain digits from 1 to 9 so that each continuous unbroken line of numbers adds up to the clue value in the filled segment to its left (for horizontal lines) or above it (for vertical lines). No number may be used more than once in any unbroken line. How is the grid filled? Answer on page 294.

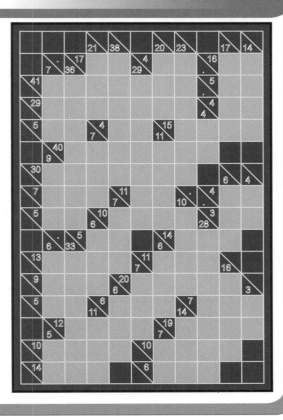

700 Nonogram 19

A number of cells in the grid below are to be shaded. Each row and column may contain one or more continuous lines of shaded cells ('blocks'). The numbers adjacent to the row or column indicate the lengths of the different blocks contained. Blocks are separated from others in the same row or column by at least one empty cell. Where are the shaded cells? A picture will emerge when the cells are shaded correctly. Answer on page 295.

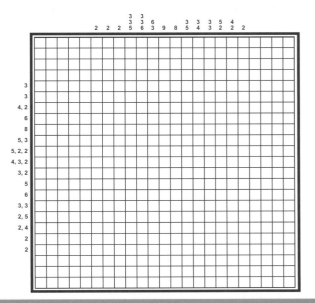

701 Futoshiki 32

Fill in the grid below so that the numbers 1 to 7 appear exactly once in each row and column. Red arrows indicate that a number is greater than its neighbour. For answer see page 274.

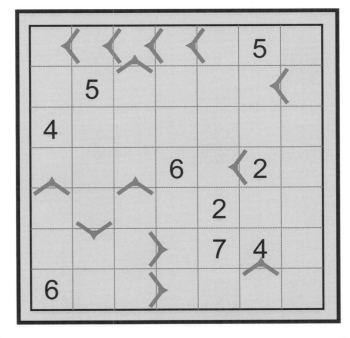

702 Sudoku 36

Fill in the grid below so that the numbers 1–9 appear exactly once in each row, column and 3x3 box. For solution see page 273.

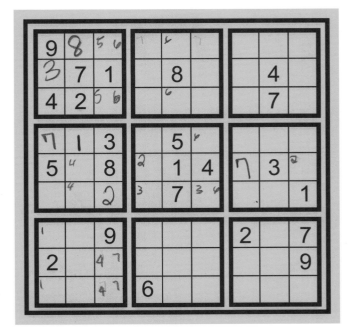

703 Battlehex 18

A number of ships of various sizes are hidden in the hexagonal grid below. The numbers next to each edge indicate how many ship segments are in the rows indicated by the directional arrows. Some ship segments and/or empty water cells have already been filled in. Where are the ships? Answer on page 296.

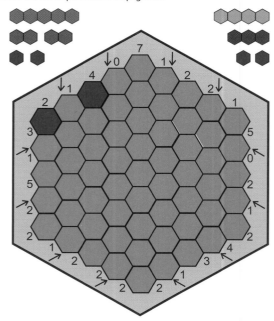

704 Map Colouring 18

The rooms of the grid are coloured so that no two rooms of the same colour ever touch. How are the rooms coloured? Answer on page 295.

705 Number Link 29

The numbered cells in the grid below indicate the start and end points of single continuous paths. These paths fill the grid completely, and do not branch, cross each other, or touch themselves to form any pool of cells (2x2 or greater).
How are the paths arranged? Answer on page 284.

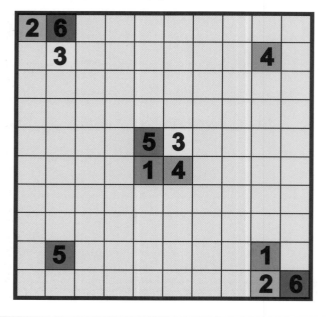

706 Fillomino 29

Each value shown in the grid below is part of a group of cells equal in number to that given value. A '6' is part of a group of six cells, for example. Groups may take any shape, but no two groups of the same size may touch each other horizontally or vertically at any point, and there are no blank cells. Not all groups need have a given value.
How are the groups arranged? Answer on page 288.

707 Minesweeper 8

The grid below contains a number of bombs hidden in empty squares. Each red flag tells you how many bombs are in the eight cells around it. Where are the bombs?
For answer see page 275.

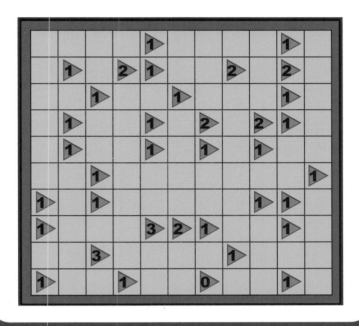

708 Slitherlink 29

A number of the intersection lines in the grid below have to be joined together to make one single complete loop. The numbers in the cell indicate how many of that cell's sides form part of the loop. Answer on page 279.

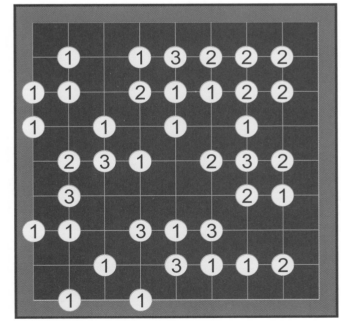

709 Tents 29

The grid below indicates a patch of woodland. Some cells contain grass, and others contain trees. Tents are placed on grass cells so that each tree has one tent next to it horizontally or vertically, although note that tents may be adjacent to more than one tree. No tent may be horizontally, vertically or diagonally adjacent to another tent. The numbers beside each row and column tell you how many tents are in that row or column. Where are the tents? Answer on page 286.

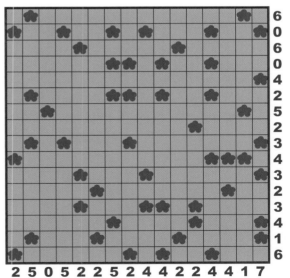

710 Gokigen Naname 29

Each cell in the grid below contains one diagonal line from corner to corner. The numbered circles show how many lines touch that corner. Fill in the grid so that the lines never form a closed circuit of any size. Answer on page 276.

711 Hitori 29

Shade out cells in the grid below so that no number appears more than once in any row or column. Shaded cells cannot touch each other horizontally or vertically, and cannot cut the unshaded cells into two or more groups – the unshaded cells must remain connected horizontally or vertically into one complex branching chain. Which cells are shaded? Answer on page 287.

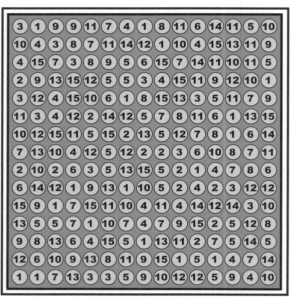

712 Dominoes 29

A full set of dominoes containing all possible pairs of numbers from (0,0) to (9,9) is laid together in one solid rectangle. The dominoes may be placed horizontally or vertically. The numbers in the grid below indicate the value of each half of each domino. How are the dominoes arranged? Answer on page 280.

0	8	5	1	9	6	8	8	4	4	2
4	1	9	0	6	5	4	3	0	0	9
0	5	3	3	2	6	0	6	9	2	2
7	2	7	6	4	1	6	8	0	1	
9	7	0	8	8	8	8	9	1	3	5
2	7	0	3	3	9	9	6	4	3	3
5	7	1	7	4	7	4	7	4	1	8
9	1	5	6	8	2	5	0	6	1	7
8	5	2	3	6	0	3	1	5	1	2
9	9	3	5	7	7	4	2	5	4	2

713 Domino placing 29

A set of dominoes containing all possible pairs of numbers from (0,0) to (7,7) is laid out vertically as shown in the blank grid below so that the larger number of each domino is on the top. The numbers above each column are from the top half of the dominoes in that column.

The numbers below each column are from the bottom half of the dominoes in that column.

The numbers to the left of each row are from the respective half-dominoes in that row. All the numbers are given to you sorted into descending numerical order. How are the dominoes laid out? Answer on page 283.

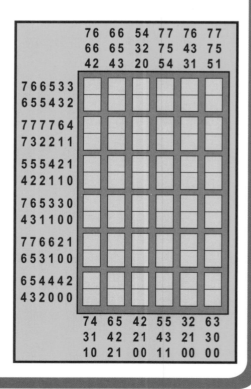

714 Bijutsukan 29

The bright cells and dark cells in the grid below represent corridors and walls respectively. Light sources shine a horizontal and vertical beam of light. A corridor cell becomes illuminated if it is in the same row or column as a light source and there is no wall cell in between them. Place light sources in the corridor cells so that every corridor cell is illuminated, and no light source illuminates another light source. The numbers in some walls tell you how many light sources are touching that wall horizontally or vertically. Answer on page 281.

715 Sikaku 29

Divide the grid below into a number of rectangular rooms. Each room must contain exactly one number, equal to the number of cells that make up the room.
Answer on page 277.

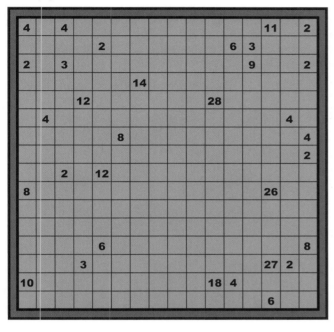

716 Futoshiki 33

Fill in the grid below so that the numbers 1 to 7 appear exactly once in each row and column. Red arrows indicate that a number is greater than its neighbour.
For answer see page 274.

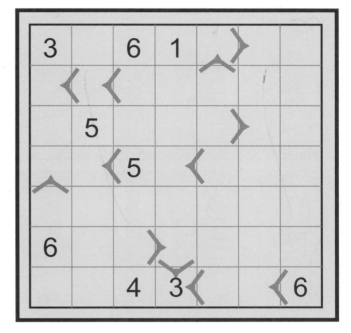

717 Silhouettes 11

Which of the six images fits the silhouette?
Answer on page 302.

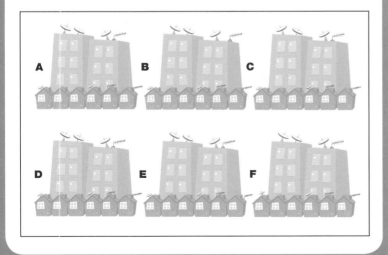

718 Tentai 22

The grid below is divided into a number of shapes. Each shape has a star at its centre, and is made up of one continuous group of cells connected horizontally and/or vertically. The shapes are all symmetrical – they stay the same when rotated by 180 degrees – but may get quite complicated. Where are the shapes? Answer on page 291.

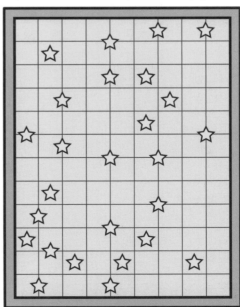

719 Who's Who 11

From the information given, can you match each grocer to his or her stall? Answer on p302.

I'm Megan, my stand's sign has a red tomato on it.

I'm Cate, my stand is full of produce.

I'm Rod, my stand does not have an awning.

I am Tony.

720 Colourminoes 26

In the grid below, each colour has a unique integer value from 0 to 6. The numbers next to each row and column indicate the total value of the cells in that row or column. The values of the cells of the grid correspond in turn to the numbers shown on a half-set of dominoes containing all possible pairs of numbers from (0,0) to (6,6) which has been laid together in one solid rectangle. Dominoes in this rectangle may be placed horizontally or vertically. What number does each colour correspond to, and how are the corresponding dominoes arranged? Answer on page 290.

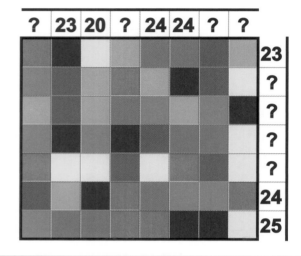

721 Battleships 27

A number of ships of various sizes are hidden in the grid below. The numbers next to each row and column indicate how many ship segments are in that row or column. Some ship segments have already been filled in. Where are the ships? Answer on page 289.

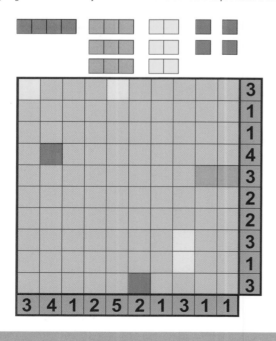

722 Nonogram 20

A number of cells in the grid below are to be shaded. Each row and column may contain one or more continuous lines of shaded cells ('blocks'). The numbers adjacent to the row or column indicate the lengths of the different blocks contained. Blocks are separated from others in the same row or column by at least one empty cell. Where are the shaded cells? A picture will emerge when the cells are shaded correctly. Answer on page 295.

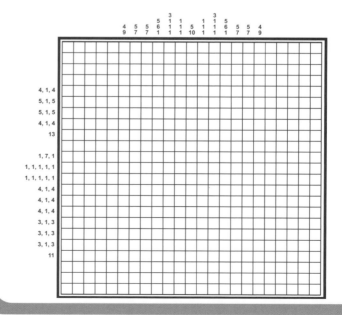

723 Missing Landmarks 21

Which famous landmark is blurred out of this photo? Answer on page 292.

724 Sudoku 37

Fill in the grid below so that the numbers 1–9 appear exactly once in each row, column and 3x3 box. For solution see page 273.

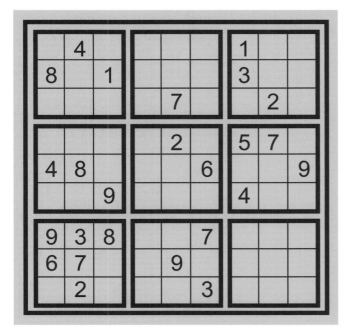

725 Kakuro 20

The empty squares in this grid contain digits from 1 to 9 so that each continuous unbroken line of numbers adds up to the clue value in the filled segment to its left (for horizontal lines) or above it (for vertical lines). No number may be used more than once in any unbroken line. How is the grid filled? Answer on page 294.

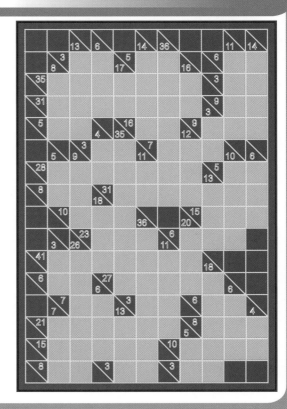

726 Futoshiki 34

Fill in the grid below so that the numbers 1 to 7 appear exactly once in each row and column. Red arrows indicate that a number is greater than its neighbour.
For answer see page 274.

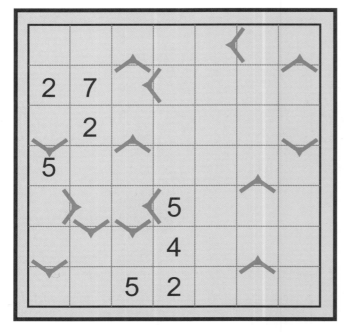

727 Gokigen Naname 30

Each cell in the grid below contains one diagonal line from corner to corner. The numbered circles show how many lines touch that corner. Fill in the grid so that the lines never form a closed circuit of any size. Answer on page 276.

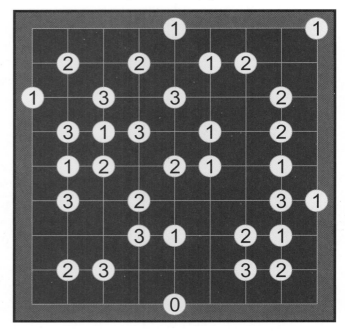

728 Masyu 15

A line passes through some or all of the cells in the grid below in such a way that it forms a single continuous non-intersecting loop. The line always exits a cell by a different side to the one it entered by, and passes through all cells containing a circle. The line travels straight through a cell with a light circle but turns in the previous and/or following cells in its path. The line turns in a cell containing a dark cell, but travels straight through both the previous and following cells in its path. Where is the line? Answer on page 301.

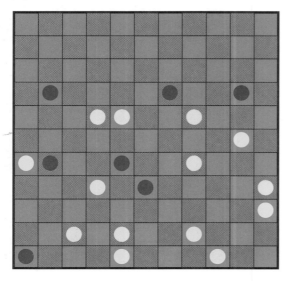

729 Hashiwokakero 15

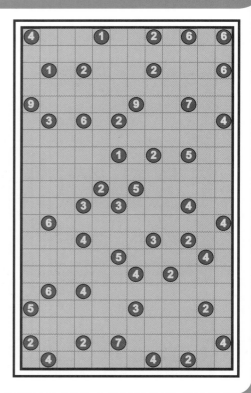

A number of straight horizontal and vertical bridges connect the islands shown. The number on each island shows how many bridges touch that island. Bridges may not cross each other, and no more than 2 bridges may connect a pair of islands.
Where are the bridges? Answer on page 297.

730 Bijutsukan 30

The bright cells and dark cells in the grid below represent corridors and walls respectively. Light sources shine a horizontal and vertical beam of light. A corridor cell becomes illuminated if it is in the same row or column as a light source and there is no wall cell in between them. Place light sources in the corridor cells so that every corridor cell is illuminated, and no light source illuminates another light source. The numbers in some walls tell you how many light sources are touching that wall horizontally or vertically. Answer on page 281.

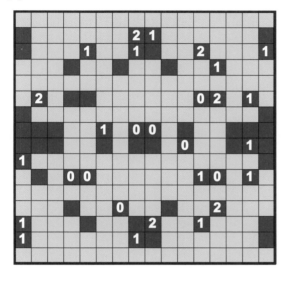

731 Sikaku 30

Divide the grid below into a number of rectangular rooms. Each room must contain exactly one number, equal to the number of cells that make up the room. Answer on page 277.

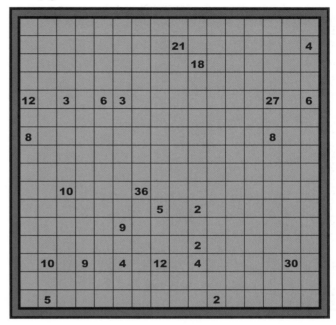

732 Number Link 30

The numbered cells in the grid below indicate the start and end points of single continuous paths. These paths fill the grid completely, and do not branch, cross each other, or touch themselves to form any pool of cells (2x2 or greater). How are the paths arranged? Answer on page 284.

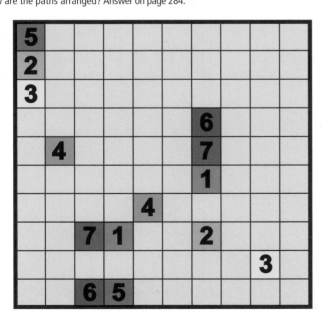

733 Match One 15

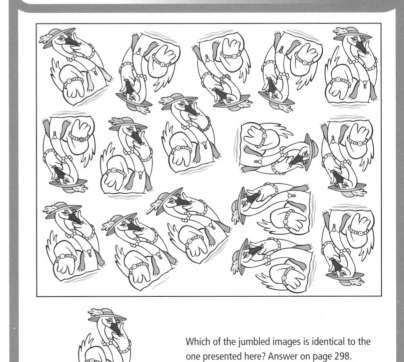

Which of the jumbled images is identical to the one presented here? Answer on page 298.

734 Hitori 30

Shade out cells in the grid below so that no number appears more than once in any row or column. Shaded cells cannot touch each other horizontally or vertically, and cannot cut the unshaded cells into two or more groups – the unshaded cells must remain connected horizontally or vertically into one complex branching chain. Which cells are shaded? Answer on page 287.

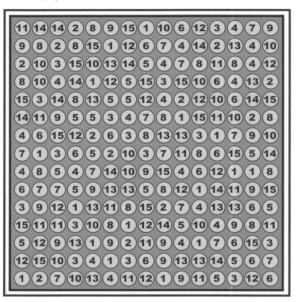

735 Mirror Image 15

Which of the five images below is an identical mirror image of the one above? Answer on page 300.

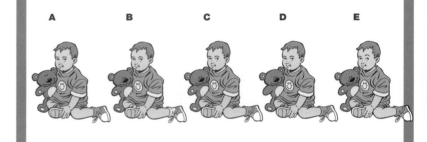

A   B   C   D   E

736 Domino placing 30

A set of dominoes containing all possible pairs of numbers from (0,0) to (7,7) is laid out vertically as shown in the blank grid below so that the larger number of each domino is on the top. The numbers above each column are from the top half of the dominoes in that column. The numbers below each column are from the bottom half of the dominoes in that column. The numbers to the left of each row are from the respective half-dominoes in that row. All the numbers are given to you sorted into descending numerical order. How are the dominoes laid out? Answer on page 283.

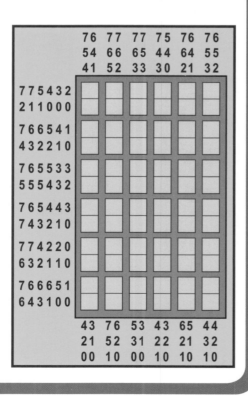

737 Slitherlink 30

A number of the intersection lines in the grid below have to be joined together to make one single complete loop. The numbers in the cell indicate how many of that cell's sides form part of the loop. Answer on page 279.

738 Dominoes 30

A full set of dominoes containing all possible pairs of numbers from (0,0) to (9,9) is laid together in one solid rectangle. The dominoes may be placed horizontally or vertically. The numbers in the grid below indicate the value of each half of each domino. How are the dominoes arranged? Answer on page 280.

9	2	1	2	5	0	6	8	6	1	3
0	1	3	3	9	4	0	0	4	0	4
0	2	9	7	6	5	7	3	6	0	5
8	4	9	6	5	2	5	8	6	9	1
3	2	4	3	5	3	6	4	8	8	1
5	4	6	3	2	9	6	2	6	5	6
7	4	2	8	7	5	7	5	2	2	8
4	8	8	3	7	1	9	2	9	4	0
1	1	4	9	0	1	1	8	8	7	7
0	9	5	3	9	6	7	7	0	3	7

739 Identicals 15

Which pair of images is identical? Answer on page 300.

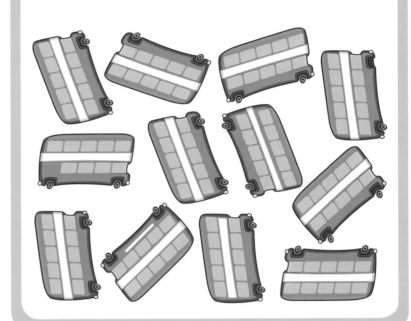

740 Fillomino 30

Each value shown in the grid below is part of a group of cells equal in number to that given value. A '6' is part of a group of six cells, for example. Groups may take any shape, but no two groups of the same size may touch each other horizontally or vertically at any point, and there are no blank cells. Not all groups need have a given value. How are the groups arranged? Answer on page 288.

741 Yudoku 15

Fill in the grid below so that the letters s, p, a, r, k, l, i, n and g appear exactly once in each row, column and 3x3 box. Answer on page 301.

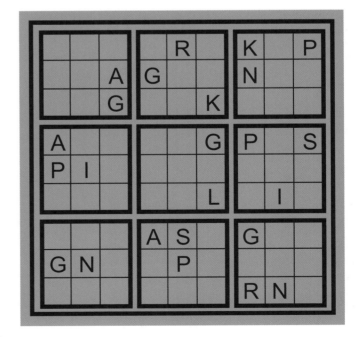

742 Suiri 15

Five friends are having a meal. From the information given below, can you work out what each meat (2) each woman (1) is having, what she is accompanying it with (3), and what she is finishing her meal with afterwards (4)?

1. Dina is either having noodles or soup with her meal, followed by either cake or chocolates.

2. May is either having stir-fry vegetables or bean shoots with her meal.

5. Either Lili or Dina is having duck or lamb followed by chocolates.

3. Min is either having chicken or lamb with rice or soup.

4. Su is either having bean shoots or soup with her beef or lamb, followed by either coffee or cake.

7. The cake is being eaten after a meal accompanied by either soup or stir-fry vegetables.

6. The duck is being followed by either coffee or ice-cream.

8. The meal being eaten with noodles is being followed by either lychees or ice-cream.

9. One of the women is eating pork.

Answer on page 299.

743 Tents 30

The grid below indicates a patch of woodland. Some cells contain grass, and others contain trees. Tents are placed on grass cells so that each tree has one tent next to it horizontally or vertically, although note that tents may be adjacent to more than one tree. No tent may be horizontally, vertically or diagonally adjacent to another tent. The numbers beside each row and column tell you how many tents are in that row or column. Where are the tents? Answer on page 286.

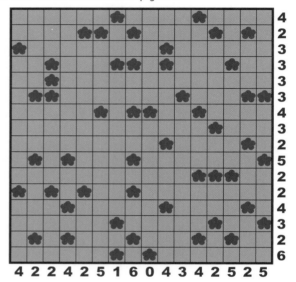

744 Battleships 28

A number of ships of various sizes are hidden in the grid below. The numbers next to each row and column indicate how many ship segments are in that row or column. Some ship segments have already been filled in. Where are the ships? Answer on page 289.

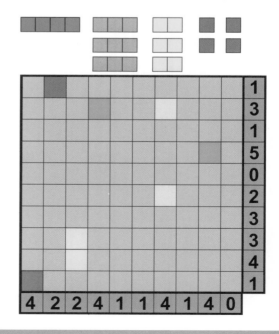

745 Detail Scene 15

The three enlarged squares appear somewhere in the large picture. Can you find them? Answer on page 299.

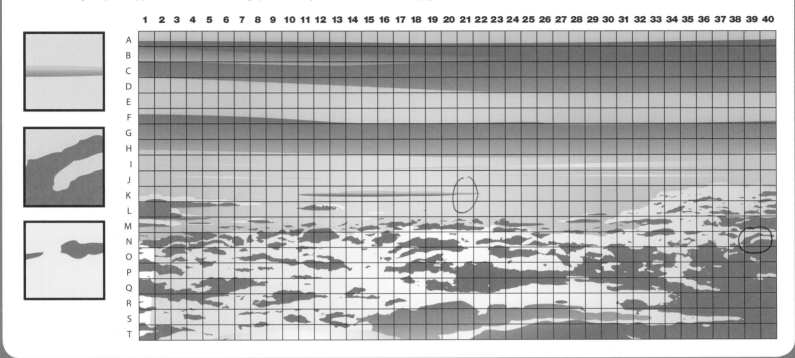

746 Colourminoes 27

In the grid below, each colour has a unique integer value from 0 to 6. The numbers next to each row and column indicate the total value of the cells in that row or column. The values of the cells of the grid correspond in turn to the numbers shown on a half-set of dominoes containing all possible pairs of numbers from (0,0) to (6,6) which has been laid together in one solid rectangle. Dominoes in this rectangle may be placed horizontally or vertically. What number does each colour correspond to, and how are the corresponding dominoes arranged? Answer on page 290.

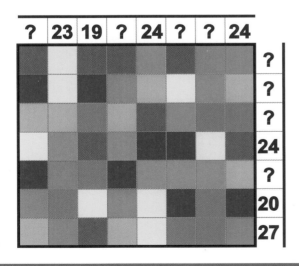

747 Tentai 23

The grid below is divided into a number of shapes. Each shape has a star at its centre, and is made up of one continuous group of cells connected horizontally and/or vertically. The shapes are all symmetrical – they stay the same when rotated by 180 degrees – but may get quite complicated. Where are the shapes? Answer on page 291.

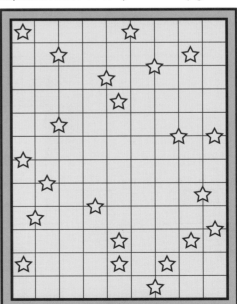

748 Battlehex 19

A number of ships of various sizes are hidden in the hexagonal grid below. The numbers next to each edge indicate how many ship segments are in the rows indicated by the directional arrows. Some ship segments and/or empty water cells have already been filled in. Where are the ships? Answer on page 296.

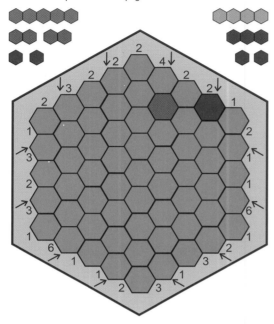

749 Sudoku 38

Fill in the grid below so that the numbers 1–9 appear exactly once in each row, column and 3x3 box. For solution see page 273.

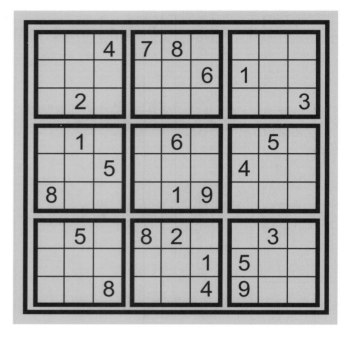

750 Map Colouring 19

The rooms of the grid are coloured so that no two rooms of the same colour ever touch. How are the rooms coloured? Answer on page 295.

751 Futoshiki 35

Fill in the grid below so that the numbers 1 to 7 appear exactly once in each row and column. Red arrows indicate that a number is greater than its neighbour. For answer see page 274.

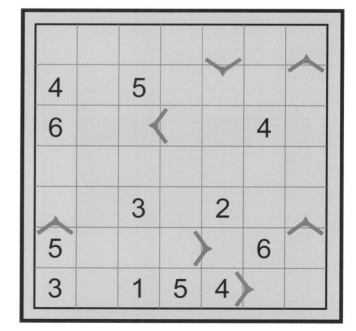

752 Missing Landmarks 22

Which famous landmark is blurred out of this photo?
Answer on page 292.

753 Fillomino 31

Each value shown in the grid below is part of a group of cells equal in number to that given value. A '6' is part of a group of six cells, for example. Groups may take any shape, but no two groups of the same size may touch each other horizontally or vertically at any point, and there are no blank cells. Not all groups need have a given value. How are the groups arranged? Answer on page 288.

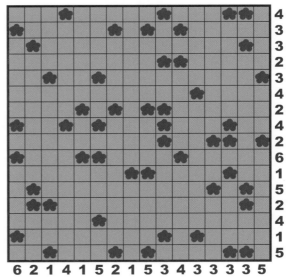

754 Hitori 31

Shade out cells in the grid below so that no number appears more than once in any row or column. Shaded cells cannot touch each other horizontally or vertically, and cannot cut the unshaded cells into two or more groups – the unshaded cells must remain connected horizontally or vertically into one complex branching chain. Which cells are shaded? Answer on page 287.

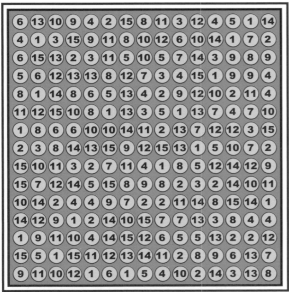

755 Tents 31

The grid below indicates a patch of woodland. Some cells contain grass, and others contain trees. Tents are placed on grass cells so that each tree has one tent next to it horizontally or vertically, although note that tents may be adjacent to more than one tree. No tent may be horizontally, vertically or diagonally adjacent to another tent. The numbers beside each row and column tell you how many tents are in that row or column. Where are the tents? Answer on page 286.

756 Dominoes 31

A full set of dominoes containing all possible pairs of numbers from (0,0) to (9,9) is laid together in one solid rectangle. The dominoes may be placed horizontally or vertically. The numbers in the grid below indicate the value of each half of each domino. How are the dominoes arranged? Answer on page 280.

2	1	0	3	7	9	3	5	7	1	1
9	1	1	2	7	5	6	2	8	5	7
9	3	7	5	4	8	5	1	6	5	3
5	7	0	1	2	0	5	8	4	9	8
4	8	3	2	8	4	4	3	7	9	0
6	0	7	5	8	8	0	3	1	7	9
3	0	4	3	0	2	0	6	6	2	9
1	1	2	5	6	5	0	4	8	6	2
9	4	8	8	4	7	9	4	4	9	2
2	0	6	1	3	6	3	6	9	7	6

757 Domino placing 31

A set of dominoes containing all possible pairs of numbers from (0,0) to (7,7) is laid out vertically as shown in the blank grid below so that the larger number of each domino is on the top. The numbers above each column are from the top half of the dominoes in that column. The numbers below each column are from the bottom half of the dominoes in that column. The numbers to the left of each row are from the respective half-dominoes in that row.

All the numbers are given to you sorted into descending numerical order. How are the dominoes laid out? Answer on page 283.

Column headers (top):
76	76	77	76	76	76
33	65	76	42	54	54
21	54	55	20	43	31

Row labels (left):
766431
633111

766655
543200

777443
742210

555421
521000

776322
542210

765430
643310

Column footers (bottom):
32	65	65	54	32	73
21	44	41	32	10	32
10	21	10	00	00	10

758 Slitherlink 31

A number of the intersection lines in the grid below have to be joined together to make one single complete loop. The numbers in the cell indicate how many of that cell's sides form part of the loop. Answer on page 279.

2	3	2			2		3
	2		2			1	2
	2	1		1		2	2
2		2	1		3		1	2
		3			1		2		1
2	2	3	0		1			3
	2		2	3	1	2		3
2			1		2			2	2
3	2	3	2		2	3	3	2
	2		3	2	2		2		3

759 Number Link 31

The numbered cells in the grid below indicate the start and end points of single continuous paths. These paths fill the grid completely, and do not branch, cross each other, or touch themselves to form any pool of cells (2x2 or greater). How are the paths arranged? Answer on page 285.

760 Sikaku 31

Divide the grid below into a number of rectangular rooms. Each room must contain exactly one number, equal to the number of cells that make up the room.
Answer on page 278.

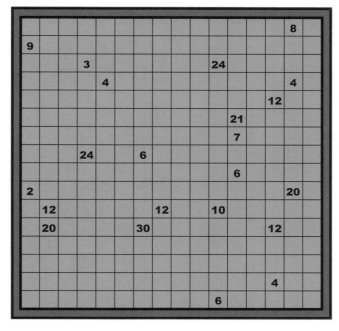

761 Gokigen Naname 31

Each cell in the grid below contains one diagonal line from corner to corner. The numbered circles show how many lines touch that corner. Fill in the grid so that the lines never form a closed circuit of any size. Answer on page 276.

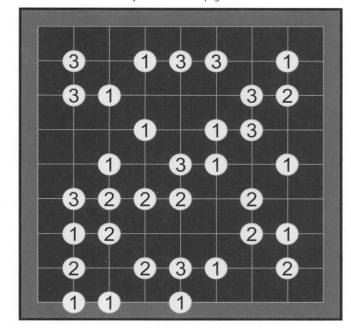

762 Bijutsukan 31

The bright cells and dark cells in the grid below represent corridors and walls respectively. Light sources shine a horizontal and vertical beam of light. A corridor cell becomes illuminated if it is in the same row or column as a light source and there is no wall cell in between them. Place light sources in the corridor cells so that every corridor cell is illuminated, and no light source illuminates another light source. The numbers in some walls tell you how many light sources are touching that wall horizontally or vertically. Answer on page 282.

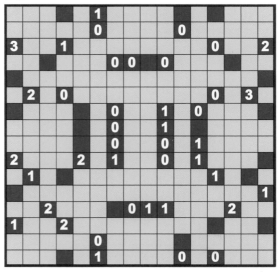

763 Artist's Errors

The artist drawing this scene has made a number of visual, conceptual and logical errors. Can you find them all?
Answer on page 304.

764 Kakuro 21

The empty squares in this grid contain digits from 1 to 9 so that each continuous unbroken line of numbers adds up to the clue value in the filled segment to its left (for horizontal lines) or above it (for vertical lines). No number may be used more than once in any unbroken line. How is the grid filled? Answer on page 294.

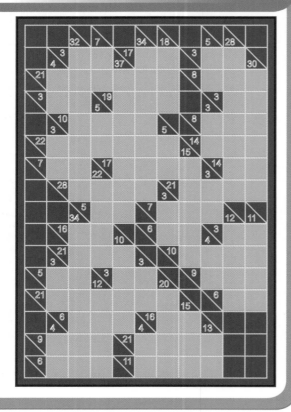

765 Nonogram 21

A number of cells in this grid are to be shaded. Each row and column may contain one or more continuous lines of shaded cells ('blocks'). The numbers adjacent to the row or column indicate the lengths of the different blocks contained. Blocks are separated from others in the same row or column by at least one empty cell. Where are the shaded cells? A picture will emerge when the cells are shaded correctly. Answer on page 295.

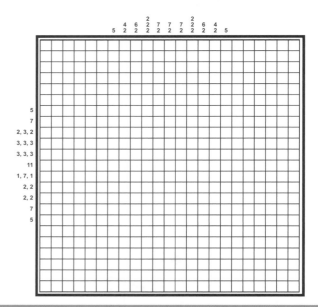

766 Sudoku 39

Fill in the grid below so that the numbers 1–9 appear exactly once in each row, column and 3x3 box. For solution see page 273.

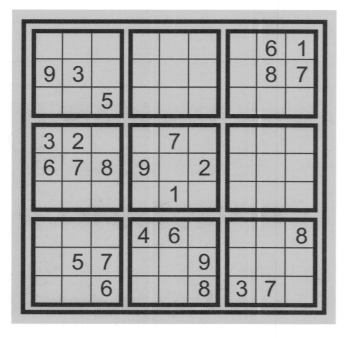

767 Battleships 29

A number of ships of various sizes are hidden in the grid below. The numbers next to each row and column indicate how many ship segments are in that row or column. Some ship segments have already been filled in. Where are the ships? Answer on page 289.

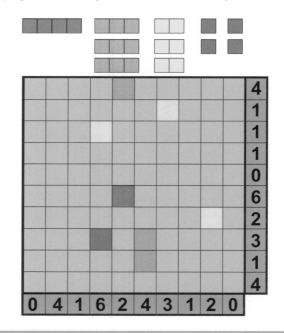

768 Colourminoes 28

In the grid below, each colour has a unique integer value from 0 to 6. The numbers next to each row and column indicate the total value of the cells in that row or column. The values of the cells of the grid correspond in turn to the numbers shown on a half-set of dominoes containing all possible pairs of numbers from (0,0) to (6,6) which has been laid together in one solid rectangle. Dominoes in this rectangle may be placed horizontally or vertically. What number does each colour correspond to, and how are the corresponding dominoes arranged? Answer on page 290.

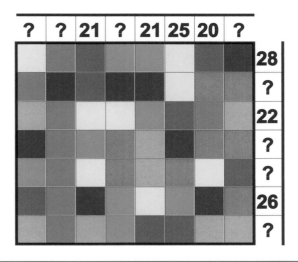

769 Tentai 24

The grid below is divided into a number of shapes. Each shape has a star at its centre, and is made up of one continuous group of cells connected horizontally and/or vertically. The shapes are all symmetrical – they stay the same when rotated by 180 degrees – but may get quite complicated. Where are the shapes? Answer on page 291.

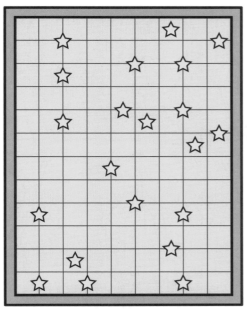

770 Silhouettes 12

Which of the six images fits the silhouette? Answer on page 302.

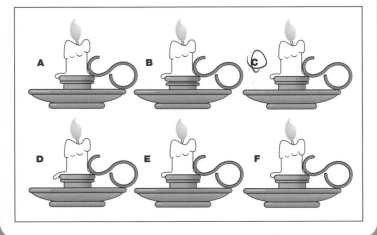

771 Futoshiki 36

Fill in the grid below so that the numbers 1 to 7 appear exactly once in each row and column. Red arrows indicate that a number is greater than its neighbour.
For answer see page 275.

772 Who's Who 12

From the information given, can you match each doctor to his patient? Answer on p302.

I'm Dr. Jerome, my patient is Brendon.

I'm Dr. Lucas, my patient, Ron, wears a shirt and has a broken arm.

I'm Dr. Lester, my patient is William.

I'm Dr. Milton, my patient is Trevor.

My doctor is carrying a thermometer.

My doctor is wearing a lab coat.

773 Hitori 32

Shade out cells in the grid below so that no number appears more than once in any row or column. Shaded cells cannot touch each other horizontally or vertically, and cannot cut the unshaded cells into two or more groups – the unshaded cells must remain connected horizontally or vertically into one complex branching chain. Which cells are shaded? Answer on page 287.

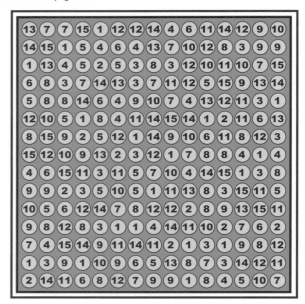

774 Slitherlink 32

A number of the intersection lines in the grid below have to be joined together to make one single complete loop. The numbers in the cell indicate how many of that cell's sides form part of the loop. Answer on page 279.

3	1	2				2		
3	2			2			2	3
				2	1	1	0	
				2	3		3	2
	2			2	0		2	
	2	2				3		
2				2			2	
1			3	0				3
	2	1		3			2	
3		2	2			2	2	

775 Mirror Image 16

Which of the five images below is an identical mirror image of the one above? Answer on page 300.

776 Detail Scene 16

The three enlarged squares appear somewhere in the large picture. Can you find them? Answer on page 299.

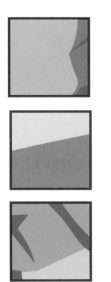

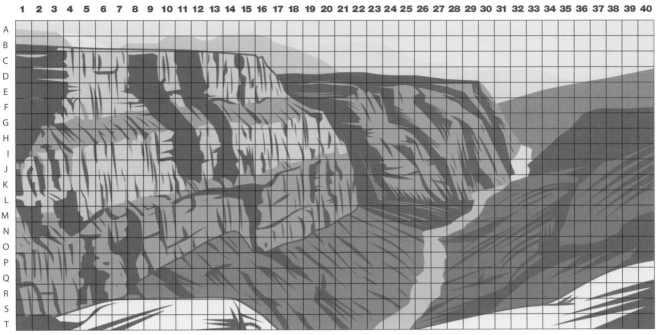

777 Spot the Difference

There are eight differences between the two pictures. Can you find them all?
Answer on p302.

778 Map Colouring 20

The rooms of the grid are coloured so that no two rooms of the same colour ever touch. How are the rooms coloured? Answer on page 295.

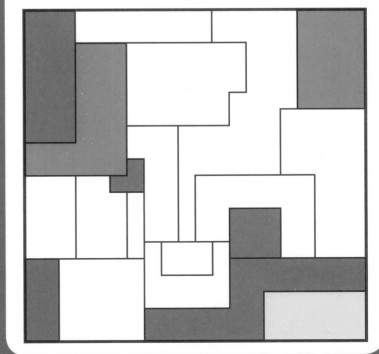

Hashiwokakero 16

A number of straight horizontal and vertical bridges connect the islands shown. The number on each island shows how many bridges touch that island. Bridges may not cross each other, and no more than 2 bridges may connect a pair of islands.

Where are the bridges?
Answer on page 297.

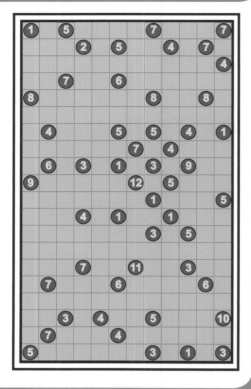

Number Link 32

The numbered cells in the grid below indicate the start and end points of single continuous paths. These paths fill the grid completely, and do not branch, cross each other, or touch themselves to form any pool of cells (2x2 or greater).
How are the paths arranged? Answer on page 285.

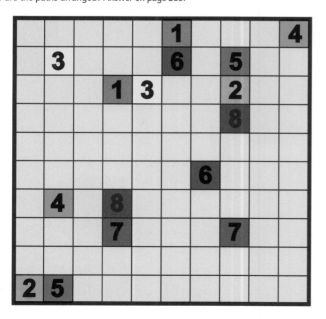

Suiri 16

Five enthusiastic photographers abroad are out photographing their favourite subjects. From the information contained below, can you work out what each person's (1) photographic preference (2) is, where (3) they are, and how many photos (4) they have taken so far?

1. Megumi is in Hannover.
2. The photographer in Berlin – not Yuri – has taken 18 pictures.
3. Ayame, who likes flowers, has taken one more picture than the photographer in Darmstadt.
4. Someone has taken 15 pictures of churches.
5. The photographer taking pictures of animals (who is not in a town with a nine-letter name) is not Megumi.
6. The Munich photographer likes houses.
7. Yukiko has taken 17 pictures, and not of strangers.
8. Someone has taken 14 photos. Someone else has taken 16.
9. One of the photographers is in Nuremberg.
10. One of the photographers is called Arisa.
Answer on page 299.

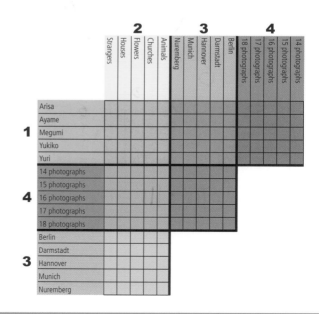

| | **2** | | | | | **3** | | | | | **4** | | | | |
	Strangers	Houses	Flowers	Churches	Animals	Nuremberg	Munich	Hannover	Darmstadt	Berlin	18 photographs	17 photographs	16 photographs	15 photographs	14 photographs
1 Arisa															
Ayame															
Megumi															
Yukiko															
Yuri															
4 14 photographs															
15 photographs															
16 photographs															
17 photographs															
18 photographs															
3 Berlin															
Darmstadt															
Hannover															
Munich															
Nuremberg															

782 Bijutsukan 32

The bright cells and dark cells in the grid below represent corridors and walls respectively. Light sources shine a horizontal and vertical beam of light. A corridor cell becomes illuminated if it is in the same row or column as a light source and there is no wall cell in between them. Place light sources in the corridor cells so that every corridor cell is illuminated, and no light source illuminates another light source. The numbers in some walls tell you how many light sources are touching that wall horizontally or vertically. Answer on page 282.

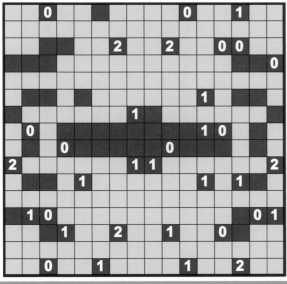

783 Sudoku 40

Fill in the grid below so that the numbers 1–9 appear exactly once in each row, column and 3x3 box. For solution see page 273.

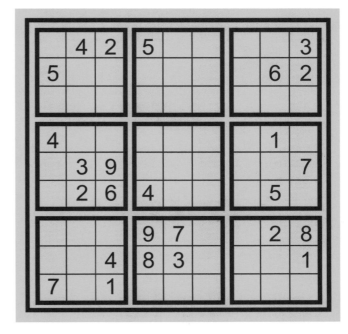

784 Battlehex 20

A number of ships of various sizes are hidden in the hexagonal grid below. The numbers next to each edge indicate how many ship segments are in the rows indicated by the directional arrows. Some ship segments and/or empty water cells have already been filled in. Where are the ships? Answer on page 296.

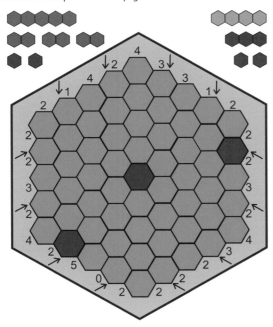

785 Killer Sudoku 8

Fill in the grid below so that the numbers 1–9 appear exactly once in each row, column and 3x3 block, and that the numbers in each dotted room add up to the value in its top right corner. Answer on page 303.

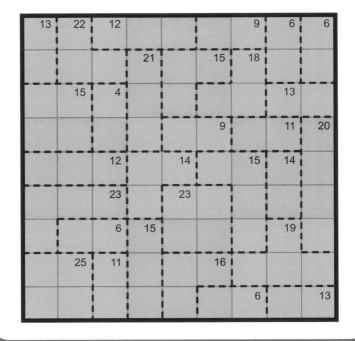

786 Fillomino 32

Each value shown in the grid below is part of a group of cells equal in number to that given value. A '6' is part of a group of six cells, for example. Groups may take any shape, but no two groups of the same size may touch each other horizontally or vertically at any point, and there are no blank cells. Not all groups need have a given value. How are the groups arranged? Answer on page 288.

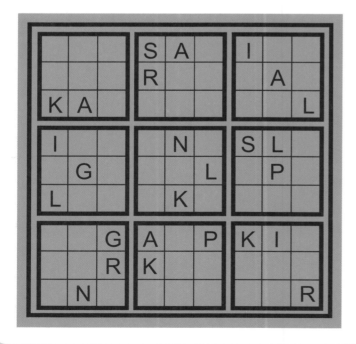

787 Domino placing 32

A set of dominoes containing all possible pairs of numbers from (0,0) to (7,7) is laid out vertically as shown in the blank grid below so that the larger number of each domino is on the top. The numbers above each column are from the top half of the dominoes in that column. The numbers below each column are from the bottom half of the dominoes in that column. The numbers to the left of each row are from the respective half-dominoes in that row. All the numbers are given to you sorted into descending numerical order. How are the dominoes laid out? Answer on page 283.

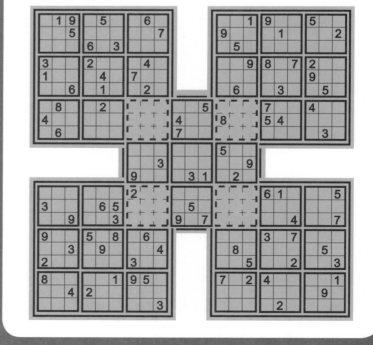

788 Yudoku 16

Fill in the grid below so that the letters s, p, a, r, k, l, i, n and g appear exactly once in each row, column and 3x3 box. Answer on page 301.

789 Samurai Sudoku 8

Fill in each 9x9 grid below so that the numbers 1–9 appear exactly once in each row, column and 3x3 block. Numbers in overlapping blocks count identically towards both grids. Answer on page 303.

790 Differences

Each copy of the picture has one flaw that none of the others share. Can you find them all? Answer on page 304.

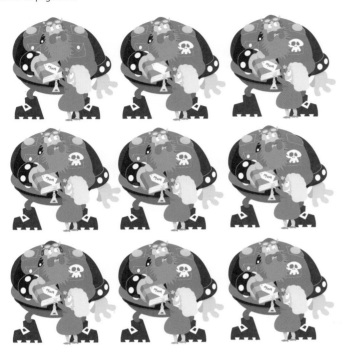

791 Tents 32

The grid below indicates a patch of woodland. Some cells contain grass, and others contain trees. Tents are placed on grass cells so that each tree has one tent next to it horizontally or vertically, although note that tents may be adjacent to more than one tree. No tent may be horizontally, vertically or diagonally adjacent to another tent. The numbers beside each row and column tell you how many tents are in that row or column. Where are the tents? Answer on page 286.

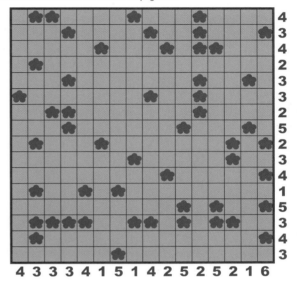

792 Gokigen Naname 32

Each cell in the grid below contains one diagonal line from corner to corner. The numbered circles show how many lines touch that corner. Fill in the grid so that the lines never form a closed circuit of any size. Answer on page 276.

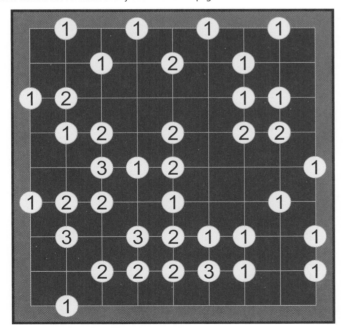

793 Dominoes 32

A full set of dominoes containing all possible pairs of numbers from (0,0) to (9,9) is laid together in one solid rectangle. The dominoes may be placed horizontally or vertically. The numbers in the grid below indicate the value of each half of each domino. How are the dominoes arranged? Answer on page 280.

3	0	9	3	6	9	4	4	4	0
8	7	7	0	1	9	6	0	1	8
6	1	1	5	3	1	1	8	9	3
4	5	7	4	2	2	4	7	3	2
8	8	1	3	8	9	3	6	5	7
2	6	8	9	5	8	6	3	7	1
3	2	7	5	4	0	0	3	4	9
9	0	7	5	8	5	0	6	3	5
6	6	2	5	7	7	5	5	2	4
0	0	7	6	2	2	1	2	0	1

794 Spot the Set

There are four different versions of the picture in the group below, each one reproduced three times. Can you identify the four sets?
Answer on page 304.

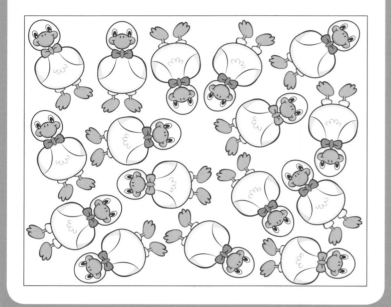

795 Match One 16

Which of the jumbled images is identical to the one presented here? Answer on page 298.

796 Super Sudoku 8

Fill in the grid below so that the digits 1, 2, 3, 4, 5, 6, 7, 8, 9, a, b, c, d, e, f and g appear exactly once in each row and column. Answer on page 303.

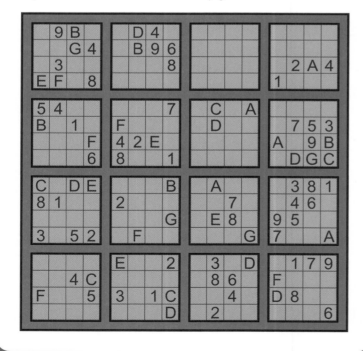

797 Sikaku 32

Divide the grid below into a number of rectangular rooms. Each room must contain exactly one number, equal to the number of cells that make up the room.
Answer on page 278.

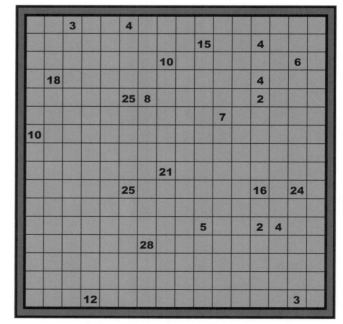

798 Masyu 16

A line passes through some or all of the cells in the grid below in such a way that it forms a single continuous non-intersecting loop. The line always exits a cell by a different side to the one it entered by, and passes through all cells containing a circle. The line travels straight through a cell with a light circle but turns in the previous and/or following cells in its path. The line turns in a cell containing a dark cell, but travels straight through both the previous and following cells in its path. Where is the line?
Answer on page 301.

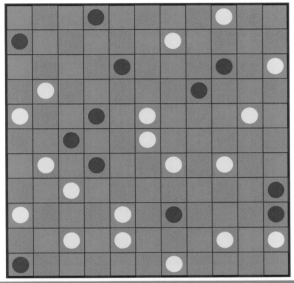

799 Identicals 16

Which pair of images is identical?
Answer on page 300.

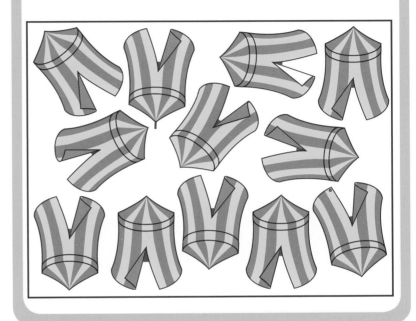

800 Missing Landmarks 23

Which famous landmark is blurred out of this photo?
Answer on page 293.

801 Battleships 30

A number of ships of various sizes are hidden in the grid below. The numbers next to each row and column indicate how many ship segments are in that row or column. Some ship segments have already been filled in. Where are the ships? Answer on page 289.

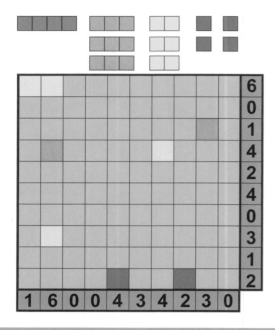

802 Colourminoes 29

In the grid below, each colour has a unique integer value from 0 to 6. The numbers next to each row and column indicate the total value of the cells in that row or column. The values of the cells of the grid correspond in turn to the numbers shown on a half-set of dominoes containing all possible pairs of numbers from (0,0) to (6,6) which has been laid together in one solid rectangle. Dominoes in this rectangle may be placed horizontally or vertically. What number does each colour correspond to, and how are the corresponding dominoes arranged? Answer on page 290.

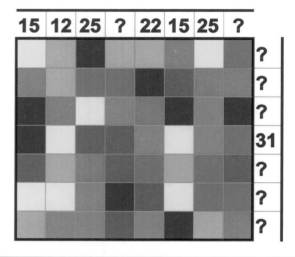

803 Futoshiki 37

Fill in the grid below so that the numbers 1 to 7 appear exactly once in each row and column. Red arrows indicate that a number is greater than its neighbour. For answer see page 275.

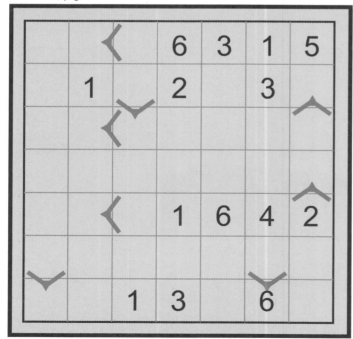

804 Kakuro 22

The empty squares in this grid contain digits from 1 to 9 so that each continuous unbroken line of numbers adds up to the clue value in the filled segment to its left (for horizontal lines) or above it (for vertical lines). No number may be used more than once in any unbroken line. How is the grid filled? Answer on page 294.

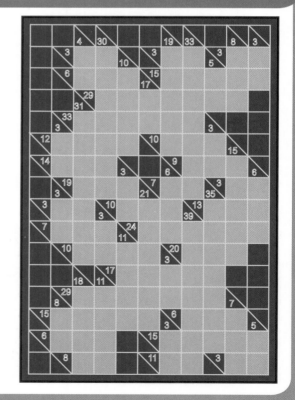

805 Nonogram 22

A number of cells in the grid below are to be shaded. Each row and column may contain one or more continuous lines of shaded cells ('blocks'). The numbers adjacent to the row or column indicate the lengths of the different blocks contained. Blocks are separated from others in the same row or column by at least one empty cell. Where are the shaded cells? A picture will emerge when the cells are shaded correctly. Answer on page 295.

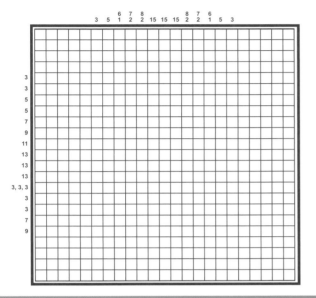

806 Sudoku 41

Fill in the grid below so that the numbers 1–9 appear exactly once in each row, column and 3x3 box. For solution see page 273.

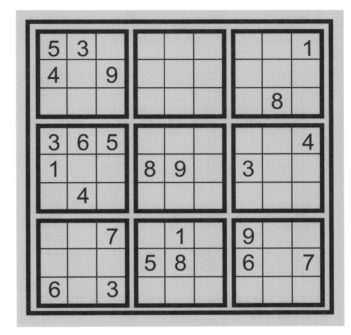

807 Kin-kon-kan 05

In the grid below, some cells contain diagonal mirrors which reflect light on both sides. One mirror is hidden in each room.

The coloured boxes around the edge indicate the start and finish of a coloured beam of light fired into the grid. These beams always travel in a straight line, but are reflected through a 90-degree angle when hitting a mirror. The number in each box shows how many grid cells its beam of light travels through before exiting again.

Where are the mirrors, and how are they placed? For solution see page 273.

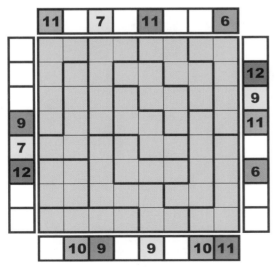

808 Dominoes 33

A full set of dominoes containing all possible pairs of numbers from (0,0) to (9,9) is laid together in one solid rectangle. The dominoes may be placed horizontally or vertically. The numbers in the grid below indicate the value of each half of each domino. How are the dominoes arranged? Answer on page 280.

2	2	0	0	7	1	0	9	6	7	8
5	5	3	8	5	1	8	5	2	6	0
9	2	1	9	9	1	5	8	4	2	7
4	2	2	7	8	3	8	1	3	0	0
4	3	3	6	4	6	4	9	6	8	1
4	6	4	7	0	6	5	6	1	0	9
7	0	1	7	3	1	0	8	5	3	7
9	2	3	5	0	4	4	2	7	7	3
8	9	9	2	6	6	4	3	4	6	5
1	9	8	8	7	2	5	9	1	3	5

809 Number Link 33

The numbered cells in the grid below indicate the start and end points of single continuous paths. These paths fill the grid completely, and do not branch, cross each other, or touch themselves to form any pool of cells (2x2 or greater).
How are the paths arranged? Answer on page 285.

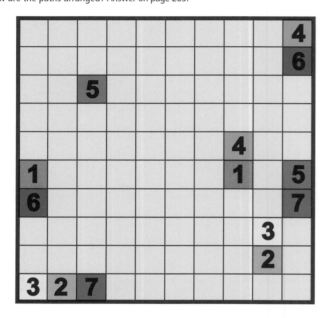

810 Domino placing 33

A set of dominoes containing all possible pairs of numbers from (0,0) to (7,7) is laid out vertically as shown in the blank grid below so that the larger number of each domino is on the top. The numbers above each column are from the top half of the dominoes in that column. The numbers below each column are from the bottom half of the dominoes in that column. The numbers to the left of each row are from the respective half-dominoes in that row.

All the numbers are given to you sorted into descending numerical order. How are the dominoes laid out? Answer on page 283.

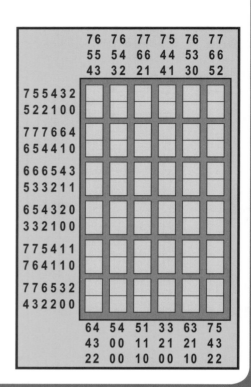

811 Tents 33

The grid below indicates a patch of woodland. Some cells contain grass, and others contain trees. Tents are placed on grass cells so that each tree has one tent next to it horizontally or vertically, although note that tents may be adjacent to more than one tree. No tent may be horizontally, vertically or diagonally adjacent to another tent. The numbers beside each row and column tell you how many tents are in that row or column. Where are the tents? Answer on page 286.

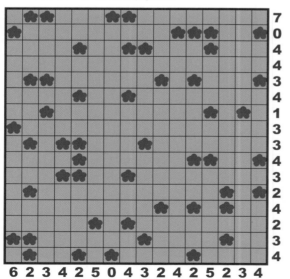

812 Minesweeper 9

The grid below contains a number of bombs hidden in empty squares. Each red flag tells you how many bombs are in the eight cells around it. Where are the bombs?
For answer see page 275.

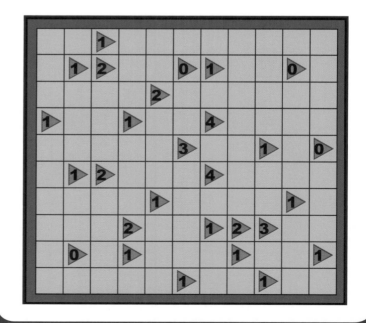

813 Fillomino 33

Each value shown in the grid below is part of a group of cells equal in number to that given value. A '6' is part of a group of six cells, for example. Groups may take any shape, but no two groups of the same size may touch each other horizontally or vertically at any point, and there are no blank cells. Not all groups need have a given value. How are the groups arranged? Answer on page 288.

814 Hitori 33

Shade out cells in the grid below so that no number appears more than once in any row or column. Shaded cells cannot touch each other horizontally or vertically, and cannot cut the unshaded cells into two or more groups – the unshaded cells must remain connected horizontally or vertically into one complex branching chain. Which cells are shaded? Answer on page 287.

815 Tentai 25

The grid below is divided into a number of shapes. Each shape has a star at its centre, and is made up of one continuous group of cells connected horizontally and/or vertically. The shapes are all symmetrical – they stay the same when rotated by 180 degrees – but may get quite complicated. Where are the shapes? Answer on page 291.

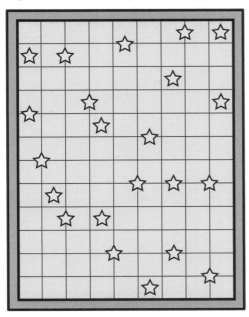

816 Slitherlink 33

A number of the intersection lines in the grid below have to be joined together to make one single complete loop. The numbers in the cell indicate how many of that cell's sides form part of the loop. Answer on page 279.

817 Sikaku 33

Divide the grid below into a number of rectangular rooms. Each room must contain exactly one number, equal to the number of cells that make up the room.
Answer on page 278.

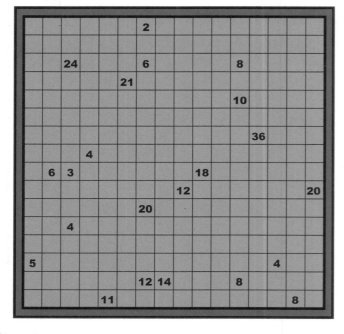

818 Gokigen Naname 33

Each cell in the grid below contains one diagonal line from corner to corner. The numbered circles show how many lines touch that corner. Fill in the grid so that the lines never form a closed circuit of any size. Answer on page 276.

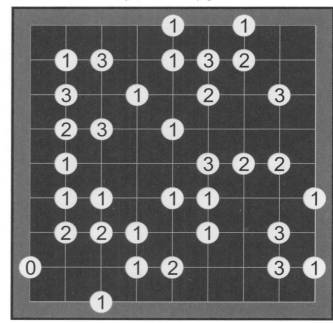

819 Bijutsukan 33

The bright cells and dark cells in the grid below represent corridors and walls respectively. Light sources shine a horizontal and vertical beam of light. A corridor cell becomes illuminated if it is in the same row or column as a light source and there is no wall cell in between them. Place light sources in the corridor cells so that every corridor cell is illuminated, and no light source illuminates another light source. The numbers in some walls tell you how many light sources are touching that wall horizontally or vertically.
Answer on page 282.

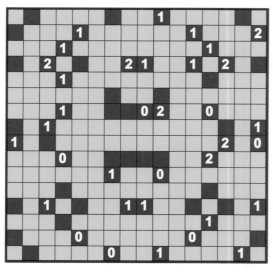

820 Futoshiki 38

Fill in the grid below so that the numbers 1 to 7 appear exactly once in each row and column. Red arrows indicate that a number is greater than its neighbour.
For answer see page 275.

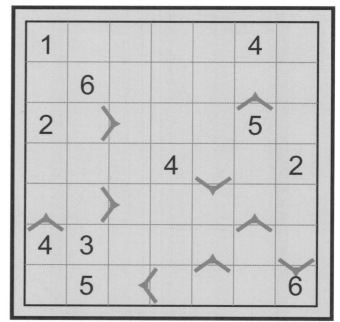

821 Battleships 31

A number of ships of various sizes are hidden in the grid below. The numbers next to each row and column indicate how many ship segments are in that row or column. Some ship segments have already been filled in. Where are the ships? Answer on page 289.

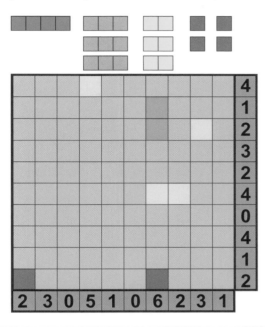

822 Map Colouring 21

The rooms of the grid are coloured so that no two rooms of the same colour ever touch. How are the rooms coloured? Answer on page 296.

823 Missing Landmarks 24

Which famous landmark is blurred out of this photo? Answer on page 293.

824 Sudoku 42

Fill in the grid below so that the numbers 1–9 appear exactly once in each row, column and 3x3 box. For solution see page 273.

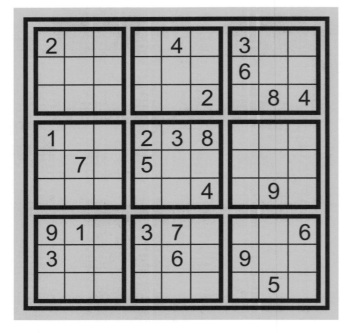

825 Colourminoes 30

In the grid below, each colour has a unique integer value from 0 to 6. The numbers next to each row and column indicate the total value of the cells in that row or column. The values of the cells of the grid correspond in turn to the numbers shown on a half-set of dominoes containing all possible pairs of numbers from (0,0) to (6,6) which has been laid together in one solid rectangle. Dominoes in this rectangle may be placed horizontally or vertically. What number does each colour correspond to, and how are the corresponding dominoes arranged? Answer on page 290.

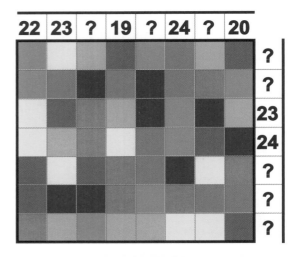

826 Battlehex 21

A number of ships of various sizes are hidden in the hexagonal grid below. The numbers next to each edge indicate how many ship segments are in the rows indicated by the directional arrows. Some ship segments and/or empty water cells have already been filled in. Where are the ships? Answer on page 296.

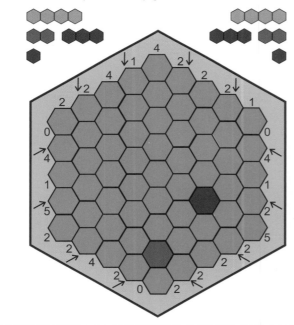

827 Fillomino 34

Each value shown in the grid below is part of a group of cells equal in number to that given value. A '6' is part of a group of six cells, for example. Groups may take any shape, but no two groups of the same size may touch each other horizontally or vertically at any point, and there are no blank cells. Not all groups need have a given value. How are the groups arranged? Answer on page 288.

828 Yudoku 17

Fill in the grid below so that the letters s, p, a, r, k, l, i, n and g appear exactly once in each row, column and 3x3 box. Answer on page 301.

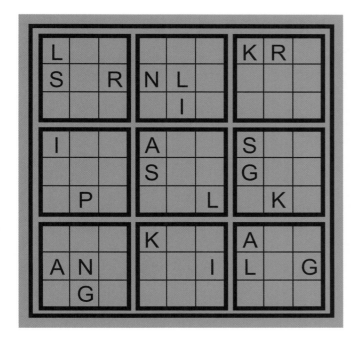

830 Match One 17

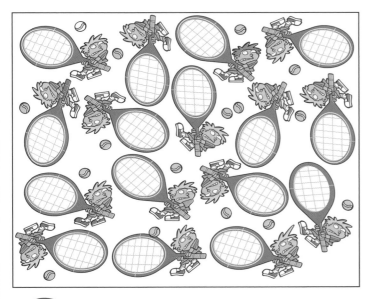

Which of the jumbled images is identical to the one presented here? Answer on page 298.

829 Suiri 17

Legend has it that five ancient Saxon lords rose to prominence in villages in what is now the English county of Oxfordshire. From the information given below, can you work out where each lord (1) originally came from (2), which village he ruled (3), and how he was known (4)?

1. Ceawlin, who was not known as the Bold, came from Essex.
2. Offa the Wild did not come from Mercia.
3. The man from Hwicce came to power in Frilford. He was not named Offa or Egbert.
3. Redwald came from Wessex. He did not rise to power in Abingdon – their ruler was known as the Bold.
4. Neither Aelle nor Ceawlin were known as the Great.
5. The lord of Chadlington was known as the Just.
6. The man from Sussex did not rule in Cassington.
7. One of the men was known as the Red.
8. One of the men ruled the village of Asthall.
Answer on page 299.

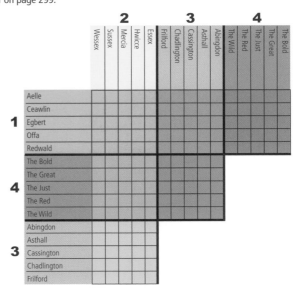

831 Hashiwokakero 17

A number of straight horizontal and vertical bridges connect the islands shown. The number on each island shows how many bridges touch that island. Bridges may not cross each other, and no more than 2 bridges may connect a pair of islands.
Where are the bridges?
Answer on page 297.

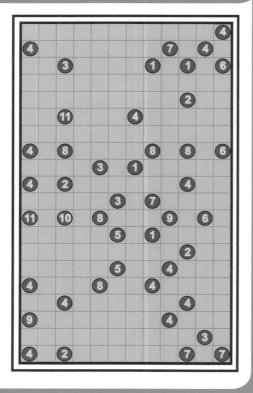

832 Identicals 17

Which pair of images is identical?
Answer on page 300.

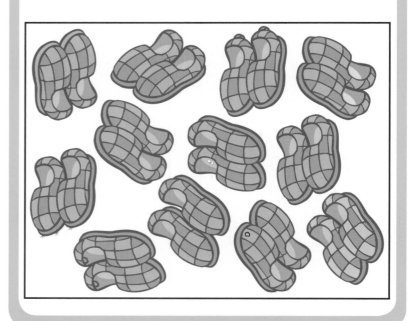

833 Detail Scene 17

The three enlarged squares appear somewhere in the large picture. Can you find them? Answer on page 299.

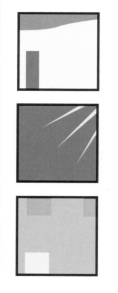

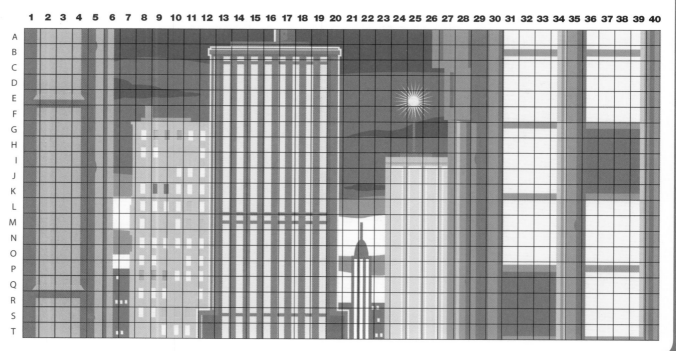

834 Mirror Image 17

Which of the five images below is an identical mirror image of the one above?
Answer on page 300.

A B C D E

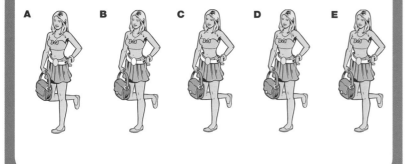

835 Domino placing 34

A set of dominoes containing all possible pairs of numbers from (0,0) to (7,7) is laid out vertically as shown in the blank grid below so that the larger number of each domino is on the top. The numbers above each column are from the top half of the dominoes in that column. The numbers below each column are from the bottom half of the dominoes in that column. The numbers to the left of each row are from the respective half-dominoes in that row. All the numbers are given to you sorted into descending numerical order. How are the dominoes laid out?
Answer on page 283.

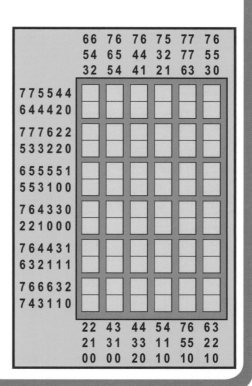

836 Number Link 34

The numbered cells in the grid below indicate the start and end points of single continuous paths. These paths fill the grid completely, and do not branch, cross each other, or touch themselves to form any pool of cells (2x2 or greater).
How are the paths arranged? Answer on page 285.

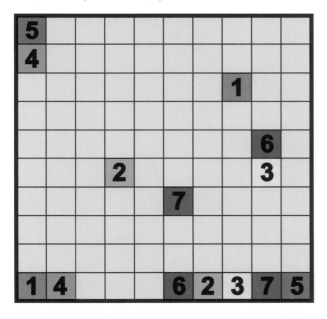

837 Tents 34

The grid below indicates a patch of woodland. Some cells contain grass, and others contain trees. Tents are placed on grass cells so that each tree has one tent next to it horizontally or vertically, although note that tents may be adjacent to more than one tree. No tent may be horizontally, vertically or diagonally adjacent to another tent. The numbers beside each row and column tell you how many tents are in that row or column. Where are the tents? Answer on page 286.

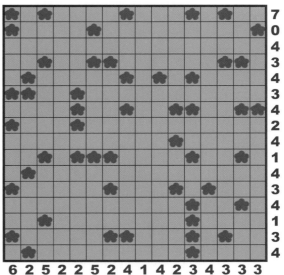

838 Masyu 17

A line passes through some or all of the cells in the grid below in such a way that it forms a single continuous non-intersecting loop. The line always exits a cell by a different side to the one it entered by, and passes through all cells containing a circle. The line travels straight through a cell with a light circle but turns in the previous and/or following cells in its path. The line turns in a cell containing a dark cell, but travels straight through both the previous and following cells in its path. Where is the line? Answer on page 301.

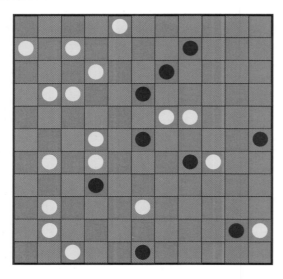

839 Sikaku 34

Divide the grid below into a number of rectangular rooms. Each room must contain exactly one number, equal to the number of cells that make up the room. Answer on page 278.

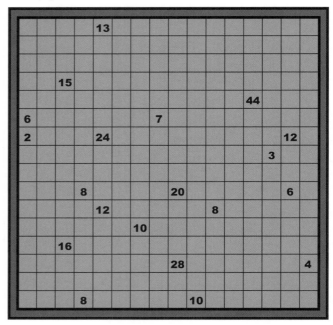

840 Bijutsukan 34

The bright cells and dark cells in the grid below represent corridors and walls respectively. Light sources shine a horizontal and vertical beam of light. A corridor cell becomes illuminated if it is in the same row or column as a light source and there is no wall cell in between them. Place light sources in the corridor cells so that every corridor cell is illuminated, and no light source illuminates another light source. The numbers in some walls tell you how many light sources are touching that wall horizontally or vertically. Answer on page 282.

841 Dominoes 34

A full set of dominoes containing all possible pairs of numbers from (0,0) to (9,9) is laid together in one solid rectangle. The dominoes may be placed horizontally or vertically. The numbers in the grid below indicate the value of each half of each domino. How are the dominoes arranged? Answer on page 280.

7	5	2	2	3	6	5	7	4	5	0
7	4	5	1	3	1	0	2	0	3	0
2	6	8	0	1	6	1	4	5	8	9
6	4	3	2	8	8	7	8	7	8	8
0	4	0	0	2	5	9	3	7	5	4
1	6	7	8	5	4	4	2	5	5	1
9	2	4	1	8	0	5	1	0	9	3
4	6	9	3	8	3	7	3	2	6	6
9	7	9	1	0	7	1	2	2	9	7
9	9	4	3	3	6	1	6	8	9	6

842 Gokigen Naname 34

Each cell in the grid below contains one diagonal line from corner to corner. The numbered circles show how many lines touch that corner. Fill in the grid so that the lines never form a closed circuit of any size. Answer on page 276.

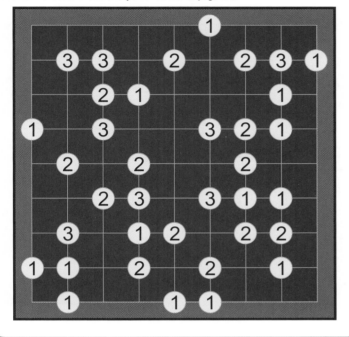

843 Hitori 34

Shade out cells in the grid below so that no number appears more than once in any row or column. Shaded cells cannot touch each other horizontally or vertically, and cannot cut the unshaded cells into two or more groups – the unshaded cells must remain connected horizontally or vertically into one complex branching chain. Which cells are shaded? Answer on page 287.

3	14	15	11	10	8	10	13	7	12	5	6	2	15	10
15	12	10	3	12	11	9	2	3	11	14	5	3	7	
11	2	1	7	5	4	15	14	11	6	8	8	15	10	10
4	1	12	14	2	11	3	9	6	3	7	10	13	10	5
8	6	3	3	15	13	2	3	11	14	14	1	9	10	
5	7	9	10	13	6	15	8	14	2	12	4	1	9	
14	5	7	9	4	4	4	3	13	15	12	14	10	2	
4	12	8	6	7	3	1	8	6	11	2	5	10	4	13
9	4	4	15	11	6	12	10	5	11	3	10	11	7	11
12	5	13	10	5	9	14	2	6	4	2	15	3	2	1
14	6	5	14	14	5	9	2	3	8	7	1	3	4	
1	2	15	2	4	11	12	3	15	9	13	13	6	14	
6	4	10	3	11	11	10	7	9	15	13	2	9	14	15
4	10	9	1	1	5	11	4	14	4	8	6	12	12	3
5	15	8	1	1	10	7	7	12	4	11	6	14	13	11

844 Slitherlink 34

A number of the intersection lines in the grid below have to be joined together to make one single complete loop. The numbers in the cell indicate how many of that cell's sides form part of the loop. Answer on page 279.

1	3	2			2	3
3		2	2	2		1
3	0					
3				3	1	2
1		1	2	2		2
3	1	1			2	1
1		2	2		3	
3		2	2	3		1
3	1	2		2	1	3
2		3	2		3	2

845 Nonogram 23

A number of cells in the grid below are to be shaded. Each row and column may contain one or more continuous lines of shaded cells ('blocks'). The numbers adjacent to the row or column indicate the lengths of the different blocks contained. Blocks are separated from others in the same row or column by at least one empty cell. Where are the shaded cells? A picture will emerge when the cells are shaded correctly. Answer on page 295.

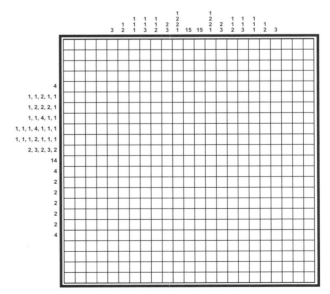

846 Kakuro 23

The empty squares in this grid contain digits from 1 to 9 so that each continuous unbroken line of numbers adds up to the clue value in the filled segment to its left (for horizontal lines) or above it (for vertical lines). No number may be used more than once in any unbroken line. How is the grid filled? Answer on page 294.

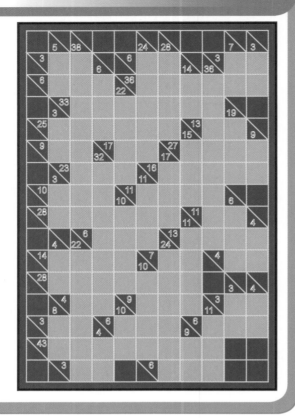

847 Who's Who 13

From the information, can you match each boyfriend and girlfriend? Answer on p302.

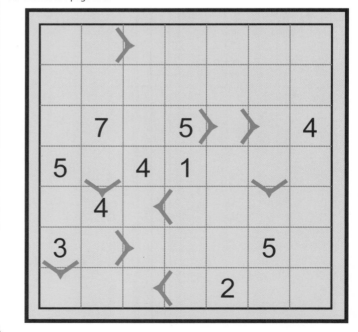

I'm Tod, my girlfriend Kerry has long hair.

I'm Eric, my girlfriend is Nia.

I'm Nate.

I'm Loz, my girlfriend is Amy.

My boyfriend has short hair.

My boyfriend has a neck chain.

I'm Rina.

848 Tentai 26

The grid below is divided into a number of shapes. Each shape has a star at its centre, and is made up of one continuous group of cells connected horizontally and/or vertically. The shapes are all symmetrical – they stay the same when rotated by 180 degrees – but may get quite complicated. Where are the shapes? Answer on page 291.

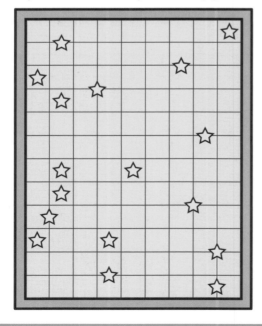

849 Futoshiki 39

Fill in the grid below so that the numbers 1 to 7 appear exactly once in each row and column. Red arrows indicate that a number is greater than its neighbour. For answer see page 275.

850 Silhouettes 13

Which of the six images fits the silhouette? Answer on page 302.

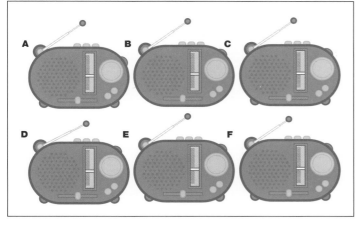

851 Sudoku 43

Fill in the grid below so that the numbers 1–9 appear exactly once in each row, column and 3x3 box. For solution see page 273.

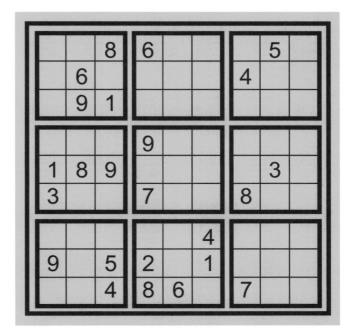

852 Battleships 32

A number of ships of various sizes are hidden in the grid below. The numbers next to each row and column indicate how many ship segments are in that row or column. Some ship segments have already been filled in. Where are the ships? Answer on page 289.

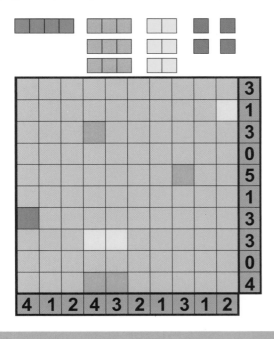

853 Colourminoes 31

In the grid below, each colour has a unique integer value from 0 to 6. The numbers next to each row and column indicate the total value of the cells in that row or column. The values of the cells of the grid correspond in turn to the numbers shown on a half-set of dominoes containing all possible pairs of numbers from (0,0) to (6,6) which has been laid together in one solid rectangle. Dominoes in this rectangle may be placed horizontally or vertically. What number does each colour correspond to, and how are the corresponding dominoes arranged? Answer on page 290.

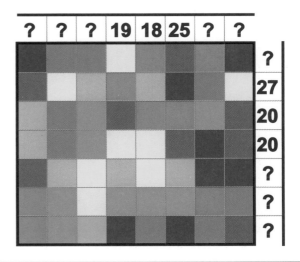

854 Fillomino 35

Each value shown in the grid below is part of a group of cells equal in number to that given value. A '6' is part of a group of six cells, for example. Groups may take any shape, but no two groups of the same size may touch each other horizontally or vertically at any point, and there are no blank cells. Not all groups need have a given value. How are the groups arranged? Answer on page 288.

7			6		3	
2		1	4			
					7	
			7			
	4		6			
4						1
2	3		1			2

855 Tents 35

The grid below indicates a patch of woodland. Some cells contain grass, and others contain trees. Tents are placed on grass cells so that each tree has one tent next to it horizontally or vertically, although note that tents may be adjacent to more than one tree. No tent may be horizontally, vertically or diagonally adjacent to another tent. The numbers beside each row and column tell you how many tents are in that row or column. Where are the tents? Answer on page 286.

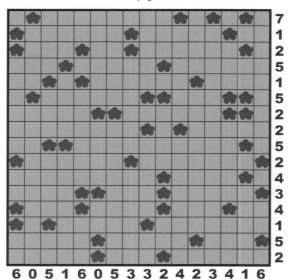

Row clues (top to bottom): 7, 1, 2, 5, 1, 5, 2, 2, 5, 2, 4, 3, 4, 1, 5, 2

Column clues (left to right): 6 0 5 1 6 0 5 3 3 2 4 2 3 4 1 6

856 Missing Landmarks 25

Which famous landmark is blurred out of this photo?
Answer on page 293.

857 Gokigen Naname 35

Each cell in the grid below contains one diagonal line from corner to corner. The numbered circles show how many lines touch that corner. Fill in the grid so that the lines never form a closed circuit of any size. Answer on page 276.

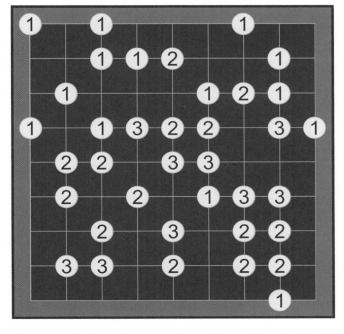

858 Bijutsukan 35

The bright cells and dark cells in the grid below represent corridors and walls respectively. Light sources shine a horizontal and vertical beam of light. A corridor cell becomes illuminated if it is in the same row or column as a light source and there is no wall cell in between them. Place light sources in the corridor cells so that every corridor cell is illuminated, and no light source illuminates another light source. The numbers in some walls tell you how many light sources are touching that wall horizontally or vertically. Answer on page 282.

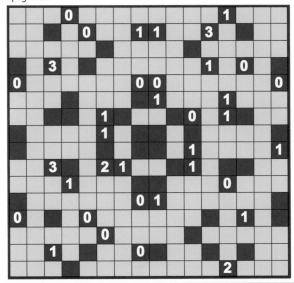

859 Domino placing 35

A set of dominoes containing all possible pairs of numbers from (0,0) to (7,7) is laid out vertically as shown in the blank grid below so that the larger number of each domino is on the top. The numbers above each column are from the top half of the dominoes in that column. The numbers below each column are from the bottom half of the dominoes in that column. The numbers to the left of each row are from the respective half-dominoes in that row. All the numbers are given to you sorted into descending numerical order. How are the dominoes laid out? Answer on page 283.

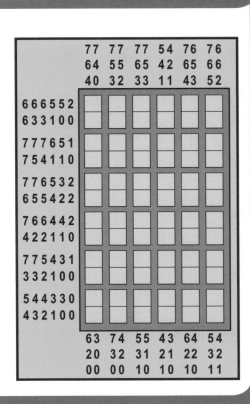

860 Slitherlink 35

A number of the intersection lines in the grid below have to be joined together to make one single complete loop. The numbers in the cell indicate how many of that cell's sides form part of the loop. Answer on page 279.

861 Number Link 35

The numbered cells in the grid below indicate the start and end points of single continuous paths. These paths fill the grid completely, and do not branch, cross each other, or touch themselves to form any pool of cells (2x2 or greater).
How are the paths arranged? Answer on page 285.

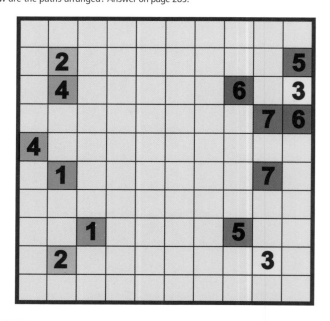

862 Sikaku 35

Divide the grid below into a number of rectangular rooms. Each room must contain exactly one number, equal to the number of cells that make up the room.
Answer on page 278.

	7									2
	4			8						
					4			20		
			5		3		8			
3									12	8	14
	3									
	4			16						
		21					6			
4										
7				21						
2			14							
			12		12					
4		21						4		
	3	4								

863 Dominoes 35

A full set of dominoes containing all possible pairs of numbers from (0,0) to (9,9) is laid together in one solid rectangle. The dominoes may be placed horizontally or vertically. The numbers in the grid below indicate the value of each half of each domino. How are the dominoes arranged? Answer on page 280.

7	5	6	6	1	9	9	7	9	0	3
4	9	2	5	3	2	3	1	6	3	8
9	9	0	1	6	0	1	7	7	2	5
4	0	9	5	5	5	4	8	4	5	2
3	5	0	0	7	2	2	2	6	1	6
4	8	5	7	7	8	9	7	3	9	1
7	8	4	4	4	9	9	3	2	2	8
3	8	6	0	4	3	6	4	1	5	5
3	8	7	2	8	8	0	4	8	6	1
0	7	0	0	3	1	6	6	1	1	2

864 Hitori 35

Shade out cells in the grid below so that no number appears more than once in any row or column. Shaded cells cannot touch each other horizontally or vertically, and cannot cut the unshaded cells into two or more groups – the unshaded cells must remain connected horizontally or vertically into one complex branching chain. Which cells are shaded? Answer on page 287.

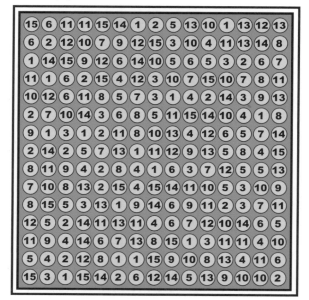

865 Sudoku 44

Fill in the grid below so that the numbers 1–9 appear exactly once in each row, column and 3x3 box. For solution see page 273.

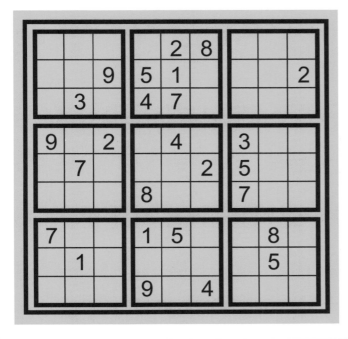

866 Battlehex 22

A number of ships of various sizes are hidden in the hexagonal grid below. The numbers next to each edge indicate how many ship segments are in the rows indicated by the directional arrows. Some ship segments and/or empty water cells have already been filled in. Where are the ships? Answer on page 296.

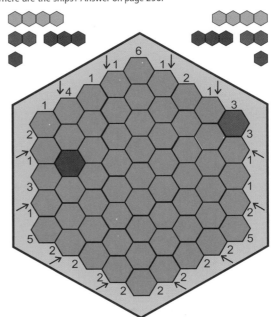

867 Futoshiki 40

Fill in the grid below so that the numbers 1 to 7 appear exactly once in each row and column. Red arrows indicate that a number is greater than its neighbour. For answer see page 275.

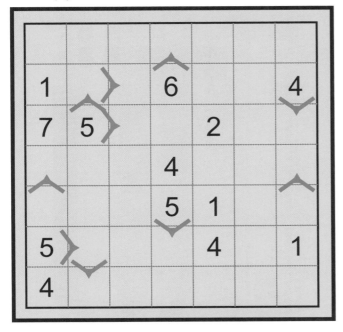

868 Map Colouring 22

The rooms of the grid are coloured so that no two rooms of the same colour ever touch. How are the rooms coloured? Answer on page 296.

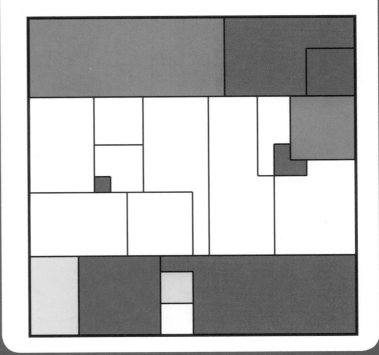

869 Kakuro 24

The empty squares in this grid contain digits from 1 to 9 so that each continuous unbroken line of numbers adds up to the clue value in the filled segment to its left (for horizontal lines) or above it (for vertical lines). No number may be used more than once in any unbroken line. How is the grid filled? Answer on page 294.

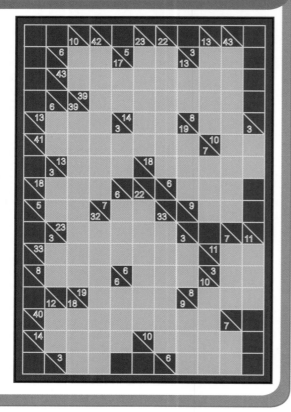

870 Nonogram 24

A number of cells in the grid below are to be shaded. Each row and column may contain one or more continuous lines of shaded cells ('blocks'). The numbers adjacent to the row or column indicate the lengths of the different blocks contained. Blocks are separated from others in the same row or column by at least one empty cell. Where are the shaded cells? A picture will emerge when the cells are shaded correctly. Answer on page 295.

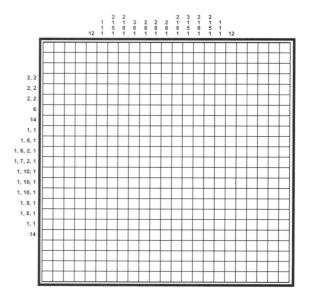

871 Artist's Errors

The artist drawing this scene has made a number of visual, conceptual and logical errors. Can you find them all?
Answer on page 304.

872 Battleships 33

A number of ships of various sizes are hidden in the grid below. The numbers next to each row and column indicate how many ship segments are in that row or column. Some ship segments have already been filled in. Where are the ships? Answer on page 289.

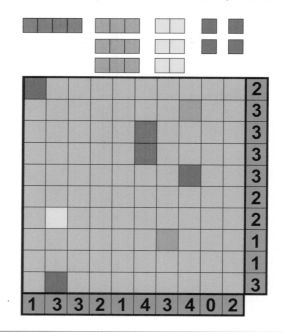

873 Tentai 27

The grid below is divided into a number of shapes. Each shape has a star at its centre, and is made up of one continuous group of cells connected horizontally and/or vertically. The shapes are all symmetrical – they stay the same when rotated by 180 degrees – but may get quite complicated. Where are the shapes? Answer on page 291.

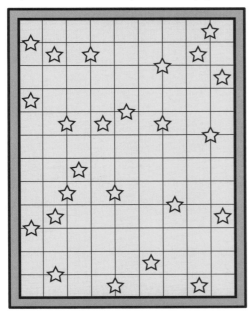

874 Colourminoes 32

In the grid below, each colour has a unique integer value from 0 to 6. The numbers next to each row and column indicate the total value of the cells in that row or column. The values of the cells of the grid correspond in turn to the numbers shown on a half-set of dominoes containing all possible pairs of numbers from (0,0) to (6,6) which has been laid together in one solid rectangle. Dominoes in this rectangle may be placed horizontally or vertically. What number does each colour correspond to, and how are the corresponding dominoes arranged? Answer on page 290.

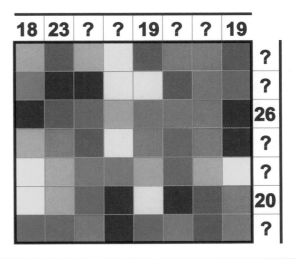

875 Samurai Sudoku 9

Fill in each 9x9 grid below so that the numbers 1–9 appear exactly once in each row, column and 3x3 block. Numbers in overlapping blocks count identically towards both grids. Answer on page 303.

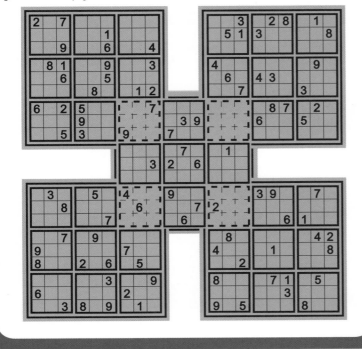

876 Fillomino 36

Each value shown in the grid below is part of a group of cells equal in number to that given value. A '6' is part of a group of six cells, for example. Groups may take any shape, but no two groups of the same size may touch each other horizontally or vertically at any point, and there are no blank cells. Not all groups need have a given value. How are the groups arranged? Answer on page 288.

Suiri 18

Five courting men are planning to serenade their new loves by the light of the full moon. From the information given below, can you work out which woman (1) is the object of which man's (2) attentions, how they met (3), and what song (4) the man is planning to sing?

1. Serena is not the object of Silvio's attentsion, nor is she going to have "I Swear" sung at her."

2. Antonio met his love buying cucumbers. He is not planning to sing her "Amazing" or "Faithfully".

3. Donatello is going to sing "Always" to his love. He did not meet her while she was oiling her motor scooter.

4. Eliana is going to have "Breathe" sung at her.

5. Silvio's love is not Mara.

6. Livio is smitten with Donata. He did not meet her watching football in a cafe – that woman is going to have "I Swear" sung at her.

7. Monica's admirer met her whilst they were buying cigarettes. She is not going to have "Amazing" sung at her.

8. One of the men found his woman in a cheap winery.

9. One of the men is called Fabrizio.

Answer on page 299.

		2 Silvio	2 Livio	2 Fabrizio	2 Donatello	2 Antonio	3 In a winery	3 Buying cigarettes	3 Watching football	3 Buying cucumbers	3 Oiling scooter	4 I Swear	4 Faithfully	4 Breathe	4 Amazing	4 Always
1	Donato															
	Eliana															
	Mara															
	Monica															
	Serena															
4	Always															
	Amazing															
	Breathe															
	Faithfully															
	I Swear															
3	Oiling scooter															
	Buying cucumbers															
	Watching football															
	Buying cigarettes															
	In a winery															

Hitori 36

Shade out cells in the grid below so that no number appears more than once in any row or column. Shaded cells cannot touch each other horizontally or vertically, and cannot cut the unshaded cells into two or more groups – the unshaded cells must remain connected horizontally or vertically into one complex branching chain. Which cells are shaded? Answer on page 287.

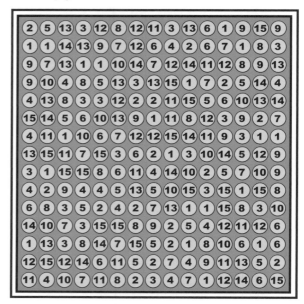

2	5	13	3	12	8	12	11	3	13	6	1	9	15	9
1	1	14	13	9	7	12	4	2	4	6	7	1	8	3
9	7	13	1	1	10	14	7	12	14	11	12	8	9	13
9	10	4	8	5	13	3	13	15	1	7	5	5	14	4
4	13	8	3	12	2	2	11	15	5	6	10	13	14	1
15	14	5	6	10	13	9	1	11	8	12	3	9	2	7
4	11	1	10	6	7	12	12	15	14	11	9	3	1	1
13	15	11	7	15	3	6	2	1	3	10	14	5	12	9
3	1	15	8	6	11	4	14	10	2	5	4	11	9	9
4	2	9	4	5	13	5	10	15	3	1	15	8	9	8
6	8	3	5	2	4	2	7	13	1	1	15	8	3	10
14	10	7	3	15	15	8	9	2	5	4	12	11	12	6
1	13	8	14	7	15	2	1	8	10	6	1	6	6	6
12	15	12	14	6	11	5	2	7	4	9	11	13	5	2
11	4	10	7	11	8	2	3	4	7	1	12	14	6	15

Spot the Difference

There are eight differences between the two pictures. Can you find them all? Answer on page 302.

880 Match One 18

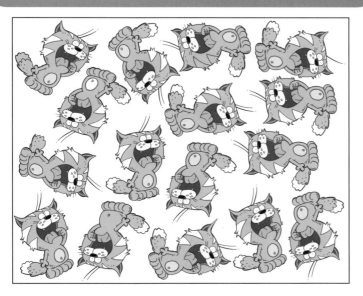

Which of the jumbled images is identical to the one presented here? Answer on page 298.

881 Bijutsukan 36

The bright cells and dark cells in the grid below represent corridors and walls respectively. Light sources shine a horizontal and vertical beam of light. A corridor cell becomes illuminated if it is in the same row or column as a light source and there is no wall cell in between them. Place light sources in the corridor cells so that every corridor cell is illuminated, and no light source illuminates another light source. The numbers in some walls tell you how many light sources are touching that wall horizontally or vertically. Answer on page 282.

882 Domino placing 36

A set of dominoes containing all possible pairs of numbers from (0,0) to (7,7) is laid out vertically as shown in the blank grid below so that the larger number of each domino is on the top. The numbers above each column are from the top half of the dominoes in that column. The numbers below each column are from the bottom half of the dominoes in that column. The numbers to the left of each row are from the respective half-dominoes in that row.

All the numbers are given to you sorted into descending numerical order. How are the dominoes laid out? Answer on page 283.

	76	77	76	76	75	77
	65	43	42	66	54	65
	43	32	10	42	31	55

665432
632000

777320
652110

776443
433110

665542
432221

776555
755310

764311
442100

52	43	76	65	43	54
22	21	42	30	33	21
11	00	00	00	11	10

883 Yudoku 18

Fill in the grid below so that the letters s, p, a, r, k, l, i, n and g appear exactly once in each row, column and 3x3 box. Answer on page 301.

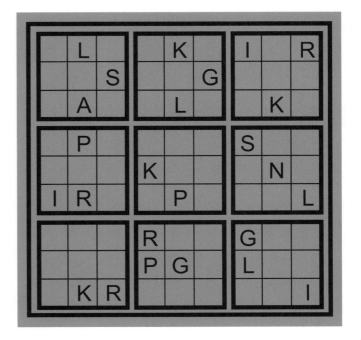

239

884 Sikaku 36

Divide the grid below into a number of rectangular rooms. Each room must contain exactly one number, equal to the number of cells that make up the room. Answer on page 278.

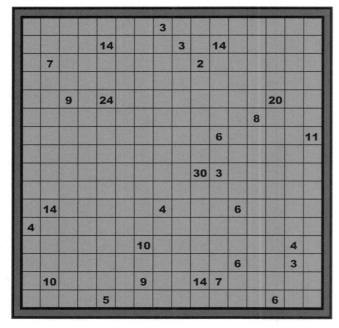

885 Super Sudoku 9

Fill in the grid below so that the digits 1, 2, 3, 4, 5, 6, 7, 8, 9, a, b, c, d, e, f and g appear exactly once in each row and column. Answer on page 303.

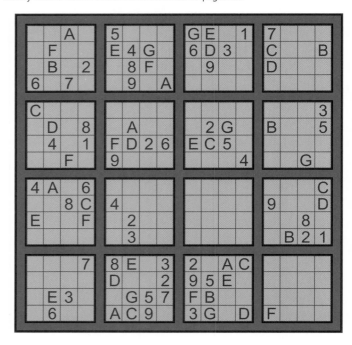

886 Detail Scene 18

The three enlarged squares appear somewhere in the large picture. Can you find them? Answer on page 299.

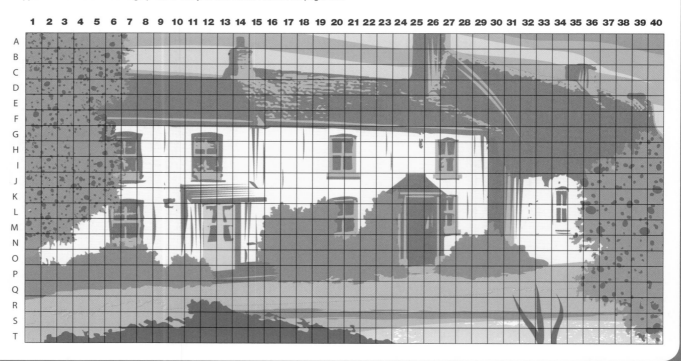

887 Slitherlink 36

A number of the intersection lines in the grid below have to be joined together to make one single complete loop. The numbers in the cell indicate how many of that cell's sides form part of the loop. Answer on page 279.

	0			2	2	1		
		1					2	2
0	1	2		0	1		2	3
		3				1	2	2
0	1			2		0		
	2			2				3
			0		1			2
3				2			0	
		2					1	1
	2	1	0	1			1	1

888 Identicals 18

Which pair of images is identical?
Answer on page 300.

889 Spot the Set

There are four different versions of the picture in the group below, each one reproduced three times. Can you identify the four sets?
Answer on page 304.

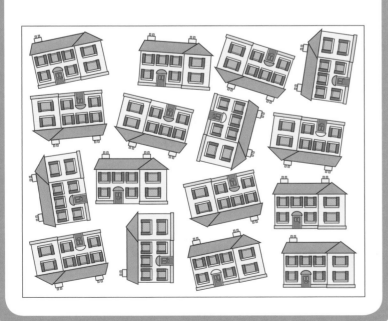

890 Gokigen Naname 36

Each cell in the grid below contains one diagonal line from corner to corner. The numbered circles show how many lines touch that corner. Fill in the grid so that the lines never form a closed circuit of any size. Answer on page 276.

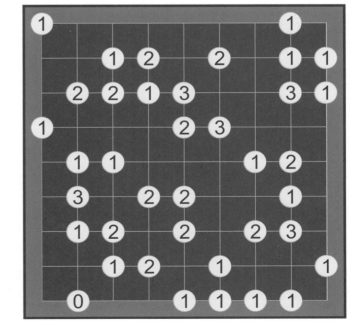

891 Killer sudoku 9

Fill in the grid below so that the numbers 1–9 appear exactly once in each row, column and 3x3 block, and that the numbers in each dotted room add up to the value in its top right corner. Answer on page 303.

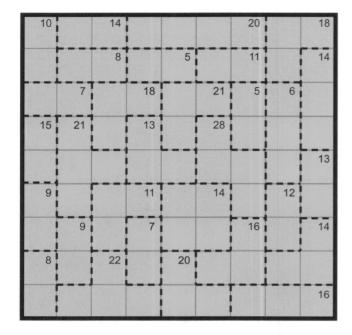

892 Hashiwokakero 18

A number of straight horizontal and vertical bridges connect the islands shown. The number on each island shows how many bridges touch that island. Bridges may not cross each other, and no more than 2 bridges may connect a pair of islands.
Where are the bridges?
Answer on page 297.

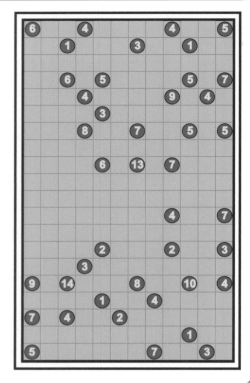

893 Sudoku 45

Fill in the grid below so that the numbers 1–9 appear exactly once in each row, column and 3x3 box. For solution see page 273.

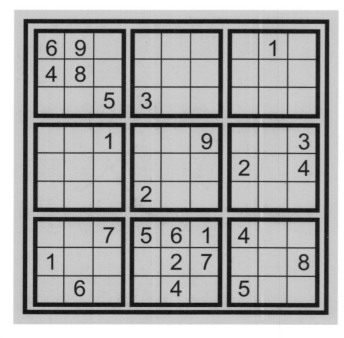

894 Differences

Each copy of the picture has one flaw that none of the others share. Can you find them all? Answer on page 304.

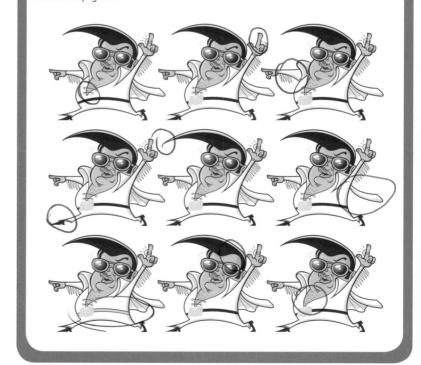

895 Masyu 18

A line passes through some or all of the cells in the grid below in such a way that it forms a single continuous non-intersecting loop. The line always exits a cell by a different side to the one it entered by, and passes through all cells containing a circle. The line travels straight through a cell with a light circle but turns in the previous and/or following cells in its path. The line turns in a cell containing a dark cell, but travels straight through both the previous and following cells in its path. Where is the line?
Answer on page 301.

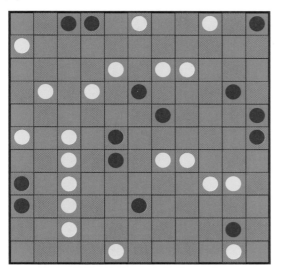

896 Number Link 36

The numbered cells in the grid below indicate the start and end points of single continuous paths. These paths fill the grid completely, and do not branch, cross each other, or touch themselves to form any pool of cells (2x2 or greater).
How are the paths arranged? Answer on page 285.

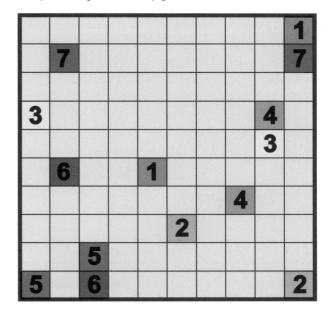

897 Mirror Image 18

Which of the five images below is an identical mirror image of the one above?
Answer on page 300.

898 Dominoes 36

A full set of dominoes containing all possible pairs of numbers from (0,0) to (9,9) is laid together in one solid rectangle. The dominoes may be placed horizontally or vertically. The numbers in the grid below indicate the value of each half of each domino. How are the dominoes arranged? Answer on page 280.

2	8	3	3	4	3	6	5	5	3	3
1	8	5	5	6	6	1	9	2	0	9
1	7	9	9	8	2	2	6	1	0	0
4	4	3	5	2	4	6	0	7	8	5
7	9	2	1	8	8	5	3	4	7	9
8	0	3	8	9	6	7	6	3	7	6
0	9	4	6	2	7	3	2	6	4	7
5	0	1	1	5	1	4	2	8	9	7
2	8	7	7	9	2	5	6	5	0	1
0	9	8	1	5	4	4	1	3	0	4

899 Tents 36

The grid below indicates a patch of woodland. Some cells contain grass, and others contain trees. Tents are placed on grass cells so that each tree has one tent next to it horizontally or vertically, although note that tents may be adjacent to more than one tree. No tent may be horizontally, vertically or diagonally adjacent to another tent. The numbers beside each row and column tell you how many tents are in that row or column. Where are the tents? Answer on page 286.

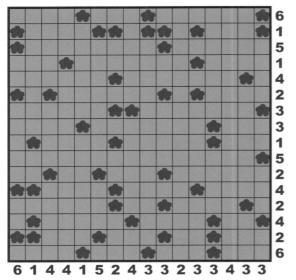

900 Futoshiki 41

Fill in the grid below so that the numbers 1 to 7 appear exactly once in each row and column. Red arrows indicate that a number is greater than its neighbour. For answer see page 275.

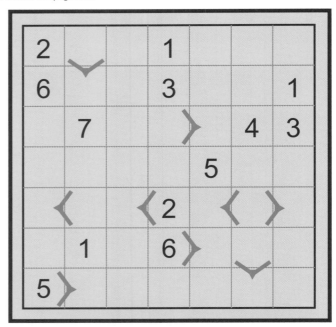

901 Missing Landmarks 26

Which famous landmark is blurred out of this photo? Answer on page 293.

902 Battleships 34

A number of ships of various sizes are hidden in the grid below. The numbers next to each row and column indicate how many ship segments are in that row or column. Some ship segments have already been filled in. Where are the ships? Answer on page 289.

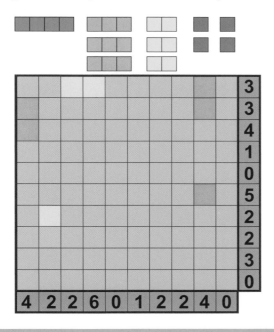

903 Sudoku 46

Fill in the grid below so that the numbers 1–9 appear exactly once in each row, column and 3x3 box. For solution see page 273.

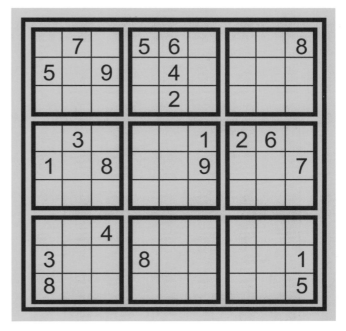

904 Battlehex 23

A number of ships of various sizes are hidden in the hexagonal grid below. The numbers next to each edge indicate how many ship segments are in the rows indicated by the directional arrows. Some ship segments and/or empty water cells have already been filled in. Where are the ships? Answer on page 296.

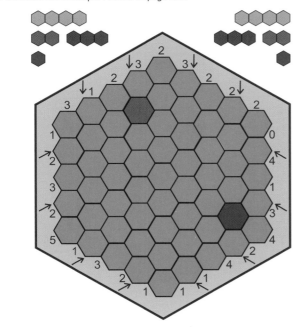

905 Map Colouring 23

The rooms of the grid are coloured so that no two rooms of the same colour ever touch. How are the rooms coloured? Answer on page 296.

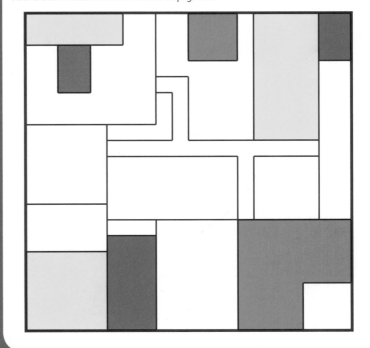

906 Colourminoes 33

In the grid below, each colour has a unique integer value from 0 to 6. The numbers next to each row and column indicate the total value of the cells in that row or column. The values of the cells of the grid correspond in turn to the numbers shown on a half-set of dominoes containing all possible pairs of numbers from (0,0) to (6,6) which has been laid together in one solid rectangle. Dominoes in this rectangle may be placed horizontally or vertically. What number does each colour correspond to, and how are the corresponding dominoes arranged? Answer on page 290.

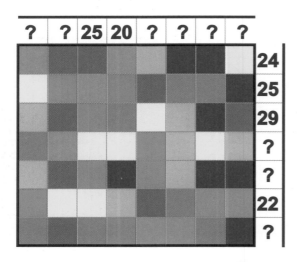

907 Futoshiki 42

Fill in the grid below so that the numbers 1 to 7 appear exactly once in each row and column. Red arrows indicate that a number is greater than its neighbour.
For answer see page 275.

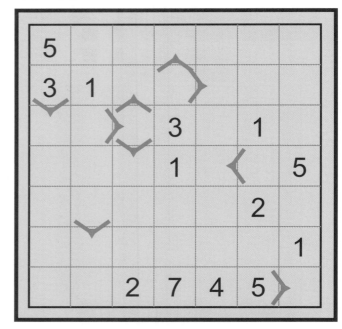

908 Who's Who 14

Using the information, can you match the policeman to the criminal? Answer on p302.

909 Silhouettes 14

Which of the six images fits the silhouette? Answer on page 302.

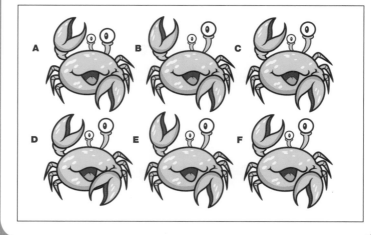

910 Tentai 28

The grid below is divided into a number of shapes. Each shape has a star at its centre, and is made up of one continuous group of cells connected horizontally and/or vertically. The shapes are all symmetrical – they stay the same when rotated by 180 degrees – but may get quite complicated. Where are the shapes? Answer on page 291.

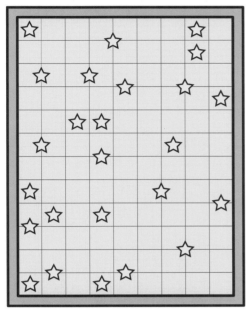

911 Kakuro 25

The empty squares in this grid contain digits from 1 to 9 so that each continuous unbroken line of numbers adds up to the clue value in the filled segment to its left (for horizontal lines) or above it (for vertical lines). No number may be used more than once in any unbroken line. How is the grid filled? Answer on page 294.

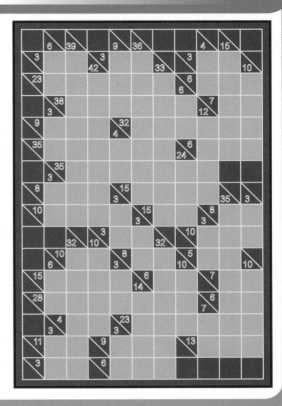

912 Bijutsukan 37

The bright cells and dark cells in the grid below represent corridors and walls respectively. Light sources shine a horizontal and vertical beam of light. A corridor cell becomes illuminated if it is in the same row or column as a light source and there is no wall cell in between them. Place light sources in the corridor cells so that every corridor cell is illuminated, and no light source illuminates another light source. The numbers in some walls tell you how many light sources are touching that wall horizontally or vertically. Answer on page 282.

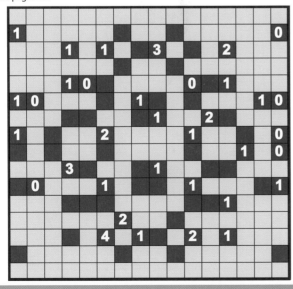

913 Fillomino 37

Each value shown in the grid below is part of a group of cells equal in number to that given value. A '6' is part of a group of six cells, for example. Groups may take any shape, but no two groups of the same size may touch each other horizontally or vertically at any point, and there are no blank cells. Not all groups need have a given value. How are the groups arranged? Answer on page 288.

914 Tents 37

The grid below indicates a patch of woodland. Some cells contain grass, and others contain trees. Tents are placed on grass cells so that each tree has one tent next to it horizontally or vertically, although note that tents may be adjacent to more than one tree. No tent may be horizontally, vertically or diagonally adjacent to another tent. The numbers beside each row and column tell you how many tents are in that row or column. Where are the tents? Answer on page 286.

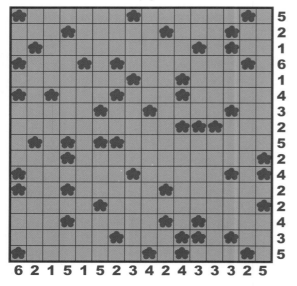

915 Sikaku 37

Divide the grid below into a number of rectangular rooms. Each room must contain exactly one number, equal to the number of cells that make up the room. Answer on page 278.

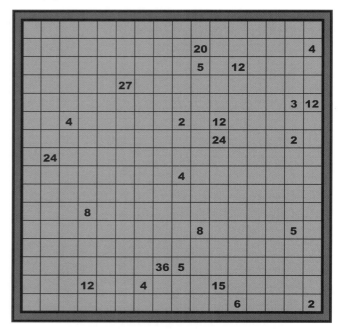

916 Dominoes 37

A full set of dominoes containing all possible pairs of numbers from (0,0) to (9,9) is laid together in one solid rectangle. The dominoes may be placed horizontally or vertically. The numbers in the grid below indicate the value of each half of each domino. How are the dominoes arranged? Answer on page 280.

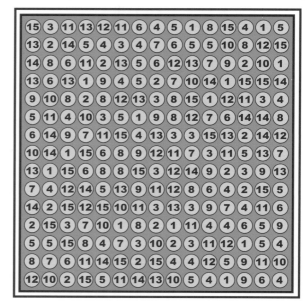

917 Hitori 37

Shade out cells in the grid below so that no number appears more than once in any row or column. Shaded cells cannot touch each other horizontally or vertically, and cannot cut the unshaded cells into two or more groups – the unshaded cells must remain connected horizontally or vertically into one complex branching chain. Which cells are shaded? Answer on page 287.

918 Nonogram 25

A number of cells in the grid below are to be shaded. Each row and column may contain one or more continuous lines of shaded cells ('blocks'). The numbers adjacent to the row or column indicate the lengths of the different blocks contained. Blocks are separated from others in the same row or column by at least one empty cell. Where are the shaded cells? A picture will emerge when the cells are shaded correctly. Answer on page 295.

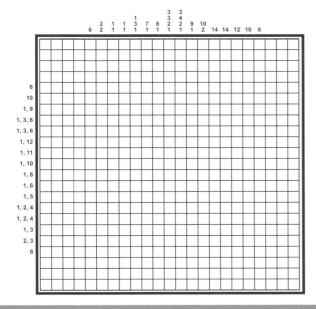

919 Slitherlink 37

A number of the intersection lines in the grid below have to be joined together to make one single complete loop. The numbers in the cell indicate how many of that cell's sides form part of the loop. Answer on page 279.

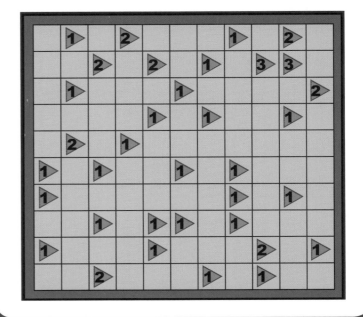

920 Number Link 37

The numbered cells in the grid below indicate the start and end points of single continuous paths. These paths fill the grid completely, and do not branch, cross each other, or touch themselves to form any pool of cells (2x2 or greater).
How are the paths arranged? Answer on page 285.

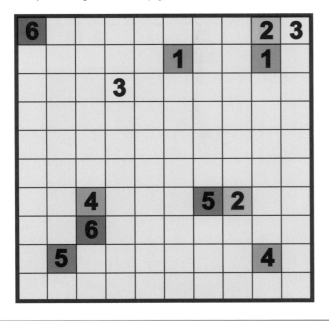

921 Minesweeper 10

The grid below contains a number of bombs hidden in empty squares. Each red flag tells you how many bombs are in the eight cells around it. Where are the bombs?
For answer see page 275.

922 Domino placing 37

A set of dominoes containing all possible pairs of numbers from (0,0) to (7,7) is laid out vertically as shown in the blank grid below so that the larger number of each domino is on the top. The numbers above each column are from the top half of the dominoes in that column. The numbers below each column are from the bottom half of the dominoes in that column. The numbers to the left of each row are from the respective half-dominoes in that row.

All the numbers are given to you sorted into descending numerical order. How are the dominoes laid out? Answer on page 283.

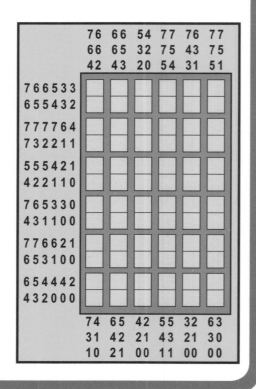

923 Gokigen Naname 37

Each cell in the grid below contains one diagonal line from corner to corner. The numbered circles show how many lines touch that corner. Fill in the grid so that the lines never form a closed circuit of any size. Answer on page 276.

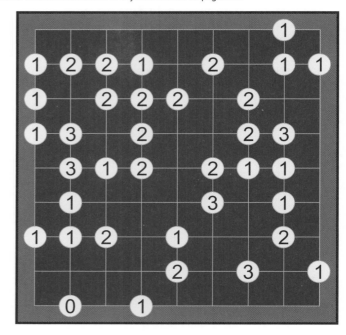

924 Sudoku 47

Fill in the grid below so that the numbers 1–9 appear exactly once in each row, column and 3x3 box. For solution see page 273.

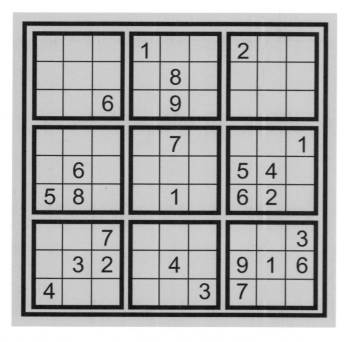

925 Battleships 35

A number of ships of various sizes are hidden in the grid below. The numbers next to each row and column indicate how many ship segments are in that row or column. Some ship segments have already been filled in. Where are the ships? Answer on page 289.

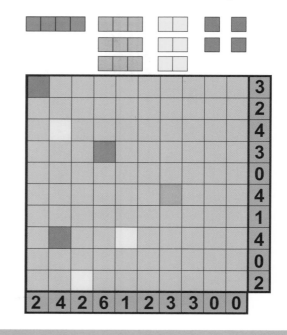

926 Missing Landmarks 27

Which famous landmark is blurred out of this photo? Answer on page 293.

927 Futoshiki 43

Fill in the grid below so that the numbers 1 to 7 appear exactly once in each row and column. Red arrows indicate that a number is greater than its neighbour. For answer see page 275.

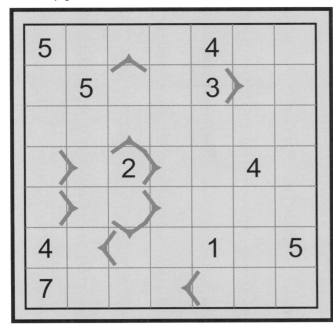

928 Identicals 19

Which pair of images is identical? Answer on page 300.

929 Dominoes 38

A full set of dominoes containing all possible pairs of numbers from (0,0) to (9,9) is laid together in one solid rectangle. The dominoes may be placed horizontally or vertically. The numbers in the grid below indicate the value of each half of each domino. How are the dominoes arranged? Answer on page 280.

9	9	4	5	2	6	8	1	2	2	4
9	6	3	4	4	5	6	7	5	1	8
5	9	9	7	6	7	5	5	6	1	7
3	4	1	1	3	3	8	0	3	5	9
8	2	0	0	3	3	9	1	4	2	7
8	8	8	2	9	3	1	0	6	9	7
8	1	2	2	9	7	5	2	1	5	8
7	8	3	0	7	8	0	2	9	5	3
2	6	1	6	7	0	6	4	0	1	4
4	3	4	0	7	4	6	0	0	5	6

930 Tents 38

The grid below indicates a patch of woodland. Some cells contain grass, and others contain trees. Tents are placed on grass cells so that each tree has one tent next to it horizontally or vertically, although note that tents may be adjacent to more than one tree. No tent may be horizontally, vertically or diagonally adjacent to another tent. The numbers beside each row and column tell you how many tents are in that row or column. Where are the tents? Answer on page 286.

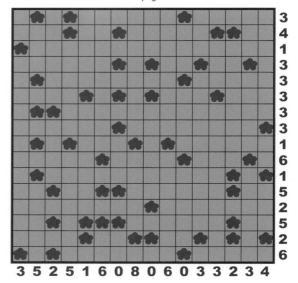

931 Mirror Image 19

Which of the five images below is an identical mirror image of the one above? Answer on page 300.

932 Gokigen Naname 38

Each cell in the grid below contains one diagonal line from corner to corner. The numbered circles show how many lines touch that corner. Fill in the grid so that the lines never form a closed circuit of any size. Answer on page 276.

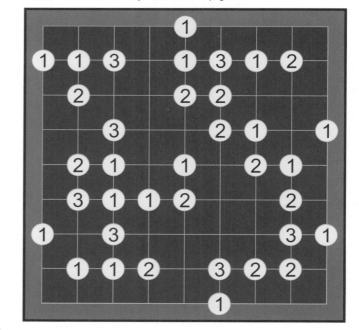

933 Domino placing 38

A set of dominoes containing all possible pairs of numbers from (0,0) to (7,7) is laid out vertically as shown in the blank grid below so that the larger number of each domino is on the top. The numbers above each column are from the top half of the dominoes in that column.

The numbers below each column are from the bottom half of the dominoes in that column. The numbers to the left of each row are from the respective half-dominoes in that row.

All the numbers are given to you sorted into descending numerical order. How are the dominoes laid out? Answer on page 283.

```
              66 76 77 77 76 55
              65 65 44 77 65 44
              33 52 21 32 40 31
    776432
    643200
    777552
    742000
    665433
    432211
    765544
    532210
    776543
    543311
    662110
    651100
              64 54 54 63 75 33
              32 42 22 21 31 20
              10 10 10 11 00 00
```

934 Slitherlink 38

A number of the intersection lines in the grid below have to be joined together to make one single complete loop. The numbers in the cell indicate how many of that cell's sides form part of the loop. Answer on page 279.

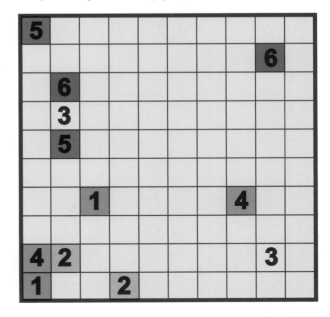

935 Hashiwokakero 19

A number of straight horizontal and vertical bridges connect the islands shown. The number on each island shows how many bridges touch that island. Bridges may not cross each other, and no more than 2 bridges may connect a pair of islands.

Where are the bridges? Answer on page 297.

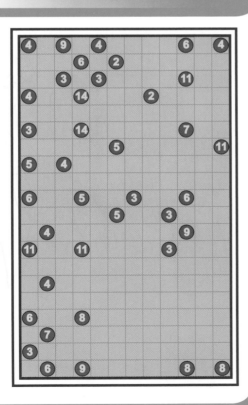

936 Number Link 38

The numbered cells in the grid below indicate the start and end points of single continuous paths. These paths fill the grid completely, and do not branch, cross each other, or touch themselves to form any pool of cells (2x2 or greater).

How are the paths arranged? Answer on page 285.

937 Fillomino 38

Each value shown in the grid below is part of a group of cells equal in number to that given value. A '6' is part of a group of six cells, for example. Groups may take any shape, but no two groups of the same size may touch each other horizontally or vertically at any point, and there are no blank cells. Not all groups need have a given value. How are the groups arranged? Answer on page 288.

938 Bijutsukan 38

The bright cells and dark cells in the grid below represent corridors and walls respectively. Light sources shine a horizontal and vertical beam of light. A corridor cell becomes illuminated if it is in the same row or column as a light source and there is no wall cell in between them. Place light sources in the corridor cells so that every corridor cell is illuminated, and no light source illuminates another light source. The numbers in some walls tell you how many light sources are touching that wall horizontally or vertically. Answer on page 282.

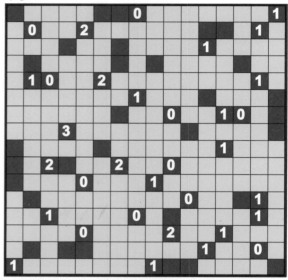

939 Yudoku 19

Fill in the grid below so that the letters s, p, a, r, k, l, i, n and g appear exactly once in each row, column and 3x3 box. Answer on page 301.

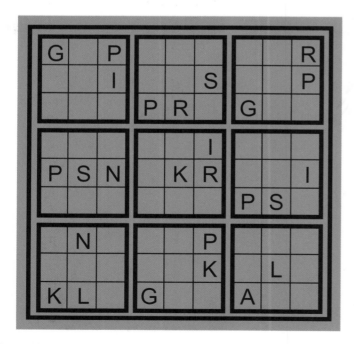

940 Match One 19

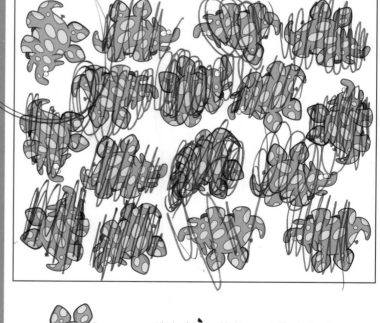

Which of the jumbled images is identical to the one presented here? Answer on page 298.

941 Suiri 19

Five neighbours like spending time in their front gardens. From the information given below, can you work out which man (1) lives in which house (2), what colour the front door is (3) and what he likes to do in his yard (4)?

1. Dave lives further up the road than the man who likes barbecues.
2. The house with the green door has a lower number than the house with the yellow door (which is not owned by the man who likes to play basketball).
3. Either Walt likes basketball and John's house has a blue door or Dave likes basketball and Walt has a blue door.
4. Mack, who has a red door, lives one up from the man who likes to read the newspaper outside (either Buck or Dave). That man in turn lives further up than the man who likes to wash his car.
5. The man at 2305, who likes sunbathing, is either Dave or Buck.
6. One of the houses has a white door.
7. The houses run from 2302 to 2306.
Answer on page 299.

942 Hitori 38

Shade out cells in the grid below so that no number appears more than once in any row or column. Shaded cells cannot touch each other horizontally or vertically, and cannot cut the unshaded cells into two or more groups – the unshaded cells must remain connected horizontally or vertically into one complex branching chain. Which cells are shaded? Answer on page 287.

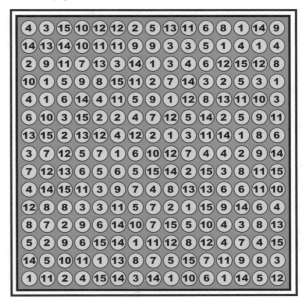

943 Masyu 19

A line passes through some or all of the cells in the grid below in such a way that it forms a single continuous non-intersecting loop. The line always exits a cell by a different side to the one it entered by, and passes through all cells containing a circle. The line travels straight through a cell with a light circle but turns in the previous and/or following cells in its path. The line turns in a cell containing a dark cell, but travels straight through both the previous and following cells in its path. Where is the line? Answer on page 301.

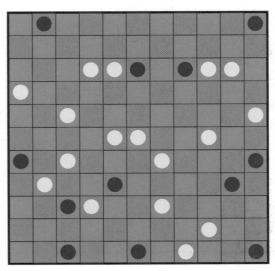

944 Detail Scene 19

The three enlarged squares appear somewhere in the large picture. Can you find them? Answer on page 299.

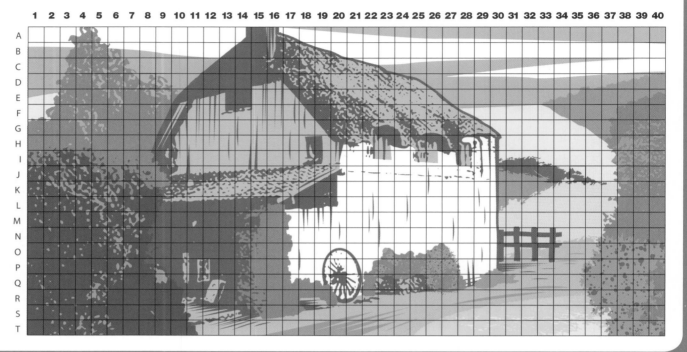

945 Sikaku 38

Divide the grid below into a number of rectangular rooms. Each room must contain exactly one number, equal to the number of cells that make up the room.
Answer on page 278.

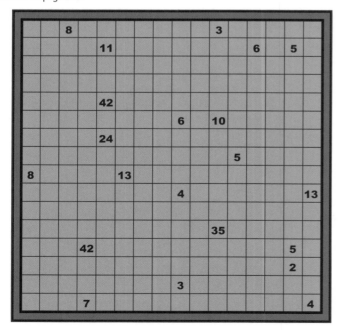

946 Colourminoes 34

In the grid below, each colour has a unique integer value from 0 to 6. The numbers next to each row and column indicate the total value of the cells in that row or column. The values of the cells of the grid correspond in turn to the numbers shown on a half-set of dominoes containing all possible pairs of numbers from (0,0) to (6,6) which has been laid together in one solid rectangle. Dominoes in this rectangle may be placed horizontally or vertically. What number does each colour correspond to, and how are the corresponding dominoes arranged? Answer on page 290.

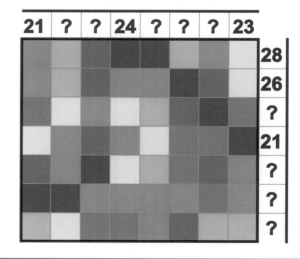

947 Tentai 29

The grid below is divided into a number of shapes. Each shape has a star at its centre, and is made up of one continuous group of cells connected horizontally and/or vertically. The shapes are all symmetrical – they stay the same when rotated by 180 degrees – but may get quite complicated. Where are the shapes? Answer on page 291.

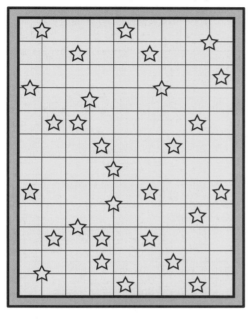

948 Battlehex 24

A number of ships of various sizes are hidden in the hexagonal grid below. The numbers next to each edge indicate how many ship segments are in the rows indicated by the directional arrows. Some ship segments and/or empty water cells have already been filled in. Where are the ships? Answer on page 296.

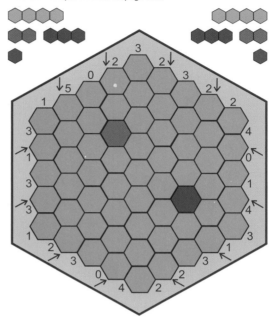

949 Sudoku 48

Fill in the grid below so that the numbers 1–9 appear exactly once in each row, column and 3x3 box. For solution see page 273.

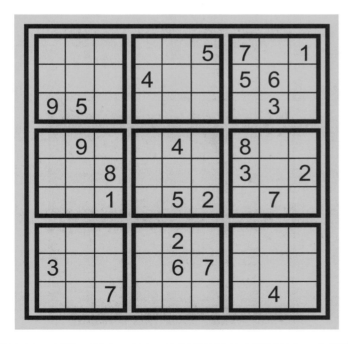

950 Map Colouring 24

The rooms of the grid are coloured so that no two rooms of the same colour ever touch. How are the rooms coloured? Answer on page 296.

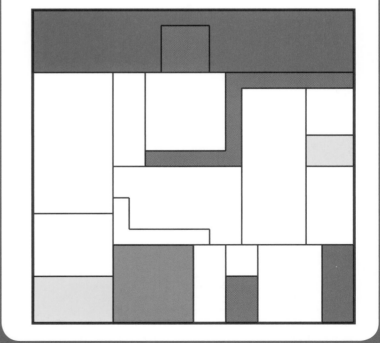

951 Kakuro 26

The empty squares in this grid contain digits from 1 to 9 so that each continuous unbroken line of numbers adds up to the clue value in the filled segment to its left (for horizontal lines) or above it (for vertical lines). No number may be used more than once in any unbroken line. How is the grid filled? Answer on page 294.

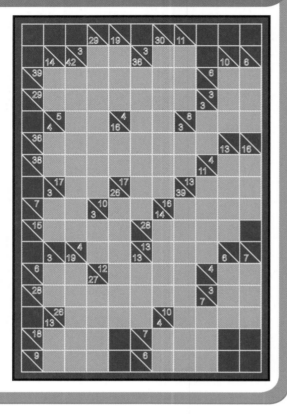

952 Nonogram 26

A number of cells in the grid below are to be shaded. Each row and column may contain one or more continuous lines of shaded cells ('blocks'). The numbers adjacent to the row or column indicate the lengths of the different blocks contained. Blocks are separated from others in the same row or column by at least one empty cell. Where are the shaded cells? A picture will emerge when the cells are shaded correctly. Answer on page 295.

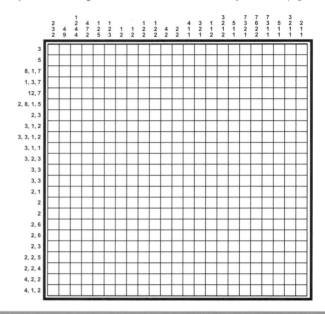

953 Futoshiki 44

Fill in the grid below so that the numbers 1 to 7 appear exactly once in each row and column. Red arrows indicate that a number is greater than its neighbour. For answer see page 275.

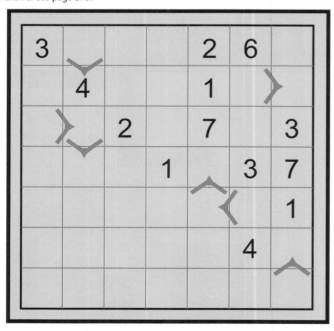

954 Battleships 36

A number of ships of various sizes are hidden in the grid below. The numbers next to each row and column indicate how many ship segments are in that row or column. Some ship segments have already been filled in. Where are the ships? Answer on page 289.

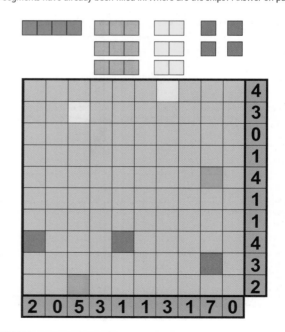

955 Number Link 39

The numbered cells in the grid below indicate the start and end points of single continuous paths. These paths fill the grid completely, and do not branch, cross each other, or touch themselves to form any pool of cells (2x2 or greater).
How are the paths arranged? Answer on page 285.

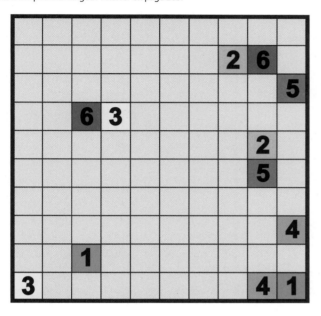

956 Slitherlink 39

A number of the intersection lines in the grid below have to be joined together to make one single complete loop. The numbers in the cell indicate how many of that cell's sides form part of the loop. Answer on page 279.

957 Fillomino 39

Each value shown in the grid below is part of a group of cells equal in number to that given value. A '6' is part of a group of six cells, for example. Groups may take any shape, but no two groups of the same size may touch each other horizontally or vertically at any point, and there are no blank cells. Not all groups need have a given value.
How are the groups arranged? Answer on page 288.

958 Bijutsukan 39

The bright cells and dark cells in the grid below represent corridors and walls respectively. Light sources shine a horizontal and vertical beam of light. A corridor cell becomes illuminated if it is in the same row or column as a light source and there is no wall cell in between them. Place light sources in the corridor cells so that every corridor cell is illuminated, and no light source illuminates another light source. The numbers in some walls tell you how many light sources are touching that wall horizontally or vertically. Answer on page 282.

959 Domino placing 39

A set of dominoes containing all possible pairs of numbers from (0,0) to (7,7) is laid out vertically as shown in the blank grid below so that the larger number of each domino is on the top. The numbers above each column are from the top half of the dominoes in that column. The numbers below each column are from the bottom half of the dominoes in that column. The numbers to the left of each row are from the respective half-dominoes in that row.

All the numbers are given to you sorted into descending numerical order. How are the dominoes laid out? Answer on page 283.

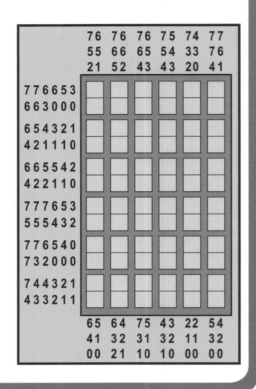

960 Sikaku 39

Divide the grid below into a number of rectangular rooms. Each room must contain exactly one number, equal to the number of cells that make up the room. Answer on page 278.

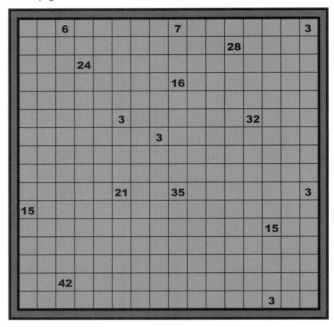

961 Tents 39

The grid below indicates a patch of woodland. Some cells contain grass, and others contain trees. Tents are placed on grass cells so that each tree has one tent next to it horizontally or vertically, although note that tents may be adjacent to more than one tree. No tent may be horizontally, vertically or diagonally adjacent to another tent. The numbers beside each row and column tell you how many tents are in that row or column. Where are the tents? Answer on page 286.

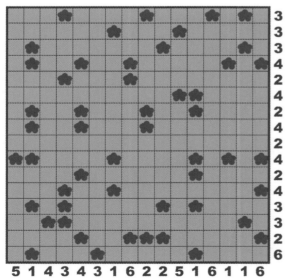

962 Dominoes 39

A full set of dominoes containing all possible pairs of numbers from (0,0) to (9,9) is laid together in one solid rectangle. The dominoes may be placed horizontally or vertically. The numbers in the grid below indicate the value of each half of each domino. How are the dominoes arranged? Answer on page 280.

1	8	1	8	1	7	5	8	1	9	4
0	6	8	6	9	5	3	3	1	9	4
5	8	0	7	0	0	7	7	5	5	2
1	8	5	1	0	6	4	0	3	7	1
6	0	4	9	3	2	3	9	8	3	3
0	6	0	4	5	6	4	8	2	9	2
2	1	9	5	0	1	6	6	7	0	6
8	9	2	7	6	4	7	7	7	9	7
9	5	5	2	3	3	4	8	4	4	5
6	1	2	2	2	4	8	3	2	9	3

963 Hitori 39

Shade out cells in the grid below so that no number appears more than once in any row or column. Shaded cells cannot touch each other horizontally or vertically, and cannot cut the unshaded cells into two or more groups – the unshaded cells must remain connected horizontally or vertically into one complex branching chain. Which cells are shaded? Answer on page 287.

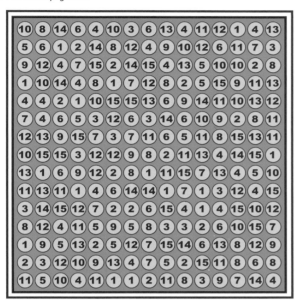

964 Gokigen Naname 39

Each cell in the grid below contains one diagonal line from corner to corner. The numbered circles show how many lines touch that corner. Fill in the grid so that the lines never form a closed circuit of any size. Answer on page 276.

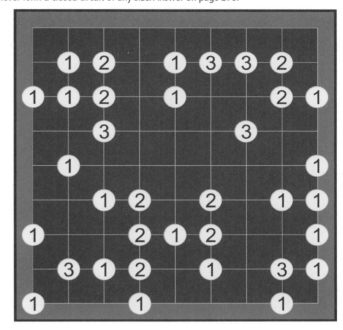

965 Colourminoes 35

In the grid below, each colour has a unique integer value from 0 to 6. The numbers next to each row and column indicate the total value of the cells in that row or column. The values of the cells of the grid correspond in turn to the numbers shown on a half-set of dominoes containing all possible pairs of numbers from (0,0) to (6,6) which has been laid together in one solid rectangle. Dominoes in this rectangle may be placed horizontally or vertically. What number does each colour correspond to, and how are the corresponding dominoes arranged? Answer on page 290.

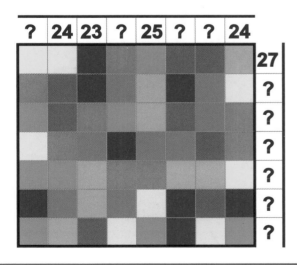

966 Sudoku 49

Fill in the grid below so that the numbers 1–9 appear exactly once in each row, column and 3x3 box. For solution see page 273.

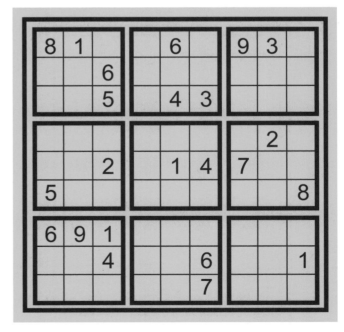

967 Missing Landmarks 28

Which famous landmark is blurred out of this photo? Answer on page 293.

968 Silhouettes 15

Which of the six images fits the silhouette? Answer on page 302.

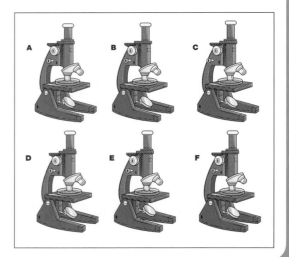

969 Tentai 30

The grid below is divided into a number of shapes. Each shape has a star at its centre, and is made up of one continuous group of cells connected horizontally and/or vertically. The shapes are all symmetrical – they stay the same when rotated by 180 degrees – but may get quite complicated. Where are the shapes? Answer on page 291.

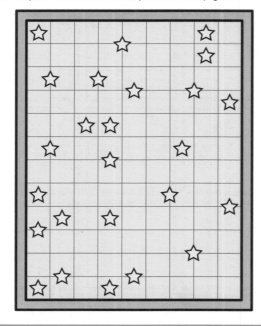

970 Futoshiki 45

Fill in the grid below so that the numbers 1 to 7 appear exactly once in each row and column. Red arrows indicate that a number is greater than its neighbour. For answer see page 275.

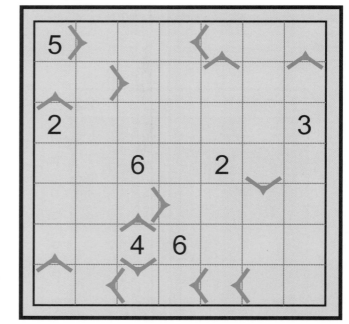

971 Who's Who 15

Using the information, can you match the reporter to their interviewee? Answer on p302.

972 Kakuro 27

The empty squares in this grid contain digits from 1 to 9 so that each continuous unbroken line of numbers adds up to the clue value in the filled segment to its left (for horizontal lines) or above it (for vertical lines). No number may be used more than once in any unbroken line. How is the grid filled? Answer on page 294.

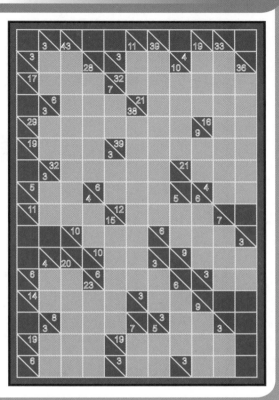

973 Artist's Errors

The artist drawing this scene has made a number of visual, conceptual and logical errors. Can you find them all? Answer on page 304.

974 Nonogram 27

A number of cells in the grid below are to be shaded. Each row and column may contain one or more continuous lines of shaded cells ('blocks'). The numbers adjacent to the row or column indicate the lengths of the different blocks contained. Blocks are separated from others in the same row or column by at least one empty cell. Where are the shaded cells? A picture will emerge when the cells are shaded correctly. Answer on page 295.

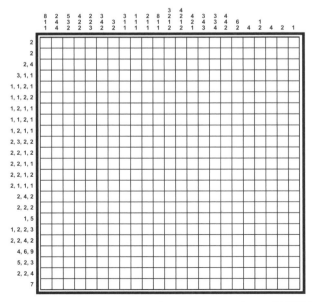

975 Domino placing 40

A set of dominoes containing all possible pairs of numbers from (0,0) to (7,7) is laid out vertically as shown in the blank grid below so that the larger number of each domino is on the top. The numbers above each column are from the top half of the dominoes in that column. The numbers below each column are from the bottom half of the dominoes in that column. The numbers to the left of each row are from the respective half-dominoes in that row. All the numbers are given to you sorted into descending numerical order. How are the dominoes laid out? Answer on page 283.

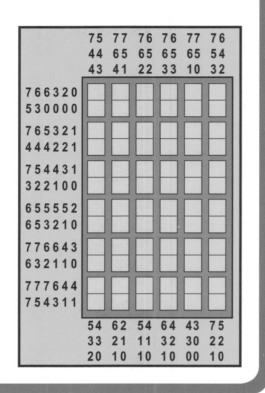

976 Match One 20

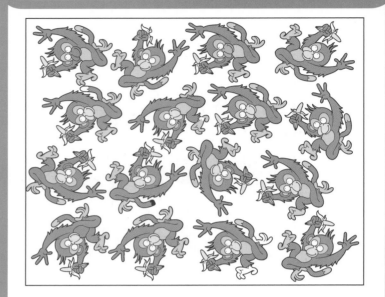

Which of the jumbled images is identical to the one presented here? Answer on page 298.

977 Tents 40

The grid below indicates a patch of woodland. Some cells contain grass, and others contain trees. Tents are placed on grass cells so that each tree has one tent next to it horizontally or vertically, although note that tents may be adjacent to more than one tree. No tent may be horizontally, vertically or diagonally adjacent to another tent. The numbers beside each row and column tell you how many tents are in that row or column. Where are the tents? Answer on page 286.

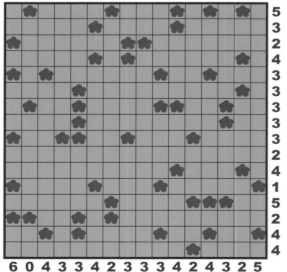

978 Sikaku 40

Divide the grid below into a number of rectangular rooms. Each room must contain exactly one number, equal to the number of cells that make up the room. Answer on page 278.

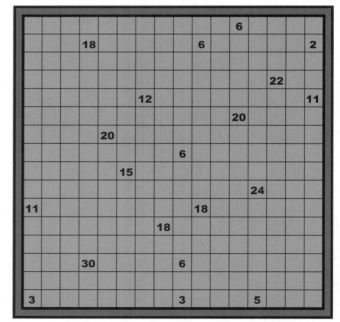

979 Super Slitherlink

A number of the intersection lines in the grid below have to be joined together to make one single complete loop. The numbers in the cell indicate how many of that cell's sides form part of the loop. Answer on page 279.

```
  2 2 2 3 2 3           1
3   3       1 2   3 2 2 2
2     2 2 3       2         2
2 3 2 3 2       3       3   2 1
2     1 2 1 2 0             2   2
3       2 1     2   1   3       2
2 1   1 1 2         2 1       3
3         2   3   1           2
1               2       3   2 2
2 2 2 0 2 0 2 0 3     3     3 0       3
  2             2           1 2
  3 1 3 1             2 1     2 3
1 2     1       1             1 2
1       3 3 1 3 2 3 2         2 2
        1       2 2 3 2 2 3
```

980 Spot the Difference

There are eight differences between the two pictures. Can you find them all? Answer on p302.

981 Samurai Sudoku 10

Fill in each 9x9 grid below so that the numbers 1–9 appear exactly once in each row, column and 3x3 block. Numbers in overlapping blocks count identically towards both grids. Answer on page 303.

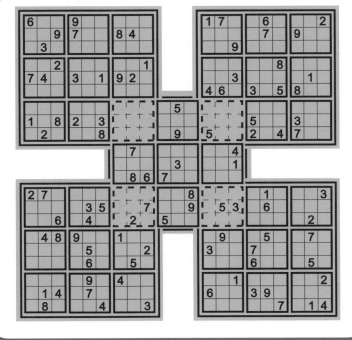

982 Hashiwokakero 20

A number of straight horizontal and vertical bridges connect the islands shown. The number on each island shows how many bridges touch that island. Bridges may not cross each other, and no more than 2 bridges may connect a pair of islands.
Where are the bridges? Answer on page 297.

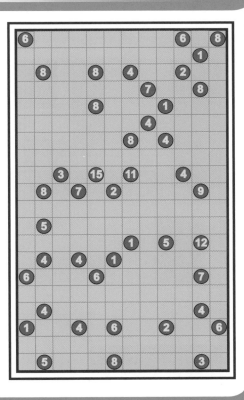

983 Hitori 40

Shade out cells in the grid below so that no number appears more than once in any row or column. Shaded cells cannot touch each other horizontally or vertically, and cannot cut the unshaded cells into two or more groups – the unshaded cells must remain connected horizontally or vertically into one complex branching chain. Which cells are shaded? Answer on page 287.

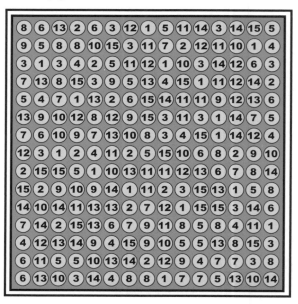

984 Killer Sudoku 10

Fill in the grid below so that the numbers 1–9 appear exactly once in each row, column and 3x3 block, and that the numbers in each dotted room add up to the value in its top right corner. Answer on page 303.

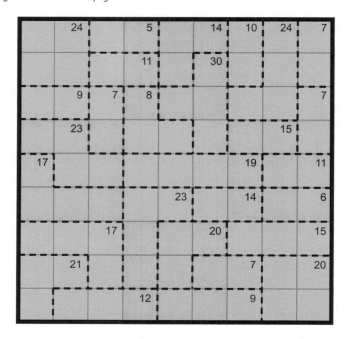

985 Map Colouring 25

The rooms of the grid are coloured so that no two rooms of the same colour ever touch. How are the rooms coloured? Answer on page 296.

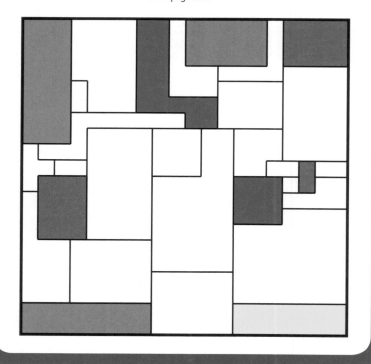

986 Identicals 20

Which pair of images is identical? Answer on page 300.

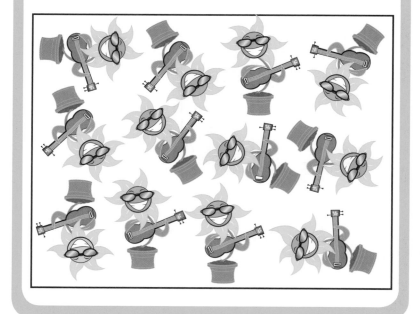

987 Fillomino 40

Each value shown in the grid below is part of a group of cells equal in number to that given value. A '6' is part of a group of six cells, for example. Groups may take any shape, but no two groups of the same size may touch each other horizontally or vertically at any point, and there are no blank cells. Not all groups need have a given value. How are the groups arranged? Answer on page 288.

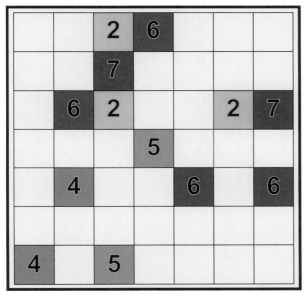

988 Masyu 20

A line passes through some or all of the cells in the grid below in such a way that it forms a single continuous non-intersecting loop. The line always exits a cell by a different side to the one it entered by, and passes through all cells containing a circle. The line travels straight through a cell with a light circle but turns in the previous and/or following cells in its path. The line turns in a cell containing a dark cell, but travels straight through both the previous and following cells in its path. Where is the line? Answer on page 301.

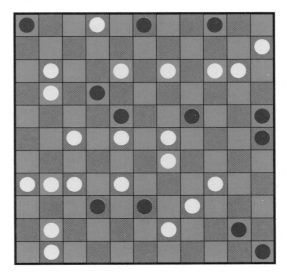

989 Detail Scene 20

The three enlarged squares appear somewhere in the large picture. Can you find them? Answer on page 299.

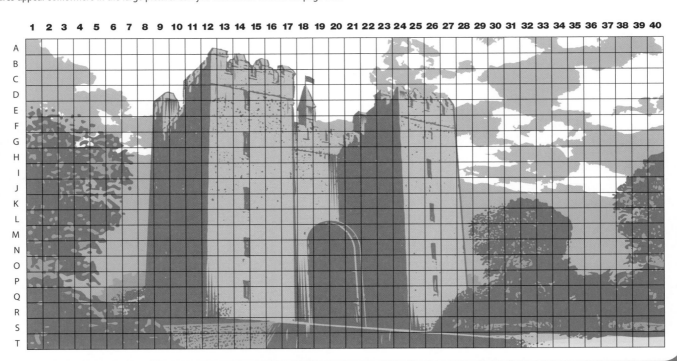

990 Mirror Image 20

Which of the five images below is an identical mirror image of the one above?
Answer on page 300.

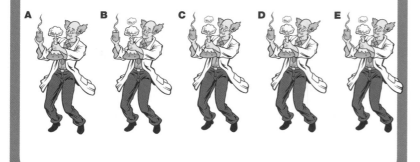

A   B   C   D   E

991 Spot the Set

There are four different versions of the picture in the group below, each one reproduced three times. Can you identify the four sets?
Answer on page 304.

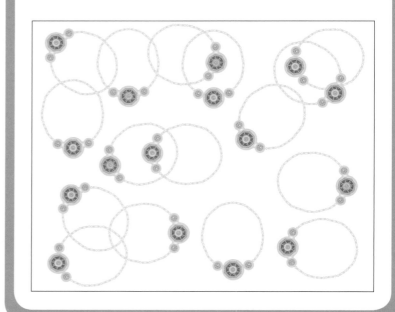

992 Bijutsukan 40

The bright cells and dark cells in the grid below represent corridors and walls respectively. Light sources shine a horizontal and vertical beam of light. A corridor cell becomes illuminated if it is in the same row or column as a light source and there is no wall cell in between them. Place light sources in the corridor cells so that every corridor cell is illuminated, and no light source illuminates another light source. The numbers in some walls tell you how many light sources are touching that wall horizontally or vertically. Answer on page 282.

993 Super Sudoku 10

Fill in the grid below so that the digits 1, 2, 3, 4, 5, 6, 7, 8, 9, a, b, c, d, e, f and g appear exactly once in each row and column. Answer on page 303.

994 Dominoes 40

A full set of dominoes containing all possible pairs of numbers from (0,0) to (9,9) is laid together in one solid rectangle. The dominoes may be placed horizontally or vertically. The numbers in the grid below indicate the value of each half of each domino. How are the dominoes arranged? Answer on page 280.

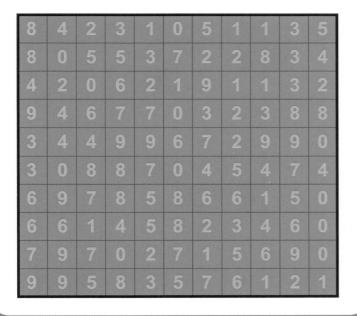

995 Sudoku 50

Fill in the grid below so that the numbers 1–9 appear exactly once in each row, column and 3x3 box. For solution see page 273.

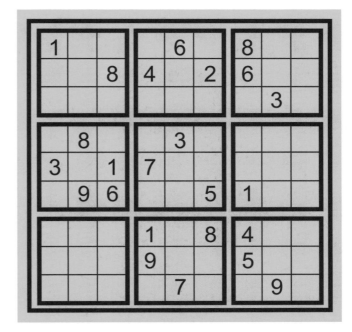

996 Differences

Each copy of the picture has one flaw that none of the others share. Can you find them all? Answer on page 304.

997 Yudoku 20

Fill in the grid below so that the letters s, p, a, r, k, l, i, n and g appear exactly once in each row, column and 3x3 box. Answer on page 301.

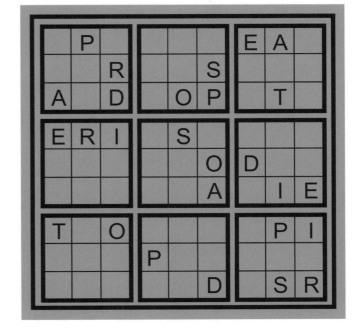

998 Battlehex 25

A number of ships of various sizes are hidden in the hexagonal grid below. The numbers next to each edge indicate how many ship segments are in the rows indicated by the directional arrows. Some ship segments and/or empty water cells have already been filled in. Where are the ships? Answer on page 296.

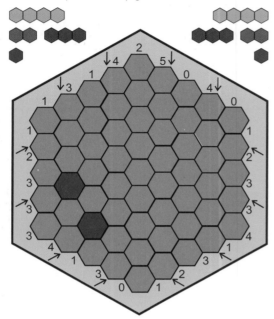

999 Number Link 40

The numbered cells in the grid below indicate the start and end points of single continuous paths. These paths fill the grid completely, and do not branch, cross each other, or touch themselves to form any pool of cells (2x2 or greater).
How are the paths arranged? Answer on page 285.

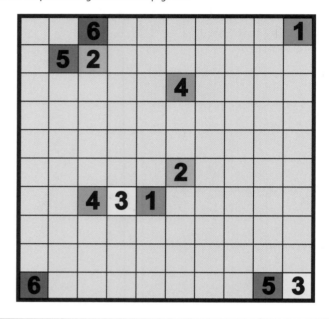

1000 Spot the Difference

There are five differences between these two pictures. Can you find them all? Answer on page 302.

1001 **Challenge sudoku**

Fill in the grid below so that the numbers 1–9 appear exactly once in each row, column and 3x3 box. Warning: this sudoku is hard.

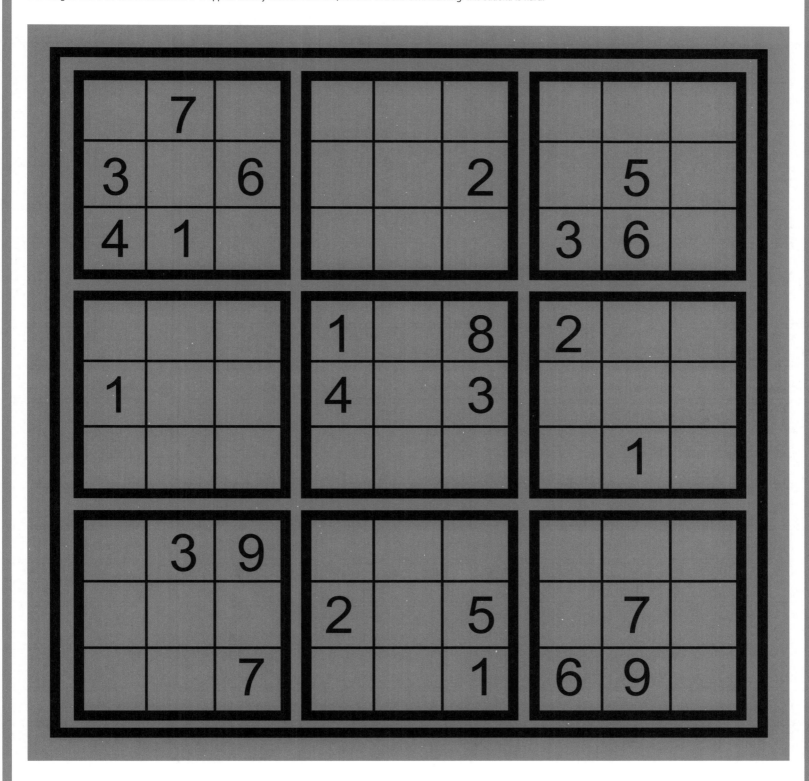

1 Sudoku 1

```
2 5 6 | 9 1 7 | 3 8 4
1 7 8 | 3 4 5 | 9 6 2
9 3 4 | 8 6 2 | 7 1 5
------+-------+------
5 6 2 | 7 3 1 | 8 4 9
3 9 7 | 2 8 4 | 1 5 6
4 8 1 | 5 9 6 | 2 7 3
------+-------+------
6 4 9 | 1 2 8 | 5 3 7
7 1 3 | 6 5 9 | 4 2 8
8 2 5 | 4 7 3 | 6 9 1
```

22 Sudoku 2

```
4 7 1 | 8 5 6 | 2 9 3
8 6 2 | 7 9 3 | 4 1 5
5 9 3 | 4 1 2 | 8 7 6
------+-------+------
2 5 7 | 9 6 8 | 1 3 4
6 8 9 | 1 3 4 | 5 2 7
1 3 4 | 2 7 5 | 9 6 8
------+-------+------
7 1 5 | 3 8 9 | 6 4 2
3 4 6 | 5 2 1 | 7 8 9
9 2 8 | 6 4 7 | 3 5 1
```

45 Sudoku 3

```
1 7 3 | 4 8 9 | 5 2 6
6 9 8 | 1 5 2 | 4 7 3
4 5 2 | 6 3 7 | 1 8 9
------+-------+------
3 4 9 | 2 1 6 | 8 5 7
5 2 1 | 9 7 8 | 6 3 4
7 8 6 | 5 4 3 | 2 9 1
------+-------+------
2 3 5 | 7 6 1 | 9 4 8
9 1 7 | 8 2 4 | 3 6 5
8 6 4 | 3 9 5 | 7 1 2
```

64 Sudoku 4

```
1 2 4 | 6 3 5 | 8 9 7
3 6 5 | 7 8 9 | 2 4 1
7 8 9 | 4 2 1 | 5 6 3
------+-------+------
5 1 2 | 9 4 8 | 7 3 6
6 4 8 | 5 7 3 | 9 1 2
9 7 3 | 1 6 2 | 4 8 5
------+-------+------
4 5 1 | 3 9 7 | 6 2 8
8 9 7 | 2 1 6 | 3 5 4
2 3 6 | 8 5 4 | 1 7 9
```

83 Sudoku 5

```
8 6 5 | 2 9 3 | 7 4 1
9 2 7 | 6 1 4 | 3 5 8
1 4 3 | 5 7 8 | 9 2 6
------+-------+------
2 5 6 | 3 8 1 | 4 9 7
4 9 1 | 7 2 5 | 6 8 3
7 3 8 | 9 4 6 | 5 1 2
------+-------+------
6 1 9 | 8 5 7 | 2 3 4
3 8 2 | 4 6 9 | 1 7 5
5 7 4 | 1 3 2 | 8 6 9
```

104 Sudoku 6

```
1 8 9 | 5 6 3 | 4 2 7
5 7 6 | 1 2 4 | 3 9 8
2 3 4 | 9 7 8 | 1 6 5
------+-------+------
6 5 8 | 2 1 7 | 9 3 4
3 4 2 | 8 5 9 | 6 7 1
7 9 1 | 3 4 6 | 5 8 2
------+-------+------
8 6 5 | 7 9 1 | 2 4 3
4 1 3 | 6 8 2 | 7 5 9
9 2 7 | 4 3 5 | 8 1 6
```

121 Sudoku 7

```
7 6 4 | 3 1 8 | 5 9 2
3 2 9 | 6 5 4 | 8 7 1
1 8 5 | 7 9 2 | 6 4 3
------+-------+------
2 7 8 | 4 6 9 | 1 3 5
5 9 1 | 2 8 3 | 4 6 7
6 4 3 | 5 7 1 | 9 2 8
------+-------+------
4 1 6 | 8 2 7 | 3 5 9
8 3 7 | 9 4 5 | 2 1 6
9 5 2 | 1 3 6 | 7 8 4
```

146 Sudoku 8

```
5 2 1 | 4 6 8 | 9 7 3
4 6 9 | 5 7 3 | 2 8 1
8 3 7 | 2 1 9 | 5 4 6
------+-------+------
3 1 2 | 9 4 6 | 7 5 8
6 8 5 | 3 2 7 | 1 9 4
7 9 4 | 1 8 5 | 6 3 2
------+-------+------
9 5 6 | 8 3 2 | 4 1 7
2 4 8 | 7 5 1 | 3 6 9
1 7 3 | 6 9 4 | 8 2 5
```

163 Sudoku 9

```
4 5 9 | 1 2 6 | 8 3 7
3 8 1 | 4 9 7 | 5 6 2
2 6 7 | 3 5 8 | 9 4 1
------+-------+------
6 9 8 | 2 1 3 | 4 7 5
5 7 2 | 8 6 4 | 1 9 3
1 3 4 | 5 7 9 | 2 8 6
------+-------+------
8 4 5 | 6 3 2 | 7 1 9
9 2 3 | 7 4 1 | 6 5 8
7 1 6 | 9 8 5 | 3 2 4
```

175 Sudoku 10

```
3 7 2 | 5 9 1 | 4 6 8
8 9 6 | 4 3 7 | 1 2 5
5 1 4 | 2 6 8 | 3 7 9
------+-------+------
2 5 1 | 6 8 9 | 7 4 3
9 6 7 | 3 2 4 | 5 8 1
4 8 3 | 7 1 5 | 6 9 2
------+-------+------
7 3 5 | 9 4 2 | 8 1 6
1 4 9 | 8 5 6 | 2 3 7
6 2 8 | 1 7 3 | 9 5 4
```

203 Sudoku 11

```
6 5 1 | 3 8 9 | 2 7 4
7 3 4 | 1 5 2 | 9 8 6
8 9 2 | 6 4 7 | 1 3 5
------+-------+------
1 4 9 | 2 3 6 | 8 5 7
2 6 3 | 5 7 8 | 4 9 1
5 8 7 | 4 9 1 | 3 6 2
------+-------+------
3 1 8 | 7 2 5 | 6 4 9
4 2 5 | 9 6 3 | 7 1 8
9 7 6 | 8 1 4 | 5 2 3
```

220 Sudoku 12

```
8 7 2 | 1 9 4 | 6 5 3
6 1 4 | 3 8 5 | 7 2 9
9 3 5 | 7 2 6 | 8 1 4
------+-------+------
2 4 6 | 8 5 7 | 9 3 1
7 9 1 | 4 6 3 | 5 8 2
3 5 8 | 9 1 2 | 4 6 7
------+-------+------
4 6 7 | 2 3 8 | 1 9 5
1 8 3 | 5 4 9 | 2 7 6
5 2 9 | 6 7 1 | 3 4 8
```

246 Sudoku 13

```
7 5 9 | 2 3 8 | 1 4 6
4 6 1 | 5 9 7 | 2 3 8
3 2 8 | 6 4 1 | 7 5 9
------+-------+------
2 7 5 | 9 8 6 | 4 1 3
1 8 4 | 3 7 5 | 6 9 2
9 3 6 | 4 1 2 | 5 8 7
------+-------+------
6 4 3 | 1 2 9 | 8 7 5
8 9 2 | 7 5 4 | 3 6 1
5 1 7 | 8 6 3 | 9 2 4
```

266 Sudoku 14

```
7 5 1 | 6 9 3 | 2 4 8
4 6 3 | 7 2 8 | 9 5 1
2 8 9 | 1 5 4 | 6 7 3
------+-------+------
5 1 2 | 3 4 6 | 7 8 9
9 7 6 | 2 8 1 | 5 3 4
3 4 8 | 5 7 9 | 1 2 6
------+-------+------
6 3 7 | 8 1 2 | 4 9 5
8 2 4 | 9 6 5 | 3 1 7
1 9 5 | 4 3 7 | 8 6 2
```

282 Sudoku 15

```
8 6 4 | 3 7 9 | 1 2 5
2 3 9 | 5 4 1 | 6 7 8
1 7 5 | 6 8 2 | 3 4 9
------+-------+------
5 4 2 | 8 6 7 | 9 3 1
9 1 6 | 2 3 4 | 8 5 7
7 8 3 | 9 1 5 | 4 6 2
------+-------+------
6 2 8 | 1 5 3 | 7 9 4
4 9 1 | 7 2 6 | 5 8 3
3 5 7 | 4 9 8 | 2 1 6
```

301 Sudoku 16

```
4 8 6 | 1 5 3 | 2 7 9
2 9 3 | 4 7 6 | 5 8 1
5 1 7 | 9 8 2 | 3 4 6
------+-------+------
6 2 1 | 5 9 4 | 7 3 8
9 5 4 | 8 3 7 | 1 6 2
3 7 8 | 6 2 1 | 9 5 4
------+-------+------
1 6 2 | 7 4 5 | 8 9 3
7 3 9 | 2 6 8 | 4 1 5
8 4 5 | 3 1 9 | 6 2 7
```

323 Sudoku 17

```
9 8 5 | 3 6 2 | 1 4 7
4 2 7 | 8 5 1 | 6 9 3
1 3 6 | 7 9 4 | 8 2 5
------+-------+------
7 4 9 | 6 2 8 | 5 3 1
3 1 2 | 4 7 5 | 9 6 8
6 5 8 | 9 1 3 | 2 7 4
------+-------+------
5 6 1 | 2 4 7 | 3 8 9
2 7 3 | 5 8 9 | 4 1 6
8 9 4 | 1 3 6 | 7 5 2
```

345 Sudoku 18

```
9 5 1 | 2 3 8 | 6 4 7
4 2 6 | 9 7 5 | 1 3 8
7 3 8 | 1 6 4 | 2 5 9
------+-------+------
1 8 4 | 6 2 9 | 5 7 3
5 6 3 | 7 4 1 | 8 9 2
2 7 9 | 5 8 3 | 4 1 6
------+-------+------
3 4 5 | 8 9 6 | 7 2 1
6 1 2 | 3 5 7 | 9 8 4
8 9 7 | 4 1 2 | 3 6 5
```

364 Sudoku 19

```
1 9 8 | 2 6 7 | 4 3 5
2 5 7 | 1 3 4 | 6 8 9
6 3 4 | 9 8 5 | 1 7 2
------+-------+------
8 7 9 | 5 4 3 | 2 1 6
4 6 3 | 8 2 1 | 5 9 7
5 1 2 | 7 9 6 | 8 4 3
------+-------+------
9 4 5 | 6 7 8 | 3 2 1
3 2 6 | 4 1 9 | 7 5 8
7 8 1 | 3 5 2 | 9 6 4
```

395 Sudoku 20

```
2 1 5 | 3 4 6 | 7 8 9
7 4 6 | 8 9 5 | 1 3 2
3 9 8 | 1 2 7 | 6 4 5
------+-------+------
4 6 9 | 2 5 1 | 8 7 3
8 5 2 | 7 6 3 | 4 9 1
1 7 3 | 4 8 9 | 2 5 6
------+-------+------
9 8 7 | 6 3 2 | 5 1 4
6 3 1 | 5 7 4 | 9 2 8
5 2 4 | 9 1 8 | 3 6 7
```

405 Sudoku 21

```
6 9 3 | 5 7 1 | 2 4 8
7 4 2 | 8 3 9 | 1 6 5
8 1 5 | 4 2 6 | 9 3 7
------+-------+------
9 6 7 | 1 8 2 | 4 5 3
2 5 8 | 3 9 4 | 6 7 1
1 3 4 | 6 5 7 | 8 9 2
------+-------+------
3 8 6 | 9 1 5 | 7 2 4
5 2 9 | 7 4 8 | 3 1 6
4 7 1 | 2 6 3 | 5 8 9
```

419 Sudoku 22

```
5 7 6 | 3 9 8 | 1 2 4
9 2 4 | 5 6 1 | 7 3 8
8 3 1 | 7 4 2 | 9 5 6
------+-------+------
7 1 8 | 4 3 5 | 6 9 2
4 9 2 | 8 1 6 | 5 7 3
3 6 5 | 9 2 7 | 4 8 1
------+-------+------
6 4 3 | 2 5 9 | 8 1 7
2 8 9 | 1 7 4 | 3 6 5
1 5 7 | 6 8 3 | 2 4 9
```

447 Sudoku 23

```
5 2 7 | 3 4 8 | 6 9 1
3 8 6 | 9 1 7 | 2 4 5
1 9 4 | 6 2 5 | 7 8 3
------+-------+------
6 4 2 | 5 3 1 | 8 7 9
8 5 9 | 7 6 2 | 1 3 4
7 1 3 | 4 8 9 | 5 2 6
------+-------+------
4 7 8 | 1 5 3 | 9 6 2
9 6 5 | 2 7 4 | 3 1 8
2 3 1 | 8 9 6 | 4 5 7
```

465 Sudoku 24

```
5 2 7 | 3 4 8 | 6 9 1
3 8 6 | 9 1 7 | 2 4 5
1 9 4 | 6 2 5 | 7 8 3
------+-------+------
6 4 2 | 5 3 1 | 8 7 9
8 5 9 | 7 6 2 | 1 3 4
7 1 3 | 4 8 9 | 5 2 6
------+-------+------
4 7 8 | 1 5 3 | 9 6 2
9 6 5 | 2 7 4 | 3 1 8
2 3 1 | 8 9 6 | 4 5 7
```

488 Sudoku 25

```
4 7 2 | 1 3 9 | 5 6 8
3 8 6 | 4 5 7 | 2 1 9
5 9 1 | 2 6 8 | 7 4 3
------+-------+------
1 6 7 | 9 8 3 | 4 5 2
2 5 9 | 6 7 4 | 3 8 1
8 3 4 | 5 2 1 | 6 9 7
------+-------+------
9 2 5 | 3 1 6 | 8 7 4
6 4 8 | 7 9 2 | 1 3 5
7 1 3 | 8 4 5 | 9 2 6
```

504 Sudoku 26

```
7 6 9 | 4 5 1 | 2 8 3
4 2 1 | 3 8 7 | 5 9 6
5 3 8 | 2 6 9 | 4 1 7
------+-------+------
8 7 4 | 5 1 2 | 6 3 9
2 9 3 | 8 4 6 | 7 5 1
6 1 5 | 9 7 3 | 8 4 2
------+-------+------
1 5 6 | 7 9 8 | 3 2 4
3 8 7 | 1 2 4 | 9 6 5
9 4 2 | 6 3 5 | 1 7 8
```

522 Sudoku 27

```
5 9 6 | 2 1 4 | 8 7 3
7 8 4 | 5 3 6 | 1 2 9
1 2 3 | 8 7 9 | 4 6 5
------+-------+------
8 4 7 | 9 6 2 | 3 5 1
6 5 2 | 3 8 1 | 9 4 7
3 1 9 | 7 4 5 | 6 8 2
------+-------+------
9 6 5 | 1 2 8 | 7 3 4
2 7 8 | 4 9 3 | 5 1 6
4 3 1 | 6 5 7 | 2 9 8
```

547 Sudoku 28

```
1 2 9 | 3 8 7 | 4 5 6
4 7 3 | 1 5 6 | 8 9 2
5 6 8 | 4 9 2 | 7 1 3
------+-------+------
6 9 4 | 7 3 8 | 5 2 1
7 5 2 | 6 1 9 | 3 8 4
3 8 1 | 5 2 4 | 9 6 7
------+-------+------
2 3 5 | 8 4 1 | 6 7 9
8 1 7 | 9 6 3 | 2 4 5
9 4 6 | 2 7 5 | 1 3 8
```

564 Sudoku 29

```
2 6 9 | 8 4 5 | 7 3 1
4 3 7 | 1 9 2 | 5 8 6
5 1 8 | 3 7 6 | 9 2 4
------+-------+------
6 5 3 | 7 2 1 | 8 4 9
9 8 1 | 4 6 3 | 2 7 5
7 2 4 | 5 8 9 | 6 1 3
------+-------+------
8 7 5 | 6 1 4 | 3 9 2
3 4 2 | 9 5 8 | 1 6 7
1 9 6 | 2 3 7 | 4 5 8
```

585 Sudoku 30

```
2 8 6 | 9 3 5 | 4 1 7
4 9 5 | 1 6 7 | 2 8 3
1 7 3 | 8 4 2 | 6 5 9
------+-------+------
5 3 2 | 4 8 9 | 7 6 1
8 4 1 | 7 5 6 | 3 9 2
7 6 9 | 3 2 1 | 5 4 8
------+-------+------
9 5 7 | 6 1 3 | 8 2 4
6 1 4 | 2 7 8 | 9 3 5
3 2 8 | 5 9 4 | 1 7 6
```

603 Sudoku 31

```
8 4 1 | 7 9 5 | 3 6 2
2 5 7 | 3 8 6 | 9 4 1
3 9 6 | 2 4 1 | 5 8 7
9 7 2 | 1 3 8 | 4 5 6
1 6 8 | 4 5 7 | 2 9 3
5 3 4 | 9 6 2 | 7 1 8
7 2 5 | 8 1 4 | 6 3 9
4 8 3 | 6 7 9 | 1 2 5
6 1 9 | 5 2 3 | 8 7 4
```

623 Sudoku 32

```
2 4 7 | 5 6 3 | 8 9 1
9 5 1 | 7 8 4 | 3 2 6
8 6 3 | 1 2 9 | 5 4 7
4 1 6 | 9 7 8 | 2 5 3
7 8 5 | 3 4 2 | 1 6 9
3 9 2 | 6 1 5 | 4 7 8
5 7 8 | 2 3 6 | 9 1 4
1 3 9 | 4 5 7 | 6 8 2
6 2 4 | 8 9 1 | 7 3 5
```

647 Sudoku 33

```
7 6 1 | 2 4 9 | 8 3 5
8 2 3 | 5 7 1 | 6 4 9
5 9 4 | 6 8 3 | 7 2 1
9 7 2 | 1 6 5 | 3 8 4
4 3 8 | 9 2 7 | 5 1 6
1 5 6 | 4 3 8 | 9 7 2
6 8 9 | 3 1 2 | 4 5 7
2 4 7 | 8 5 6 | 1 9 3
3 1 5 | 7 9 4 | 2 6 8
```

667 Sudoku 34

```
1 8 7 | 4 3 6 | 5 2 9
9 5 6 | 1 2 7 | 3 8 4
2 4 3 | 5 9 8 | 6 7 1
4 7 5 | 9 8 1 | 2 3 6
6 3 9 | 7 5 2 | 4 1 8
8 1 2 | 6 4 3 | 7 9 5
5 2 4 | 3 1 9 | 8 6 7
7 9 8 | 2 6 5 | 1 4 3
3 6 1 | 8 7 4 | 9 5 2
```

686 Sudoku 35

```
6 5 3 | 8 2 7 | 9 4 1
7 4 1 | 3 9 5 | 6 8 2
2 8 9 | 1 4 6 | 7 5 3
8 9 4 | 7 1 3 | 2 6 5
1 7 6 | 2 5 4 | 8 3 9
5 3 2 | 6 8 9 | 1 7 4
3 6 8 | 4 7 1 | 5 2 9
9 2 7 | 5 3 8 | 4 1 6
4 1 5 | 9 6 2 | 8 3 7
```

702 Sudoku 36

```
9 8 6 | 4 2 7 | 3 1 5
3 7 1 | 5 8 9 | 6 4 2
4 2 5 | 3 6 1 | 9 7 8
7 1 3 | 9 5 6 | 8 2 4
5 9 8 | 2 1 4 | 7 3 6
6 4 2 | 8 7 3 | 5 9 1
8 3 9 | 1 4 5 | 2 6 7
2 6 4 | 7 3 8 | 1 5 9
1 5 7 | 6 9 2 | 4 8 3
```

724 Sudoku 37

```
7 4 2 | 9 3 5 | 1 8 6
8 9 1 | 6 4 2 | 3 5 7
5 6 3 | 1 7 8 | 9 2 4
3 1 6 | 4 2 9 | 5 7 8
4 8 7 | 3 5 6 | 2 1 9
2 5 9 | 7 8 1 | 4 6 3
9 3 8 | 5 1 7 | 6 4 2
6 7 5 | 2 9 4 | 8 3 1
1 2 4 | 8 6 3 | 7 9 5
```

749 Sudoku 38

```
7 8 2 | 3 9 5 | 4 6 1
9 3 4 | 6 2 1 | 5 8 7
1 6 5 | 7 8 4 | 2 9 3
3 2 1 | 5 7 6 | 8 4 9
6 7 8 | 9 4 2 | 1 3 5
5 4 9 | 8 1 3 | 7 2 6
2 1 3 | 4 6 7 | 9 5 8
8 5 7 | 2 3 9 | 6 1 4
4 9 6 | 1 5 8 | 3 7 2
```

766 Sudoku 39

```
7 8 2 | 3 9 5 | 4 6 1
9 3 4 | 6 2 1 | 5 8 7
1 6 5 | 7 8 4 | 2 9 3
3 2 1 | 5 7 6 | 8 4 9
6 7 8 | 9 4 2 | 1 3 5
5 4 9 | 8 1 3 | 7 2 6
2 1 3 | 4 6 7 | 9 5 8
8 5 7 | 2 3 9 | 6 1 4
4 9 6 | 1 5 8 | 3 7 2
```

783 Sudoku 40

```
6 4 2 | 5 1 8 | 7 9 3
5 7 8 | 3 4 9 | 1 6 2
9 1 3 | 7 6 2 | 5 8 4
4 5 7 | 2 9 3 | 8 1 6
8 3 9 | 1 5 6 | 2 4 7
1 2 6 | 4 8 7 | 3 5 9
3 6 5 | 9 7 1 | 4 2 8
2 9 4 | 8 3 5 | 6 7 1
7 8 1 | 6 2 4 | 9 3 5
```

806 Sudoku 41

```
5 3 6 | 9 7 8 | 4 2 1
4 8 9 | 2 5 1 | 7 3 6
7 2 1 | 4 3 6 | 5 8 9
3 6 5 | 1 2 7 | 8 9 4
1 7 2 | 8 9 4 | 3 6 5
9 4 8 | 3 6 5 | 1 7 2
8 5 7 | 6 1 2 | 9 4 3
2 9 4 | 5 8 3 | 6 1 7
6 1 3 | 7 4 9 | 2 5 8
```

824 Sudoku 42

```
2 8 9 | 6 4 7 | 3 1 5
4 5 7 | 1 8 3 | 6 2 9
6 3 1 | 9 5 2 | 7 8 4
1 9 4 | 2 3 8 | 5 6 7
8 7 2 | 5 9 6 | 4 3 1
5 6 3 | 7 1 4 | 8 9 2
6 9 7 | 8 2 1 | 4 5 3
8 3 2 | 5 4 7 | 9 1 6
4 1 5 | 9 6 3 | 7 8 2
```

851 Sudoku 43

```
4 2 8 | 6 9 7 | 3 5 1
7 6 3 | 1 5 2 | 4 9 8
5 9 1 | 3 4 8 | 2 7 6
6 5 7 | 9 8 3 | 1 4 2
1 8 9 | 4 2 6 | 5 3 7
3 4 2 | 7 1 5 | 8 6 9
8 1 6 | 5 7 4 | 9 2 3
9 7 5 | 2 3 1 | 6 8 4
2 3 4 | 8 6 9 | 7 1 5
```

865 Sudoku 44

```
1 5 7 | 6 2 8 | 4 9 3
4 6 9 | 5 1 3 | 8 7 2
2 3 8 | 4 7 9 | 6 1 5
9 8 2 | 7 4 5 | 3 6 1
6 7 1 | 3 9 2 | 5 4 8
3 4 5 | 8 6 1 | 7 2 9
7 9 3 | 1 5 6 | 2 8 4
8 1 4 | 2 3 7 | 9 5 6
5 2 6 | 9 8 4 | 1 3 7
```

893 Sudoku 45

```
6 9 3 | 7 5 4 | 8 1 2
4 8 2 | 1 9 6 | 7 3 5
7 1 5 | 3 8 2 | 9 4 6
5 2 1 | 4 7 9 | 6 8 3
3 7 8 | 6 1 5 | 2 9 4
9 4 6 | 2 3 8 | 1 5 7
8 3 7 | 5 6 1 | 4 2 9
1 5 4 | 9 2 7 | 3 6 8
2 6 9 | 8 4 3 | 5 7 1
```

903 Sudoku 46

```
4 7 2 | 5 6 3 | 9 1 8
5 8 9 | 1 4 7 | 6 3 2
6 1 3 | 9 2 8 | 7 5 4
7 3 5 | 4 8 1 | 2 6 9
1 2 8 | 6 3 9 | 5 4 7
9 4 6 | 7 5 2 | 1 8 3
2 9 4 | 3 1 5 | 8 7 6
3 5 7 | 8 9 6 | 4 2 1
8 6 1 | 2 7 4 | 3 9 5
```

924 Sudoku 47

```
3 7 8 | 1 5 6 | 2 9 4
1 4 9 | 7 8 2 | 3 6 5
2 5 6 | 3 9 4 | 1 7 8
9 2 4 | 6 7 5 | 8 3 1
7 6 1 | 2 3 8 | 5 4 9
5 8 3 | 4 1 9 | 6 2 7
6 9 7 | 8 2 1 | 4 5 3
8 3 2 | 5 4 7 | 9 1 6
4 1 5 | 9 6 3 | 7 8 2
```

949 Sudoku 48

```
8 4 3 | 6 9 5 | 7 2 1
7 1 2 | 4 3 8 | 5 6 9
9 5 6 | 2 7 1 | 4 3 8
2 9 5 | 7 4 3 | 8 1 6
4 7 8 | 9 1 6 | 3 5 2
3 6 1 | 8 5 2 | 9 7 4
5 6 9 | 3 2 4 | 1 8 7
3 8 4 | 1 6 7 | 2 9 5
1 2 7 | 5 8 9 | 6 4 3
```

966 Sudoku 49

```
8 1 7 | 2 6 5 | 9 3 4
4 3 6 | 9 8 1 | 5 7 2
9 2 5 | 7 4 3 | 8 1 6
1 4 8 | 5 7 9 | 6 2 3
3 6 2 | 8 1 4 | 7 9 5
5 7 9 | 6 3 2 | 1 4 8
6 9 1 | 4 2 8 | 3 5 7
7 5 4 | 3 9 6 | 2 8 1
2 8 3 | 1 5 7 | 4 6 9
```

995 Sudoku 50

```
1 5 9 | 3 6 7 | 8 2 4
7 3 8 | 4 1 2 | 6 5 9
4 6 2 | 5 8 9 | 7 3 1
5 8 7 | 2 3 1 | 9 4 6
3 4 1 | 7 9 6 | 2 8 5
2 9 6 | 8 4 5 | 1 7 3
9 2 3 | 1 5 8 | 4 6 7
6 7 4 | 9 2 3 | 5 1 8
8 1 5 | 6 7 4 | 3 9 2
```

2 Kin-kon-kan 1

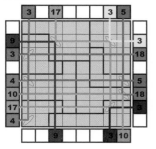

201 Kin-kon-kan 2

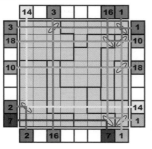

403 Kin-kon-kan 3

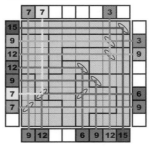

604 Kin-kon-kan 4

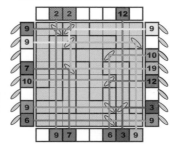

807 Kin-kon-kan 5

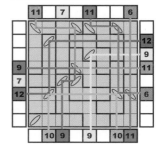

3 Futoshiki 1

```
6 4 5 7 3 2 1
7 5 2 3 1 4 6
2 6 7 4 5 1 3
3 1 4 5 2 6 7
5 3 6 1 4 7 2
1 7 3 2 6 5 4
4 2 1 6 7 3 5
```

24 Futoshiki 2

```
7 1 6 3 4 2 5
3 2 7 1 5 4 6
1 3 4 7 6 5 2
2 6 5 4 1 3 7
4 7 2 5 3 6 1
5 4 1 6 2 7 3
6 5 3 2 7 1 4
```

49 Futoshiki 3

```
5 3 2 7 4 6 1
1 4 7 6 5 3 2
6 1 5 3 2 4 7
4 7 1 2 3 5 6
3 2 4 1 6 7 5
2 6 3 5 7 1 4
7 5 6 4 1 2 3
```

68 Futoshiki 4

```
2 6 3 1 7 4 5
1 2 5 6 4 7 3
5 4 7 3 2 1 6
7 3 4 2 6 5 1
6 5 1 4 3 2 7
4 1 6 7 5 3 2
3 7 2 5 1 6 4
```

97 Futoshiki 5

```
1 5 6 3 2 7 4
4 1 2 7 6 3 5
2 4 3 1 7 5 6
3 6 7 2 5 4 1
5 7 4 6 3 1 2
6 3 1 5 4 2 7
7 2 5 4 1 6 3
```

118 Futoshiki 6 144 Futoshiki 7 162 Futoshiki 8 168 Futoshiki 9 202 Futoshiki 10

223 Futoshiki 11 248 Futoshiki 12 267 Futoshiki 13 298 Futoshiki 14 317 Futoshiki 15

344 Futoshiki 16 352 Futoshiki 17 368 Futoshiki 18 401 Futoshiki 19 420 Futoshiki 20

451 Futoshiki 21 468 Futoshiki 22 498 Futoshiki 23 520 Futoshiki 24 529 Futoshiki 25

553 Futoshiki 26 569 Futoshiki 27 274 Futoshiki 28 621 Futoshiki 29 645 Futoshiki 30

669 Futoshiki 31 701 Futoshiki 32 716 Futoshiki 33 726 Futoshiki 34 751 Futoshiki 35

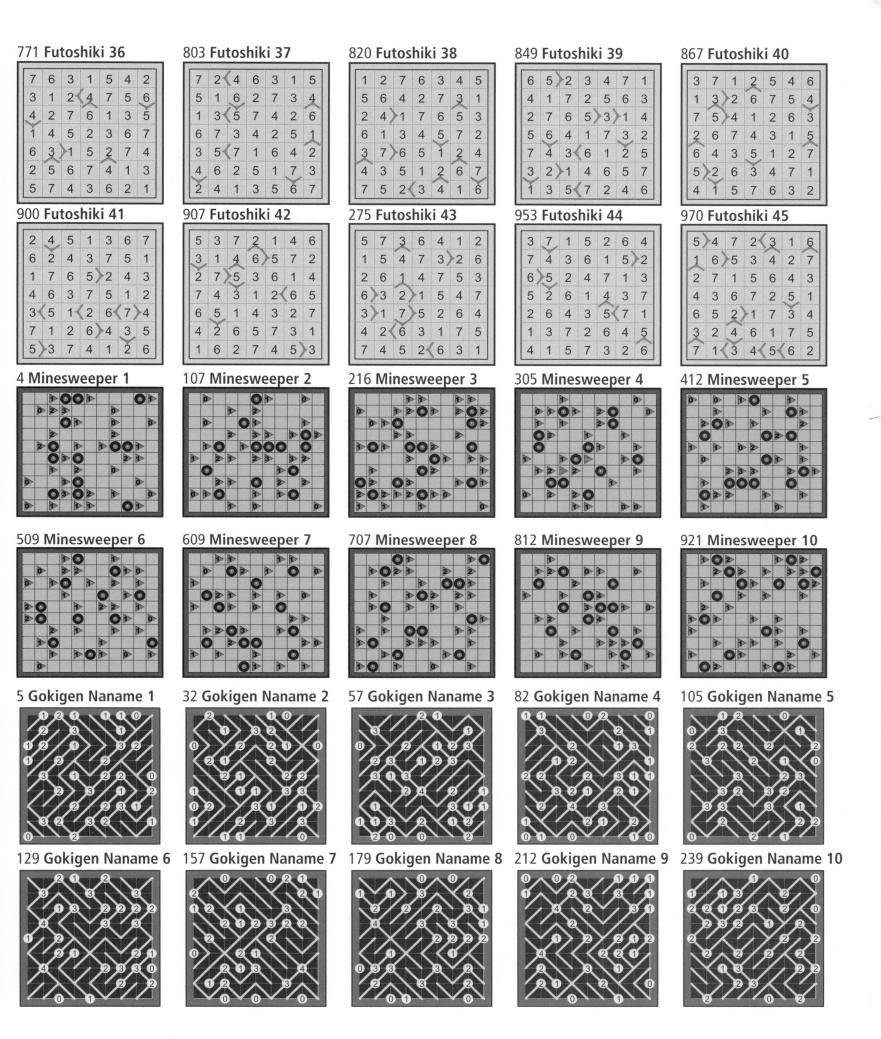

771 **Futoshiki 36**

803 **Futoshiki 37**

820 **Futoshiki 38**

849 **Futoshiki 39**

867 **Futoshiki 40**

900 **Futoshiki 41**

907 **Futoshiki 42**

275 **Futoshiki 43**

953 **Futoshiki 44**

970 **Futoshiki 45**

4 **Minesweeper 1**

107 **Minesweeper 2**

216 **Minesweeper 3**

305 **Minesweeper 4**

412 **Minesweeper 5**

509 **Minesweeper 6**

609 **Minesweeper 7**

707 **Minesweeper 8**

812 **Minesweeper 9**

921 **Minesweeper 10**

5 **Gokigen Naname 1**

32 **Gokigen Naname 2**

57 **Gokigen Naname 3**

82 **Gokigen Naname 4**

105 **Gokigen Naname 5**

129 **Gokigen Naname 6**

157 **Gokigen Naname 7**

179 **Gokigen Naname 8**

212 **Gokigen Naname 9**

239 **Gokigen Naname 10**

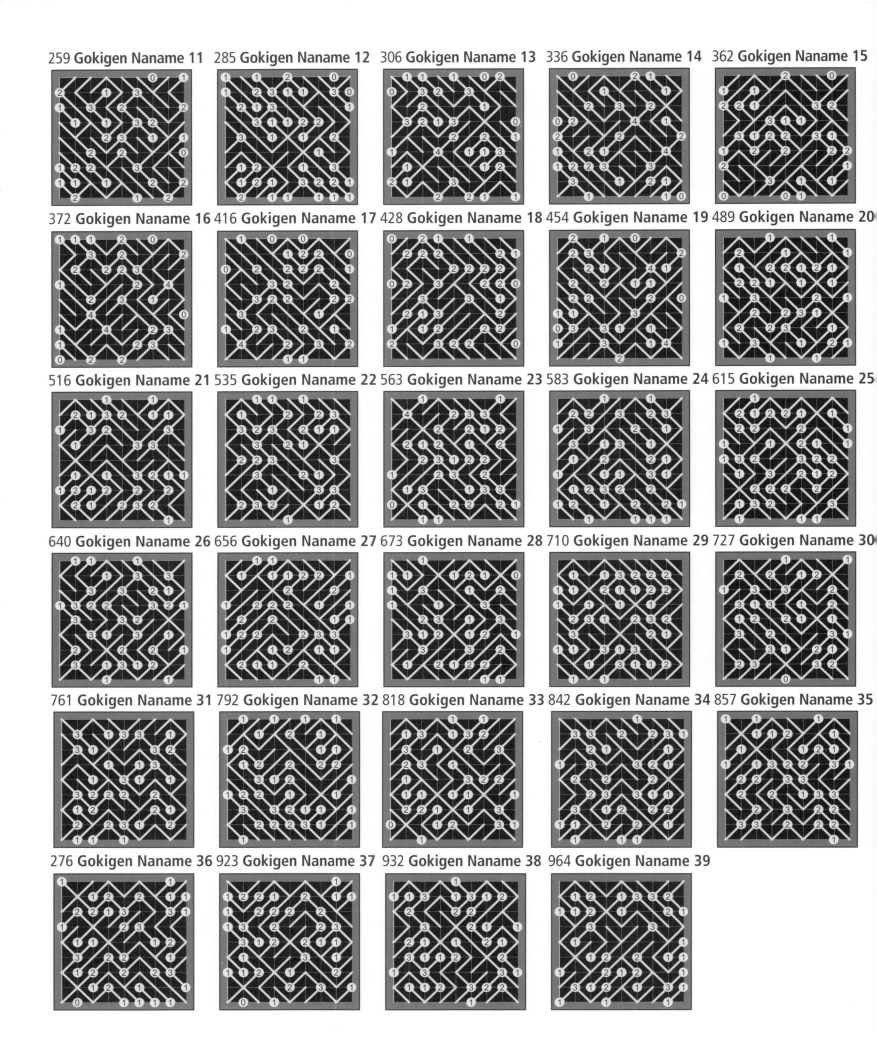

259 **Gokigen Naname 11** 285 **Gokigen Naname 12** 306 **Gokigen Naname 13** 336 **Gokigen Naname 14** 362 **Gokigen Naname 15**

372 **Gokigen Naname 16** 416 **Gokigen Naname 17** 428 **Gokigen Naname 18** 454 **Gokigen Naname 19** 489 **Gokigen Naname 20**

516 **Gokigen Naname 21** 535 **Gokigen Naname 22** 563 **Gokigen Naname 23** 583 **Gokigen Naname 24** 615 **Gokigen Naname 25**

640 **Gokigen Naname 26** 656 **Gokigen Naname 27** 673 **Gokigen Naname 28** 710 **Gokigen Naname 29** 727 **Gokigen Naname 30**

761 **Gokigen Naname 31** 792 **Gokigen Naname 32** 818 **Gokigen Naname 33** 842 **Gokigen Naname 34** 857 **Gokigen Naname 35**

276 **Gokigen Naname 36** 923 **Gokigen Naname 37** 932 **Gokigen Naname 38** 964 **Gokigen Naname 39**

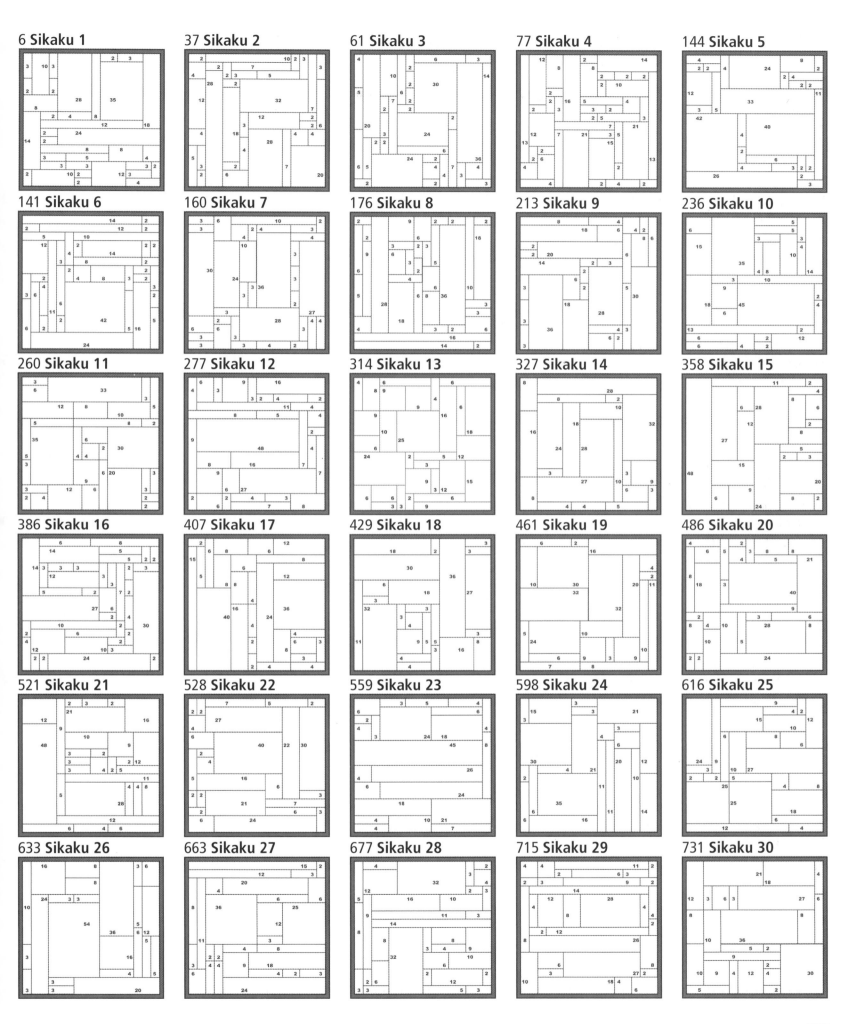

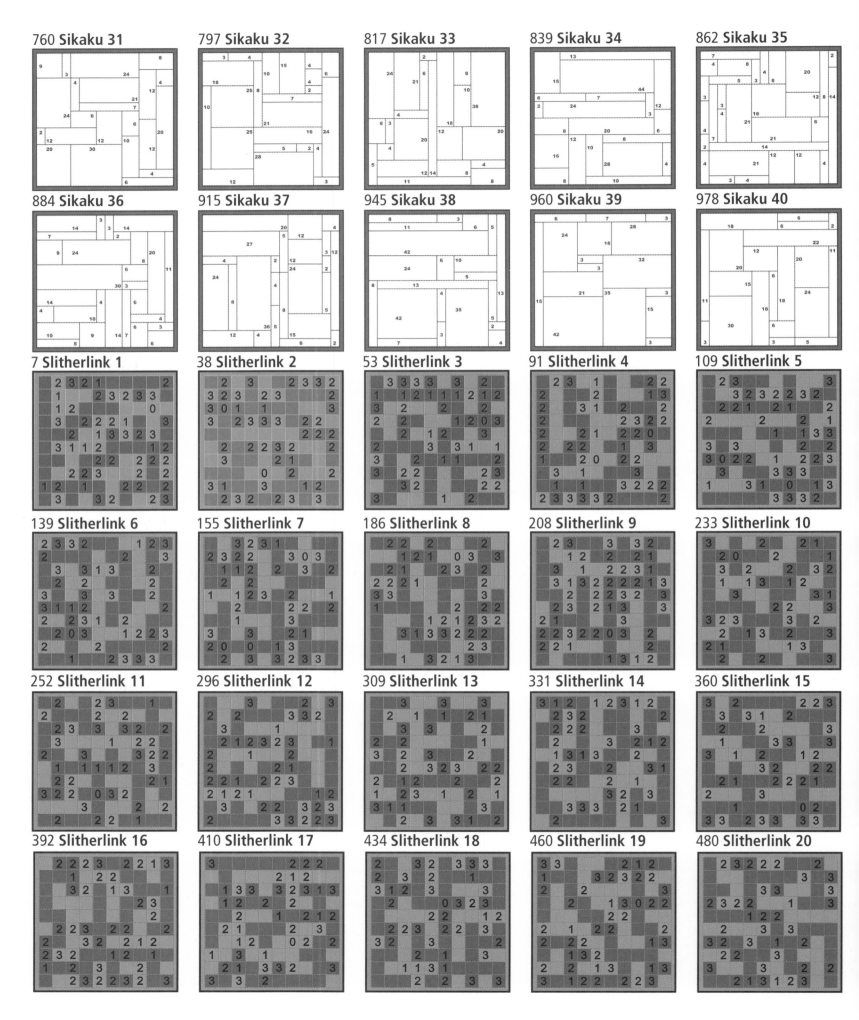

760 **Sikaku 31**   797 **Sikaku 32**   817 **Sikaku 33**   839 **Sikaku 34**   862 **Sikaku 35**

884 **Sikaku 36**   915 **Sikaku 37**   945 **Sikaku 38**   960 **Sikaku 39**   978 **Sikaku 40**

7 **Slitherlink 1**   38 **Slitherlink 2**   53 **Slitherlink 3**   91 **Slitherlink 4**   109 **Slitherlink 5**

139 **Slitherlink 6**   155 **Slitherlink 7**   186 **Slitherlink 8**   208 **Slitherlink 9**   233 **Slitherlink 10**

252 **Slitherlink 11**   296 **Slitherlink 12**   309 **Slitherlink 13**   331 **Slitherlink 14**   360 **Slitherlink 15**

392 **Slitherlink 16**   410 **Slitherlink 17**   434 **Slitherlink 18**   460 **Slitherlink 19**   480 **Slitherlink 20**

505 Slitherlink 21
279 Slitherlink 22
562 Slitherlink 23
279 Slitherlink 24
607 Slitherlink 25

635 Slitherlink 26
655 Slitherlink 27
695 Slitherlink 28
708 Slitherlink 29
737 Slitherlink 30

758 Slitherlink 31
774 Slitherlink 32
816 Slitherlink 33
844 Slitherlink 34
860 Slitherlink 35

887 Slitherlink 36
919 Slitherlink 37
934 Slitherlink 38
956 Slitherlink 39
979 Super Slitherlink

8 Dominoes 1
30 Dominoes 2
56 Dominoes 3
94 Dominoes 4
110 Dominoes 5

135 Dominoes 6
158 Dominoes 7
185 Dominoes 8
215 Dominoes 9
242 Dominoes 10

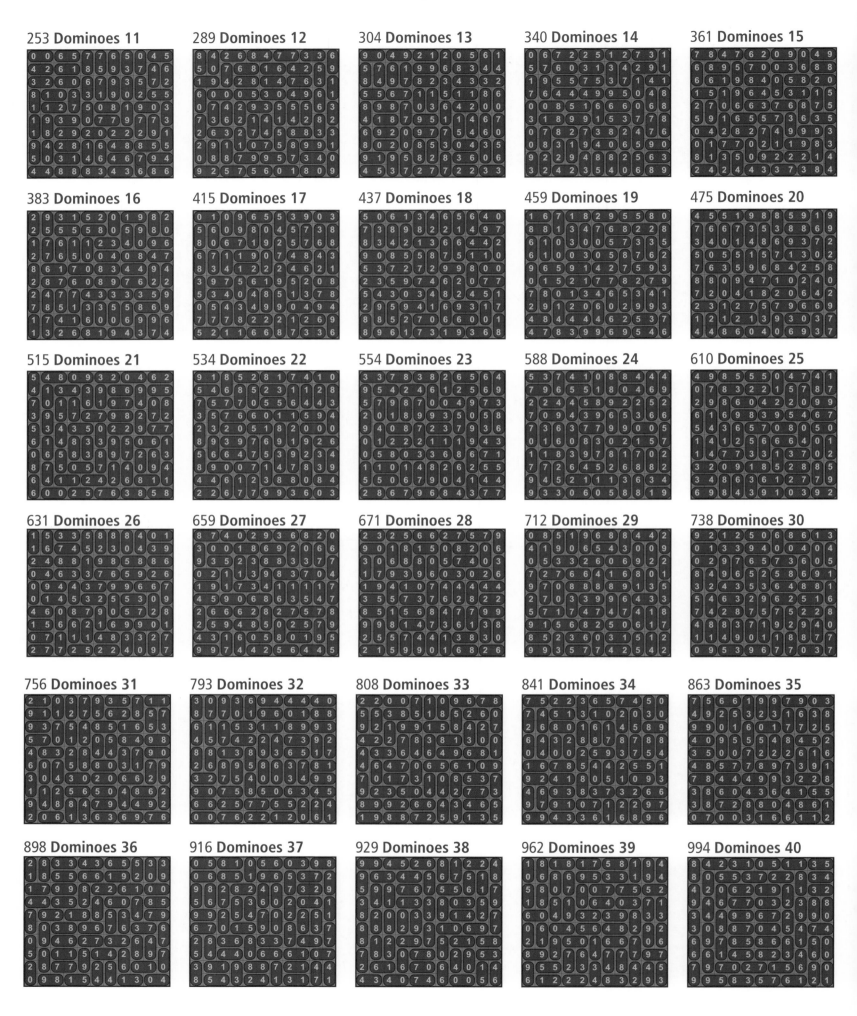

253 **Dominoes 11** 289 **Dominoes 12** 304 **Dominoes 13** 340 **Dominoes 14** 361 **Dominoes 15**

383 **Dominoes 16** 415 **Dominoes 17** 437 **Dominoes 18** 459 **Dominoes 19** 475 **Dominoes 20**

515 **Dominoes 21** 534 **Dominoes 22** 554 **Dominoes 23** 588 **Dominoes 24** 610 **Dominoes 25**

631 **Dominoes 26** 659 **Dominoes 27** 671 **Dominoes 28** 712 **Dominoes 29** 738 **Dominoes 30**

756 **Dominoes 31** 793 **Dominoes 32** 808 **Dominoes 33** 841 **Dominoes 34** 863 **Dominoes 35**

898 **Dominoes 36** 916 **Dominoes 37** 929 **Dominoes 38** 962 **Dominoes 39** 994 **Dominoes 40**

9 **Bijutsukan 1**

33 **Bijutsukan 2**

54 **Bijutsukan 3**

73 **Bijutsukan 4**

108 **Bijutsukan 5**

130 **Bijutsukan 6**

154 **Bijutsukan 7**

192 **Bijutsukan 8**

218 **Bijutsukan 9**

240 **Bijutsukan 10**

255 **Bijutsukan 11**

279 **Bijutsukan 12**

313 **Bijutsukan 13**

328 **Bijutsukan 14**

354 **Bijutsukan 15**

373 **Bijutsukan 16**

406 **Bijutsukan 17**

438 **Bijutsukan 18**

452 **Bijutsukan 19**

477 **Bijutsukan 20**

514 **Bijutsukan 21**

526 **Bijutsukan 22**

556 **Bijutsukan 23**

599 **Bijutsukan 24**

606 **Bijutsukan 25**

632 **Bijutsukan 26**

665 **Bijutsukan 27**

694 **Bijutsukan 28**

714 **Bijutsukan 29**

730 **Bijutsukan 30**

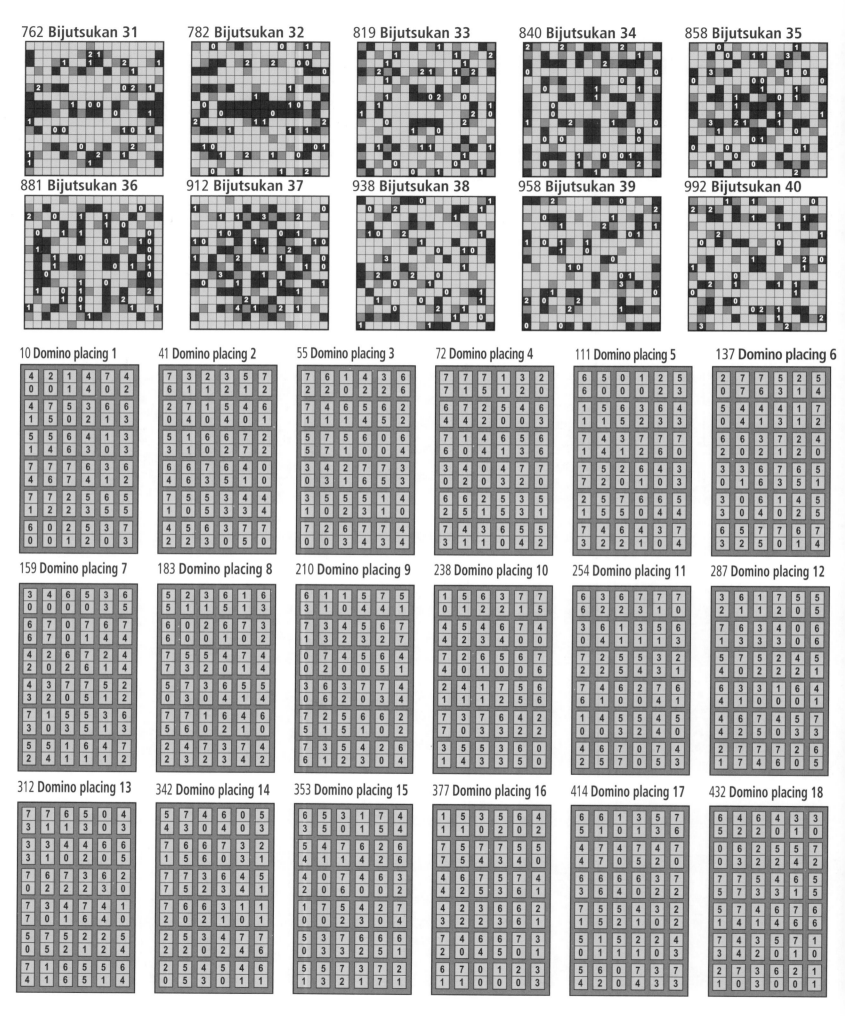

762 Bijutsukan 31
782 Bijutsukan 32
819 Bijutsukan 33
840 Bijutsukan 34
858 Bijutsukan 35
881 Bijutsukan 36
912 Bijutsukan 37
938 Bijutsukan 38
958 Bijutsukan 39
992 Bijutsukan 40

10 Domino placing 1
41 Domino placing 2
55 Domino placing 3
72 Domino placing 4
111 Domino placing 5
137 Domino placing 6

159 Domino placing 7
183 Domino placing 8
210 Domino placing 9
238 Domino placing 10
254 Domino placing 11
287 Domino placing 12

312 Domino placing 13
342 Domino placing 14
353 Domino placing 15
377 Domino placing 16
414 Domino placing 17
432 Domino placing 18

458 Domino placing 19

```
5 2 6 6 7 3
2 0 2 1 1 0
5 4 0 7 1 7
4 4 0 4 1 7
5 6 4 7 5 3
5 0 2 5 0 3
6 6 7 4 5 2
4 5 3 0 1 1
1 7 7 4 3 2
0 2 0 3 2 2
7 6 3 5 6 4
6 3 1 3 6 1
```

493 Domino placing 20

```
0 4 5 6 3 6
0 3 0 6 0 3
2 5 3 7 7 6
1 2 2 0 4 0
7 5 1 1 6 7
7 5 0 1 2 2
6 7 5 7 4 7
1 6 1 1 1 5
5 2 3 7 6 4
4 0 1 3 4 0
2 6 4 3 4 5
2 5 4 3 2 3
```

507 Domino placing 21

```
4 6 4 1 3 0
2 3 3 0 3 0
1 1 7 5 7 5
1 0 5 2 1 1
6 6 2 7 2 3
6 2 1 3 2 2
6 6 4 7 6 7
5 1 4 7 0 2
7 5 5 5 4 3
6 0 5 3 0 0
7 5 4 6 3 2
4 4 1 4 1 0
```

533 Domino placing 22

```
5 6 7 1 3 6
3 1 0 1 1 3
6 7 2 7 5 7
4 4 1 7 2 5
6 5 7 5 4 4
2 5 2 4 1 4
5 6 7 4 6 7
1 6 3 2 0 1
3 4 5 3 0 3
2 3 0 3 0 0
6 2 7 4 1 2
5 2 6 0 0 0
```

561 Domino placing 23

```
5 7 6 7 3 0
4 1 2 6 1 0
7 7 4 2 7 1
2 7 4 0 0 1
2 6 1 3 5 3
1 4 0 3 2 2
2 5 5 6 4 7
2 5 0 6 3 5
6 7 6 7 6 5
5 3 1 4 3 3
3 6 4 5 4 4
0 0 1 1 2 0
```

576 Domino placing 24

```
7 4 1 7 4 6
5 2 0 2 4 1
2 4 5 5 7 5
0 0 4 3 0 1
6 7 7 6 3 6
6 1 3 2 2 4
4 6 5 5 3 0
1 3 0 2 0 0
3 6 4 7 6 5
3 5 3 7 0 5
1 2 7 2 3 7
1 2 6 1 1 4
```

612 Domino placing 25

```
3 2 4 7 4 0
1 2 1 1 2 0
3 6 6 5 3 7
0 1 2 2 2 0
7 7 4 6 5 7
7 4 0 3 1 6
2 5 6 6 6 5
0 4 6 5 4 3
7 2 1 7 1 5
3 1 0 5 1 5
5 4 7 4 6 3
0 4 2 3 0 3
```

642 Domino placing 26

```
6 1 6 7 3 4
5 1 1 1 1 3
2 7 2 7 7 5
1 0 2 5 6 1
6 6 4 3 3 4
6 0 2 3 0 4
0 2 5 3 7 4
0 0 5 2 3 1
7 5 5 5 6 7
7 0 2 3 4 2
7 4 5 6 6 1
4 0 4 3 2 0
```

658 Domino placing 27

```
7 3 6 4 7 7
3 2 5 3 1 5
2 5 3 5 4 7
2 5 3 1 0 2
6 6 5 7 4 6
3 0 0 7 4 2
5 5 4 4 3 6
2 3 1 2 0 4
1 6 7 5 3 0
0 1 6 4 1 0
7 7 2 1 2 6
0 4 0 1 1 6
```

678 Domino placing 28

```
7 6 5 4 1 3
6 4 0 3 0 3
7 3 7 6 2 7
3 2 4 5 0 2
0 6 2 1 7 6
0 1 1 1 7 6
7 6 4 4 2 3
5 2 4 2 2 1
4 6 7 4 7 5
0 3 1 1 0 4
3 5 5 6 5 5
0 5 3 0 2 1
```

713 Domino placing 29

```
6 6 3 5 3 7
4 5 2 5 3 6
7 6 4 7 7 7
7 2 1 1 2 3
2 5 5 5 4 1
1 2 4 1 2 0
6 3 0 7 3 5
1 1 0 4 0 3
6 6 2 7 1 7
3 6 0 5 1 0
4 4 2 4 6 5
0 4 2 3 0 0
```

736 Domino placing 30

```
7 2 3 7 4 5
2 0 0 1 0 1
6 5 6 4 1 7
0 2 3 2 1 4
5 6 5 3 7 3
4 5 5 2 5 3
4 7 3 4 6 5
3 7 1 4 2 0
4 7 7 0 2 2
1 6 3 0 1 2
1 6 7 5 6 6
0 1 0 3 6 4
```

757 Domino placing 31

```
3 6 6 7 4 1
1 6 1 3 3 1
6 6 5 6 7 5
2 4 0 5 0 3
7 4 7 4 3 7
2 2 1 4 0 7
1 5 5 2 5 4
0 1 5 0 2 0
2 7 7 2 6 3
1 5 4 2 0 2
3 5 7 0 4 6
3 4 6 0 1 3
```

787 Domino placing 32

```
5 6 4 3 1 4
0 4 4 2 0 3
2 7 7 1 5 4
1 6 1 1 4 1
2 6 3 7 5 7
0 6 3 3 3 0
4 4 7 5 6 6
0 2 7 1 0 2
5 7 7 7 6 6
5 5 4 2 5 1
0 2 6 3 5 3
0 2 3 0 2 1
```

810 Domino placing 33

```
5 2 7 4 3 5
2 0 1 0 2 5
6 7 7 4 6 7
4 0 5 1 6 4
4 6 6 5 3 6
2 5 1 3 1 3
3 5 2 4 0 6
3 0 1 3 0 2
7 4 1 1 5 7
6 4 1 0 1 7
5 3 6 7 7 2
4 0 0 2 3 2
```

835 Domino placing 34

```
4 5 4 7 7 5
0 4 4 4 6 2
2 6 7 2 7 7
2 3 3 0 5 2
5 5 1 5 6 5
0 3 0 5 5 1
6 7 4 3 3 0
2 0 2 1 0 0
3 4 4 1 7 6
2 1 3 1 1 6
6 6 6 2 7 3
1 0 4 1 7 3
```

859 Domino placing 35

```
6 5 6 5 6 2
0 0 3 3 6 1
7 7 5 1 7 6
0 7 5 1 4 1
7 5 7 2 3 6
6 4 5 2 2 5
4 2 7 4 6 6
2 0 1 1 2 4
4 7 3 1 5 7
3 2 0 0 1 3
0 3 3 4 4 5
0 3 1 4 0 2
```

882 Domino placing 36

```
6 3 6 2 4 5
2 0 6 0 3 0
7 2 0 7 3 7
2 1 0 6 1 5
4 3 4 6 7 7
1 3 4 0 3 1
6 4 2 6 5 5
1 2 2 3 4 2
5 7 7 6 5 5
5 0 7 5 3 1
3 7 1 4 1 6
2 4 0 0 1 4
```

922 Domino placing 37

```
4 4 5 7 6 7
4 0 4 0 4 3
2 1 3 6 5 4
0 1 0 6 3 1
6 7 5 4 1 5
0 2 2 3 0 0
5 2 6 7 5 6
5 1 5 7 1 1
3 2 0 4 6 3
3 2 0 2 3 2
7 7 3 6 7 7
6 4 1 2 5 1
```

933 Domino placing 38

```
3 7 2 7 6 4
0 4 2 6 0 3
5 2 7 7 7 5
4 0 0 2 7 0
6 5 4 3 6 3
2 1 4 1 3 2
6 5 4 7 5 4
1 2 2 3 5 0
3 6 7 7 4 5
3 4 5 1 1 3
6 6 1 2 0 1
6 5 1 1 0 0
```

959 Domino placing 39

```
7 6 6 5 3 7
6 6 0 3 0 0
5 6 4 3 2 1
4 2 1 1 1 0
2 5 6 5 4 6
0 1 1 2 2 4
6 7 5 7 3 7
5 4 5 3 2 5
5 6 7 4 0 7
0 3 7 0 0 2
1 2 3 4 7 4
1 2 3 4 1 3
```

975 Domino placing 40

```
7 6 2 3 0 6
3 0 0 0 0 5
3 1 6 5 7 2
2 1 4 4 4 2
4 7 5 3 1 4
0 2 1 3 0 2
5 5 2 6 5 5
5 2 1 6 3 0
4 7 6 6 7 3
3 6 1 2 0 1
4 4 7 7 6 7
4 1 5 1 3 7
```

11 Number Link 1

39 Number Link 2

62 Number Link 3

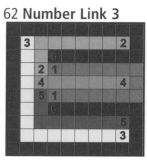

76 Number Link 4

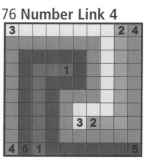

106 Number Link 5

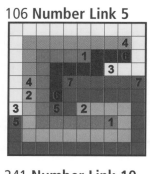

140 Number Link 6

156 Number Link 7

196 Number Link 8

209 Number Link 9

241 Number Link 10

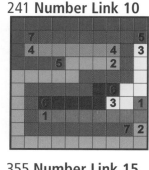

258 Number Link 11

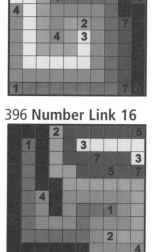

292 Number Link 12

311 Number Link 13

324 Number Link 14

355 Number Link 15

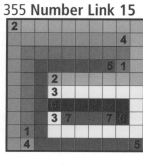

396 Number Link 16

411 Number Link 17

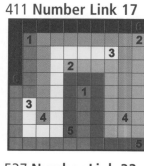

439 Number Link 18

456 Number Link 19

483 Number Link 20

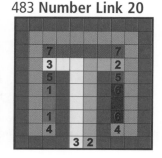

510 Number Link 21

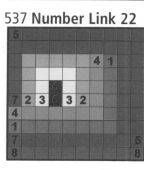

537 Number Link 22

558 Number Link 23

580 Number Link 24

614 Number Link 25

641 Number Link 26

657 Number Link 27

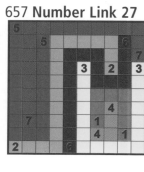

696 Number Link 28

705 Number Link 29

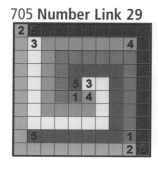

732 Number Link 30

759 **Number Link 31**

780 **Number Link 32**

809 **Number Link 33**

836 **Number Link 34**

861 **Number Link 35**

896 **Number Link 36**

920 **Number Link 37**

936 **Number Link 38**

955 **Number Link 39**

999 **Number Link 40**

12 **Tents 1**

26 **Tents 2**

60 **Tents 3**

79 **Tents 4**

113 **Tents 5**

142 **Tents 6**

151 **Tents 7**

198 **Tents 8**

214 **Tents 9**

234 **Tents 10**

257 **Tents 11**

273 **Tents 12**

310 **Tents 13**

326 **Tents 14**

359 **Tents 15**

391 **Tents 16**

413 **Tents 17**

431 **Tents 18**

457 **Tents 19**

491 **Tents 20**

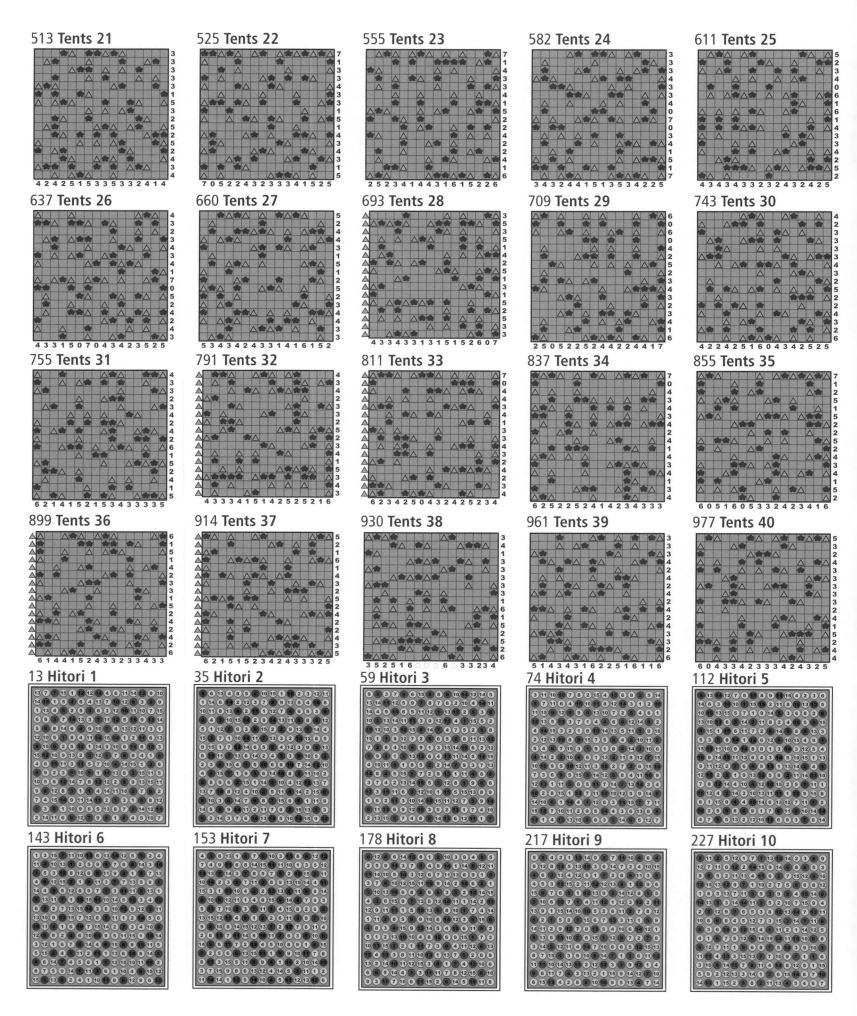

513 **Tents 21**

525 **Tents 22**

555 **Tents 23**

582 **Tents 24**

611 **Tents 25**

637 **Tents 26**

660 **Tents 27**

693 **Tents 28**

709 **Tents 29**

743 **Tents 30**

755 **Tents 31**

791 **Tents 32**

811 **Tents 33**

837 **Tents 34**

855 **Tents 35**

899 **Tents 36**

914 **Tents 37**

930 **Tents 38**

961 **Tents 39**

977 **Tents 40**

13 **Hitori 1**

35 **Hitori 2**

59 **Hitori 3**

74 **Hitori 4**

112 **Hitori 5**

143 **Hitori 6**

153 **Hitori 7**

178 **Hitori 8**

217 **Hitori 9**

227 **Hitori 10**

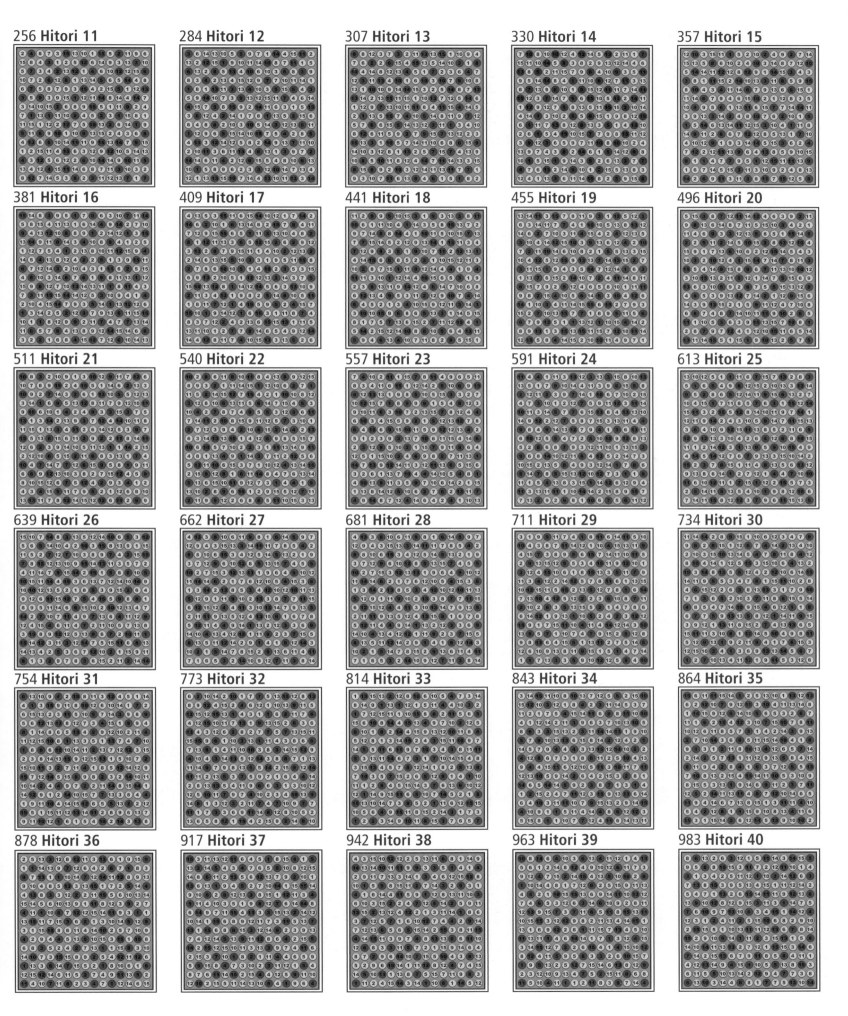

256 **Hitori 11**

284 **Hitori 12**

307 **Hitori 13**

330 **Hitori 14**

357 **Hitori 15**

381 **Hitori 16**

409 **Hitori 17**

441 **Hitori 18**

455 **Hitori 19**

496 **Hitori 20**

511 **Hitori 21**

540 **Hitori 22**

557 **Hitori 23**

591 **Hitori 24**

613 **Hitori 25**

639 **Hitori 26**

662 **Hitori 27**

681 **Hitori 28**

711 **Hitori 29**

734 **Hitori 30**

754 **Hitori 31**

773 **Hitori 32**

814 **Hitori 33**

843 **Hitori 34**

864 **Hitori 35**

878 **Hitori 36**

917 **Hitori 37**

942 **Hitori 38**

963 **Hitori 39**

983 **Hitori 40**

14 Fillomino 1

27 Fillomino
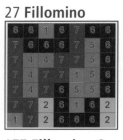

58 Fillomino 3

88 Fillomino 4

115 Fillomino 5

133 Fillomino 6

152 Fillomino 7

177 Fillomino 8

219 Fillomino 9

231 Fillomino 10

261 Fillomino 11

294 Fillomino 12

308 Fillomino 13

335 Fillomino 14

356 Fillomino 15

384 Fillomino 16

408 Fillomino 17

442 Fillomino 18

453 Fillomino 19

476 Fillomino 20

508 Fillomino 21

539 Fillomino 22

560 Fillomino 23

596 Fillomino 24

608 Fillomino 25

627 Fillomino 26

664 Fillomino 27

683 Fillomino 28

706 Fillomino 29

740 Fillomino 30

753 Fillomino 31

786 Fillomino 32

813 Fillomino 33

827 Fillomino 34

854 Fillomino 35

876 Fillomino 36

913 Fillomino 37

937 Fillomino 38

957 Fillomino 39

987 Fillomino 40
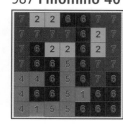

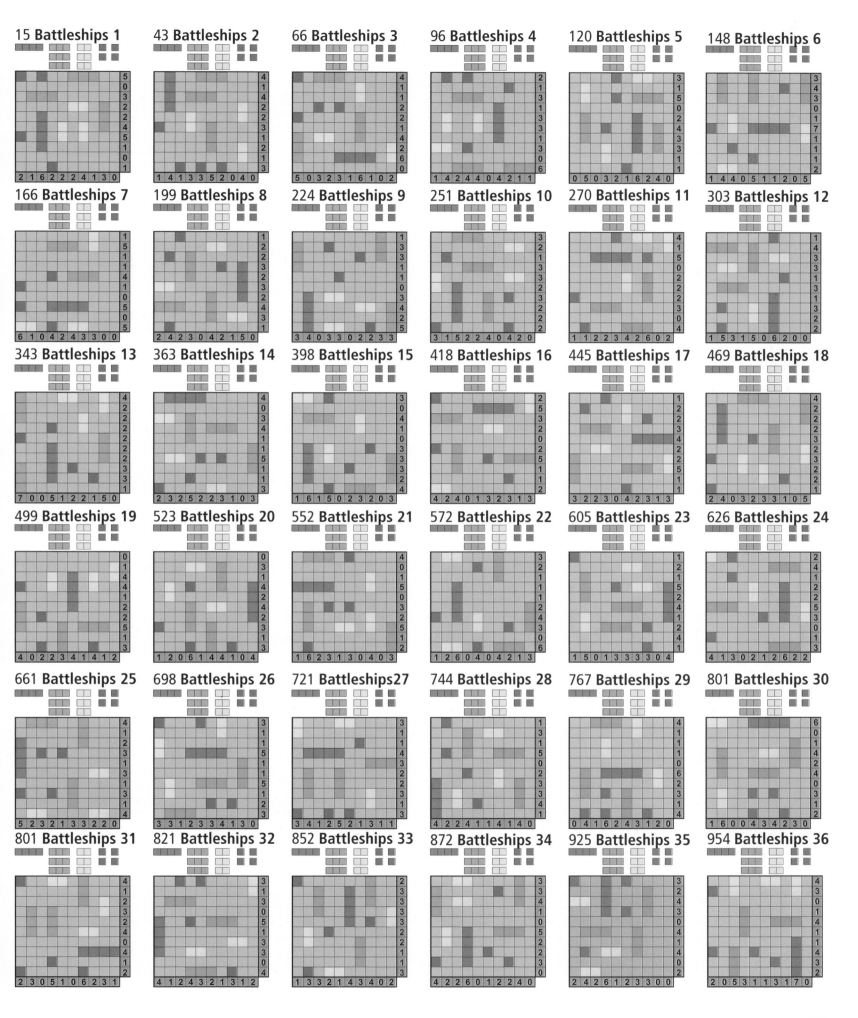

289

290

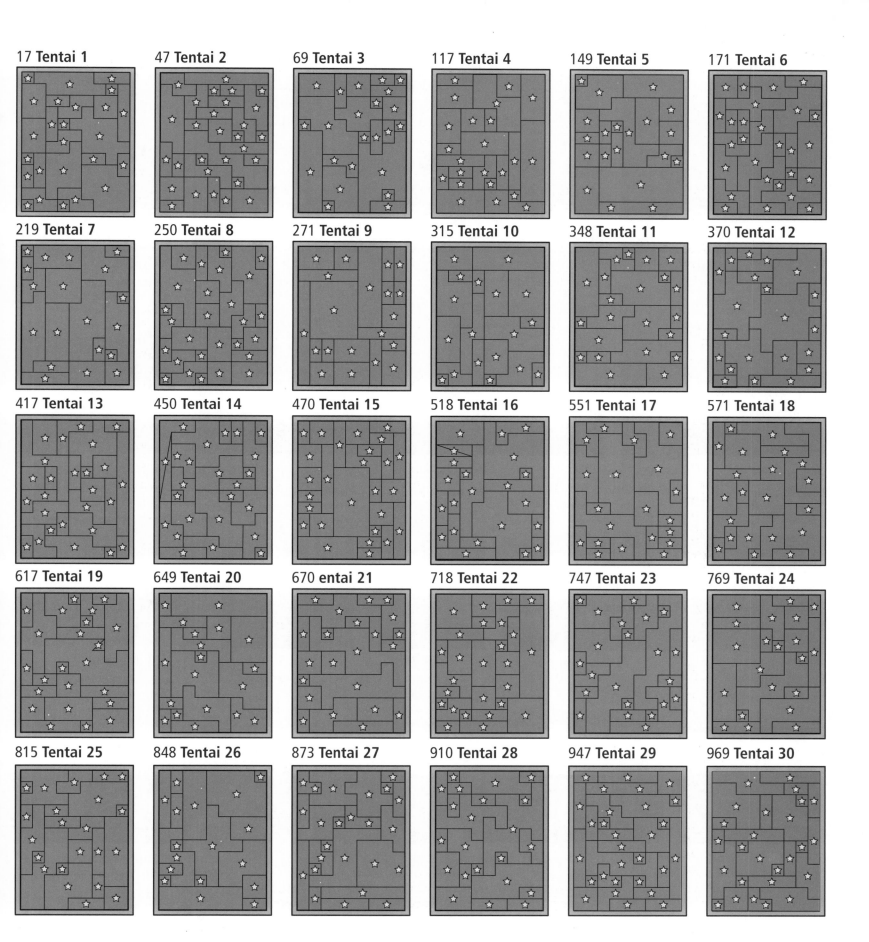

17 Tentai 1　47 Tentai 2　69 Tentai 3　117 Tentai 4　149 Tentai 5　171 Tentai 6

219 Tentai 7　250 Tentai 8　271 Tentai 9　315 Tentai 10　348 Tentai 11　370 Tentai 12

417 Tentai 13　450 Tentai 14　470 Tentai 15　518 Tentai 16　551 Tentai 17　571 Tentai 18

617 Tentai 19　649 Tentai 20　670 entai 21　718 Tentai 22　747 Tentai 23　769 Tentai 24

815 Tentai 25　848 Tentai 26　873 Tentai 27　910 Tentai 28　947 Tentai 29　969 Tentai 30

18 Missing Landmarks 1
The Landmark is Sugar Loaf Mountain (Pao de Açucar), Rio de Janeiro, Brazil.

50 Missing Landmarks 2
The Landmark is The Great Wall of China.

95 Missing Landmarks 3
The Landmark is The Space Needle, Seattle, USA.

136 Missing Landmarks 4
The Landmark is The Imperial Palace, Tokyo, Japan.

161 Missing Landmarks 5
The Landmark is The Statue of Liberty, New York, USA.

200 Missing Landmarks 6
The Landmark is The Washington Monument, Washington DC, USA.

225 Missing Landmarks 7
The Landmark is The CN Tower, (Canada's National Tower), Toronto, Canada.

265 Missing Landmarks 8
The Landmark is The Golden Pavilion, Kyoto, Japan.

300 Missing Landmarks 9
The Landmark is The Vatican, Rome, Italy.

334 Missing Landmarks 10
The Landmark is Stonehenge, England.

366 Missing Landmarks 11
The Landmark is The (leaning) Tower of Pisa, Italy.

404 Missing Landmarks 12
The Landmark is The Acropolis, Athens, Greece.

433 Missing Landmarks 13
The Landmark is The Sphinx of Giza, Egypt (with the Pyramid of Khafre in the background).

471 Missing Landmarks 14
The Landmark is The Arc de Triomphe, Paris, France.

506 Missing Landmarks 15
The Landmark is The Brandenburg Gate, Berlin, Germany.

549 Missing Landmarks 16
The Landmark is Mount Rushmore, South Dakota, USA.

573 Missing Landmarks 17
The Landmark is The Taj Mahal, India.

620 Missing Landmarks 18
The Landmark is The Houses of Parliament (and/or Big Ben), London, England.

651 Missing Landmarks 19
The Landmark is Sugar Loaf Mountain (Pao de Açucar), Rio de Janeiro, Brazil.

672 Missing Landmarks 20
The Landmark is St Basil's Cathedral, Moscow.

723 Missing Landmarks 21
The Landmark is Sydney Opera House, Sydney, Australia.

752 Missing Landmarks 22
The Landmark is The Tower of London, London, England.

800 Missing Landmarks 23
The Landmark is The London Eye (Millennium Wheel), London, England.

823 Missing Landmarks 24
The Landmark is Notre Dame de Paris Cathedral, Paris, France.

856 Missing Landmarks 25
The Landmark is The Sears Tower (233 South Wacker Drive), Chicago, Illinois.

901 Missing Landmarks 26
The Landmark is The Eiffel Tower, Paris, France.

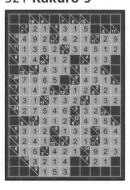

926 Missing Landmarks 27
The Landmark is The White House, Washington DC, USA.

967 Missing Landmarks 28
The Landmark is The Space Needle, Seattle, Washington, USA.

19 Kakuro 1
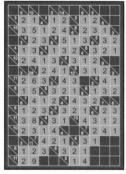

52 Kakuro 2
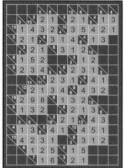

98 Kakuro 3
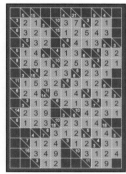

125 Kakuro 4
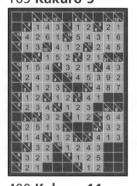

165 Kakuro 5
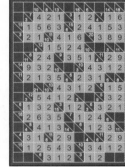

206 Kakuro 6
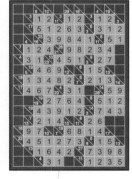

245 Kakuro 7
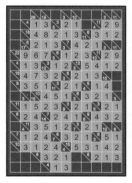

269 Kakuro 8
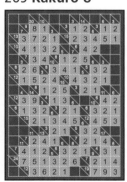

321 Kakuro 9
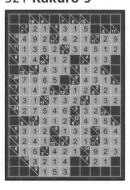

350 Kakuro 10
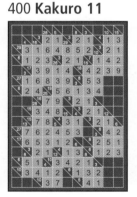

400 Kakuro 11

423 Kakuro 12

467 Kakuro 13
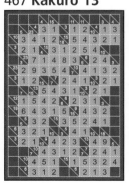

500 Kakuro 14

545 Kakuro 15
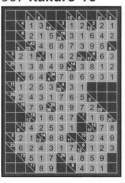

567 Kakuro 16
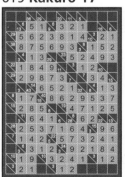

619 Kakuro 17
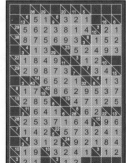

652 Kakuro 18

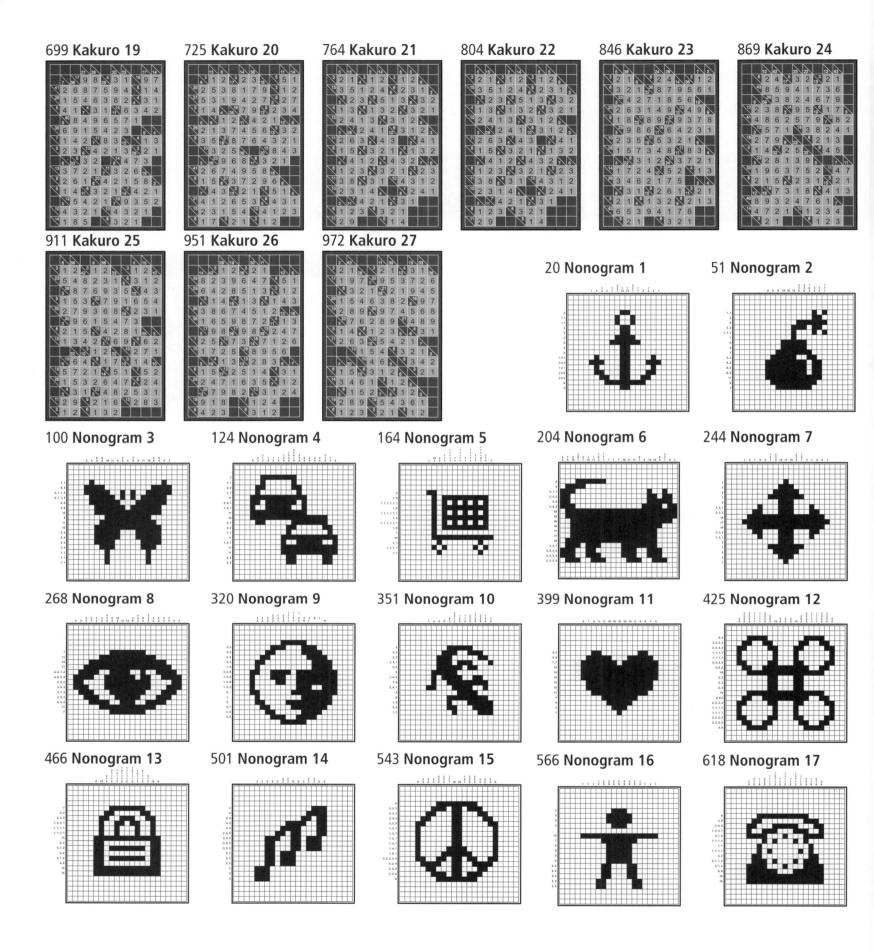

699 Kakuro 19 **725 Kakuro 20** **764 Kakuro 21** **804 Kakuro 22** **846 Kakuro 23** **869 Kakuro 24**

911 Kakuro 25 **951 Kakuro 26** **972 Kakuro 27**

20 Nonogram 1 **51 Nonogram 2**

100 Nonogram 3 **124 Nonogram 4** **164 Nonogram 5** **204 Nonogram 6** **244 Nonogram 7**

268 Nonogram 8 **320 Nonogram 9** **351 Nonogram 10** **399 Nonogram 11** **425 Nonogram 12**

466 Nonogram 13 **501 Nonogram 14** **543 Nonogram 15** **566 Nonogram 16** **618 Nonogram 17**

650 Nonogram 18

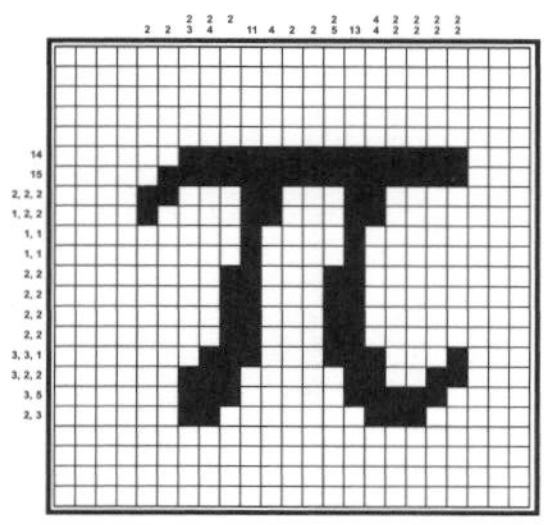

700 Nonogram 19

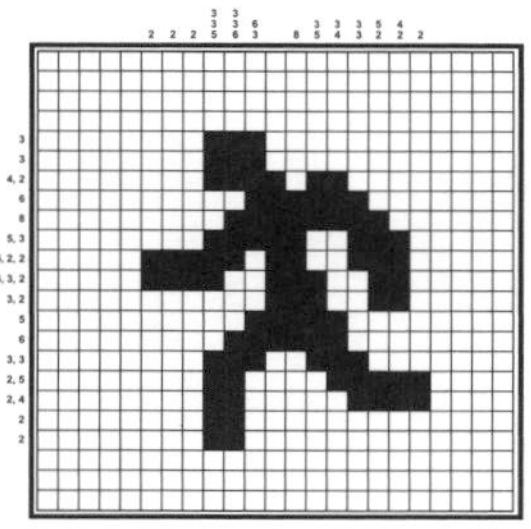

722 Nonogram 20

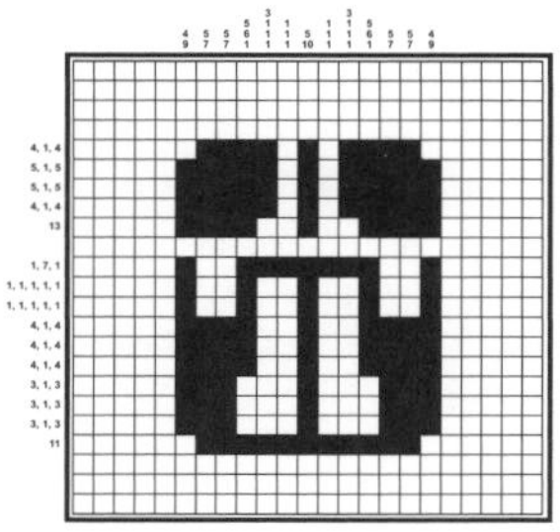

765 Nonogram 21

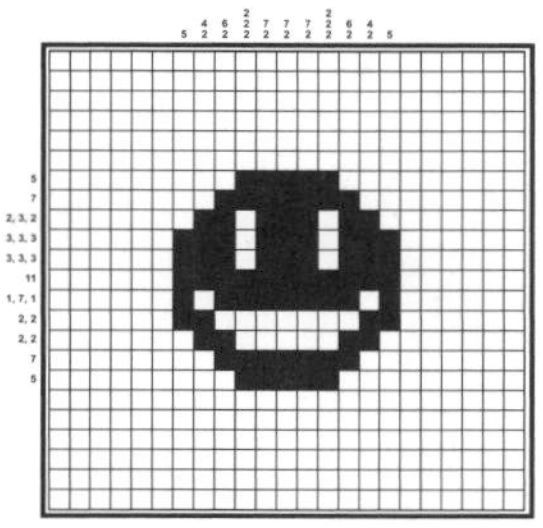

805 Nonogram 22

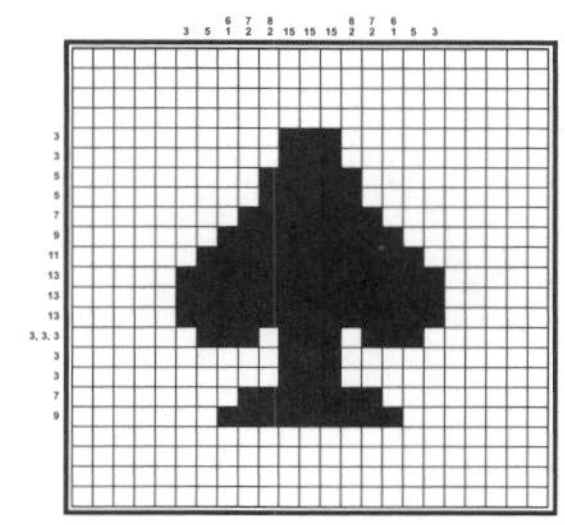

845 Nonogram 23

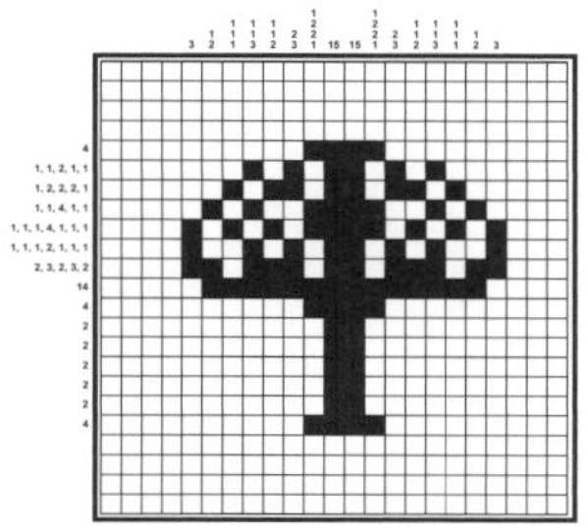

870 Nonogram 24

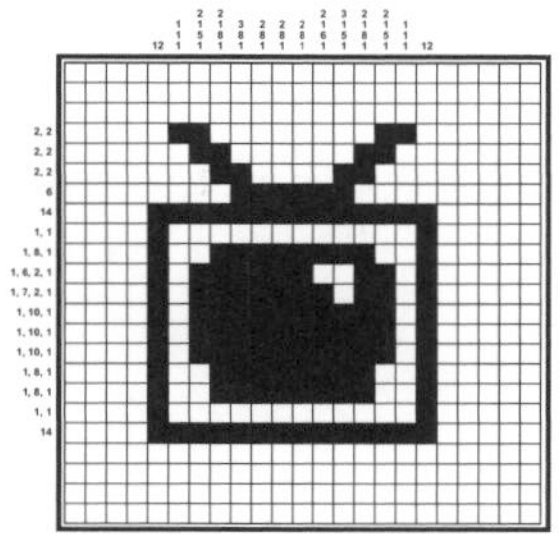

918 Nonogram 25

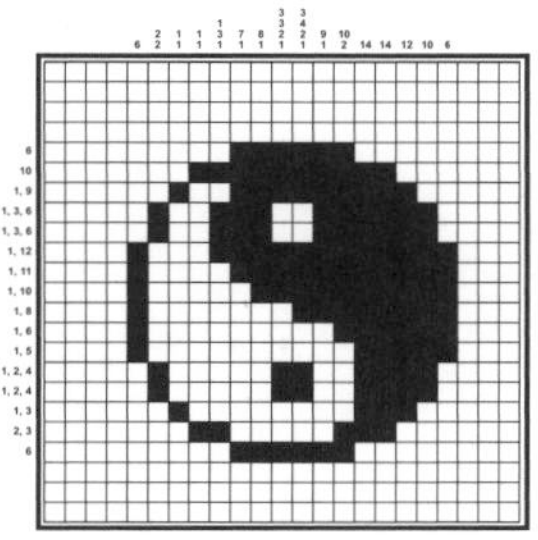

952 Nonogram 26

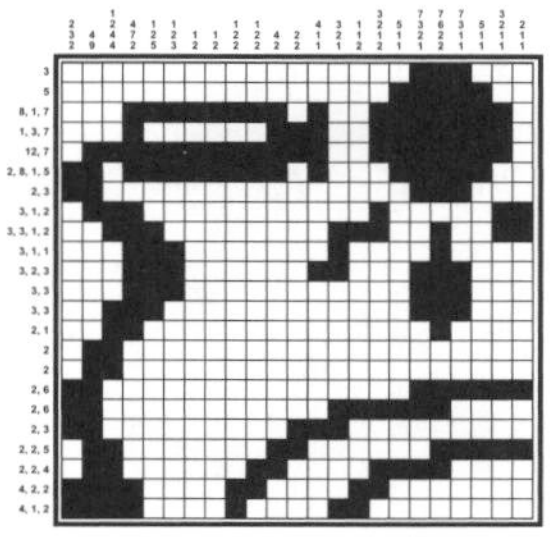

974 Nonogram 27

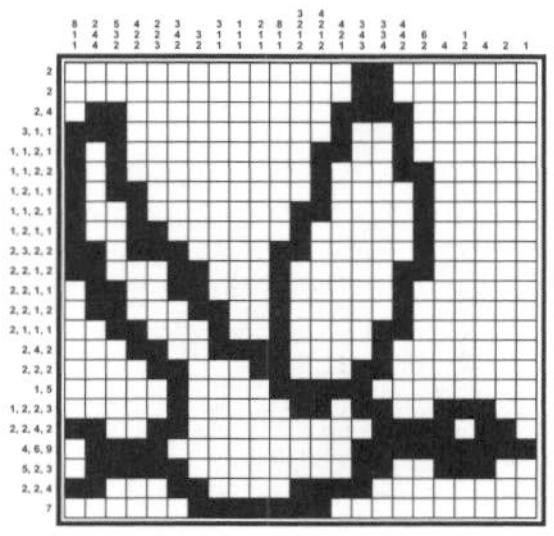

21 Map Colouring 1

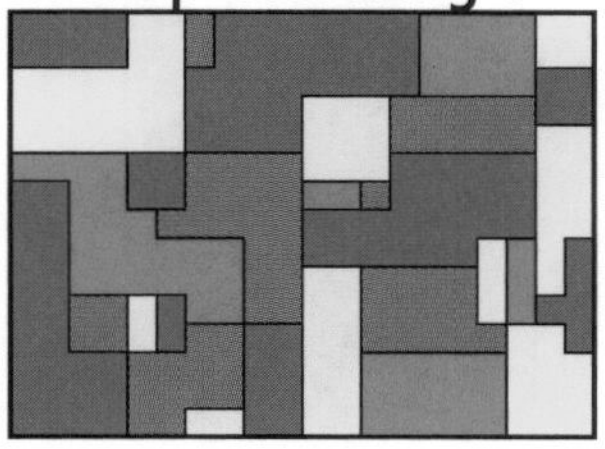

65 Map Colouring 2

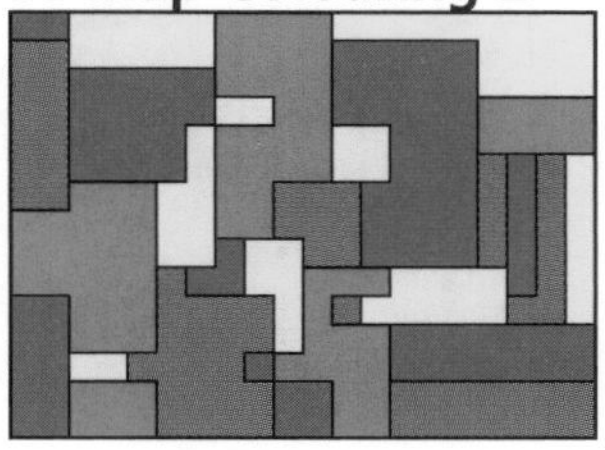

103 Map Colouring 3

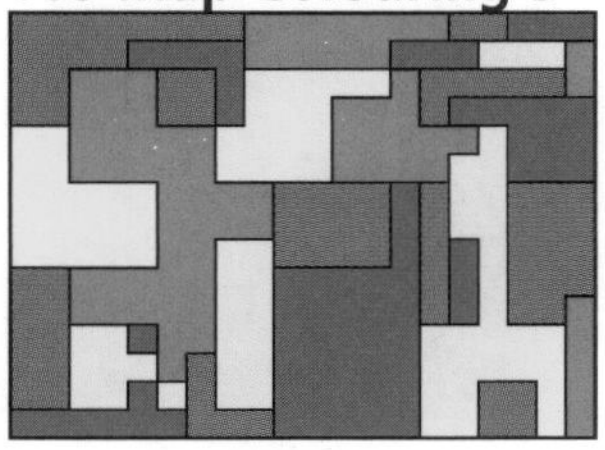

147 Map Colouring 4

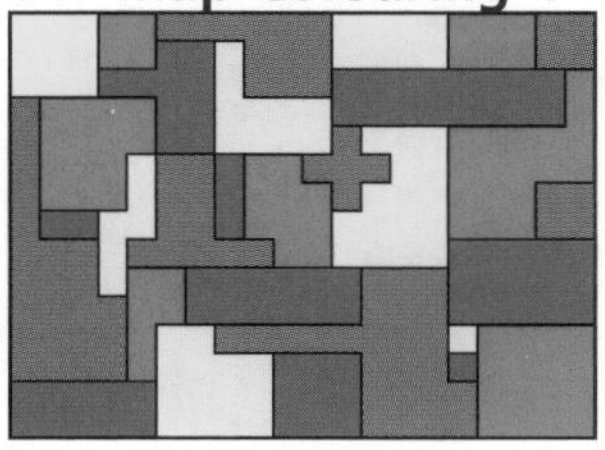

189 Map Colouring 5

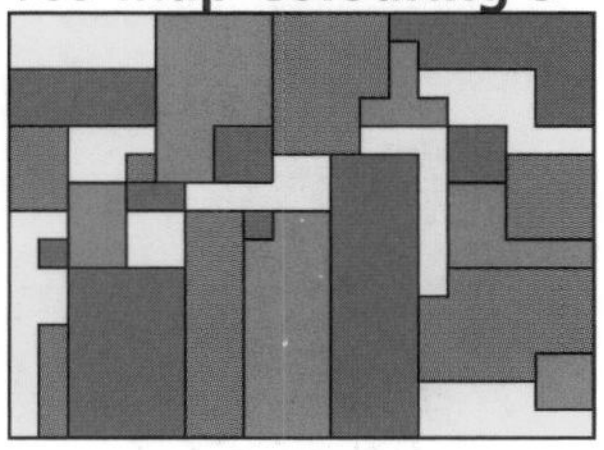

222 Map Colouring 6

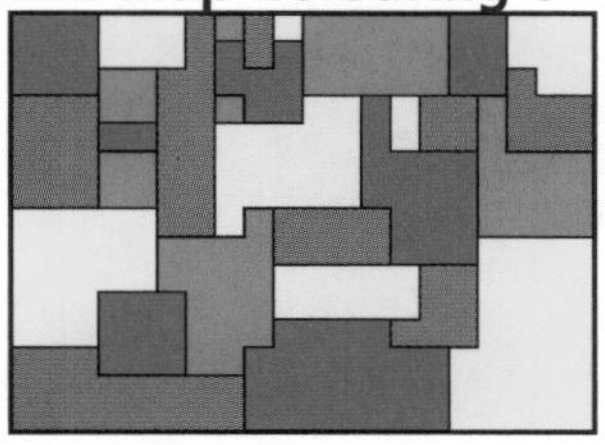

262 Map Colouring 7

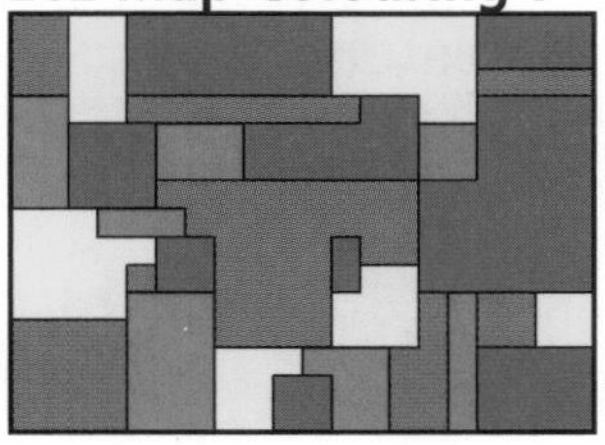

299 Map Colouring 8

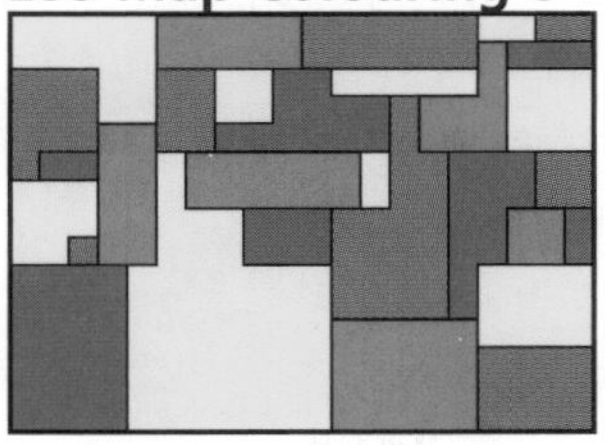

347 Map Colouring 9

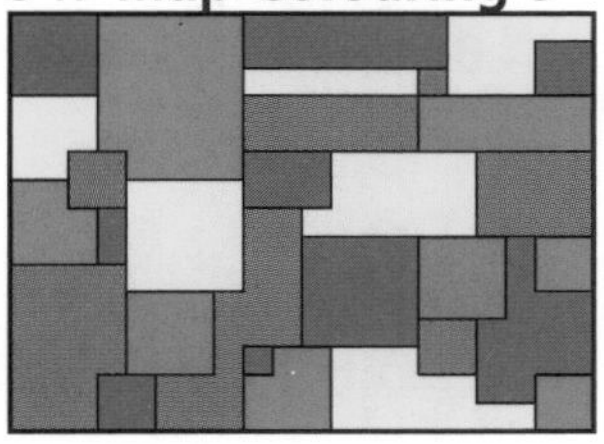

374 Map Colouring 10

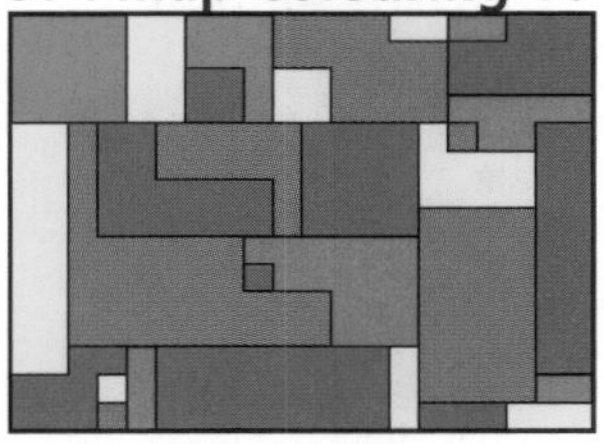

422 Map Colouring 11

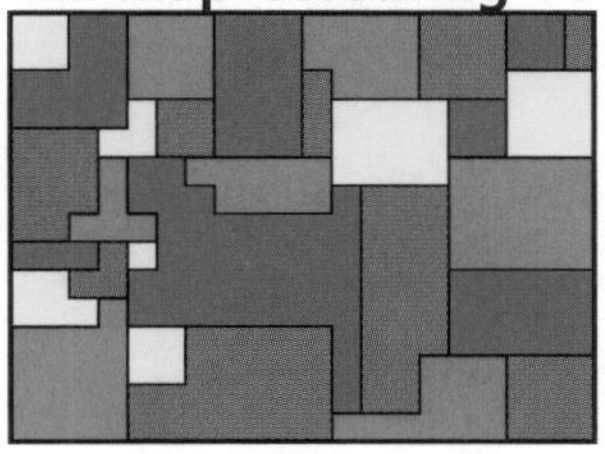

463 Map Colouring 12

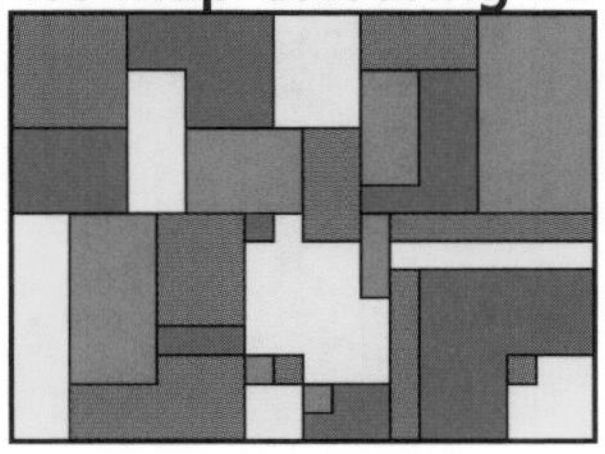

503 Map Colouring 13

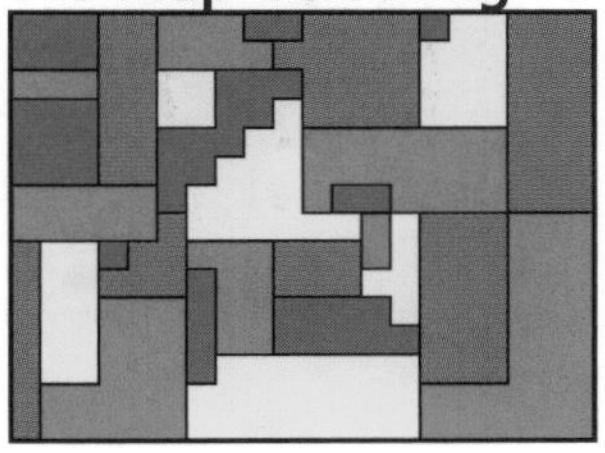

550 Map Colouring 14

577 Map Colouring 15

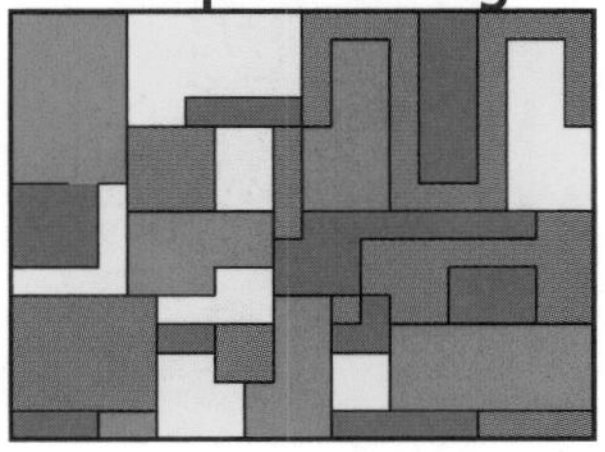

624 Map Colouring 16

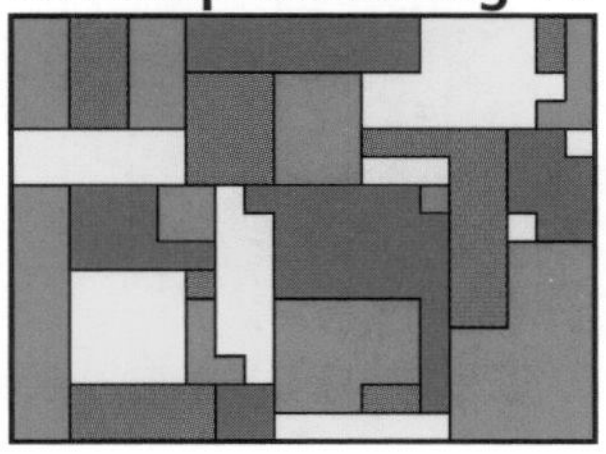

668 Map Colouring 17

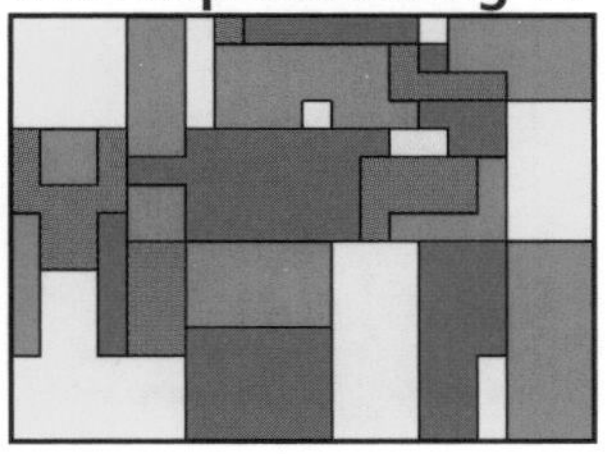

704 Map Colouring 18

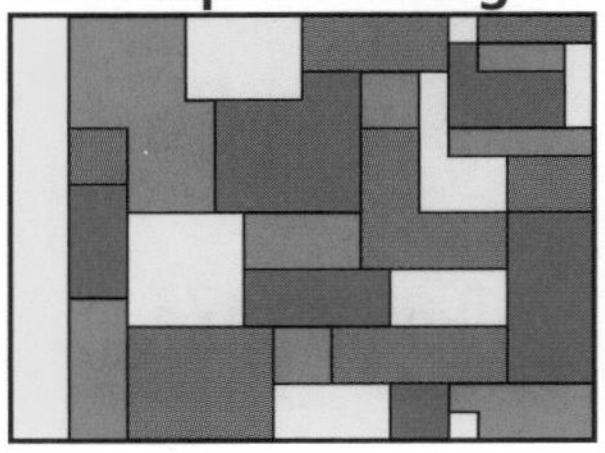

750 Map Colouring 19

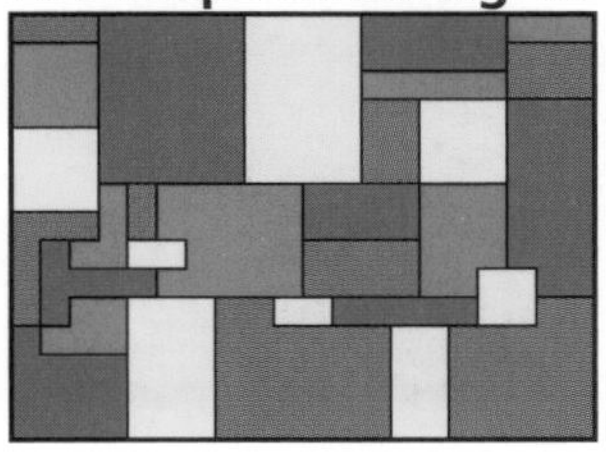

778 Map Colouring 20

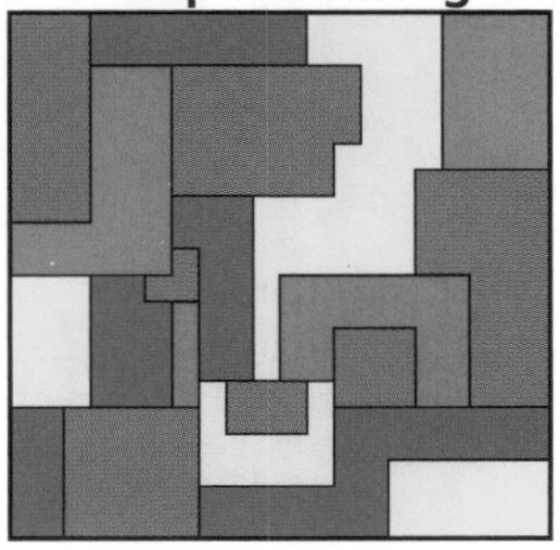

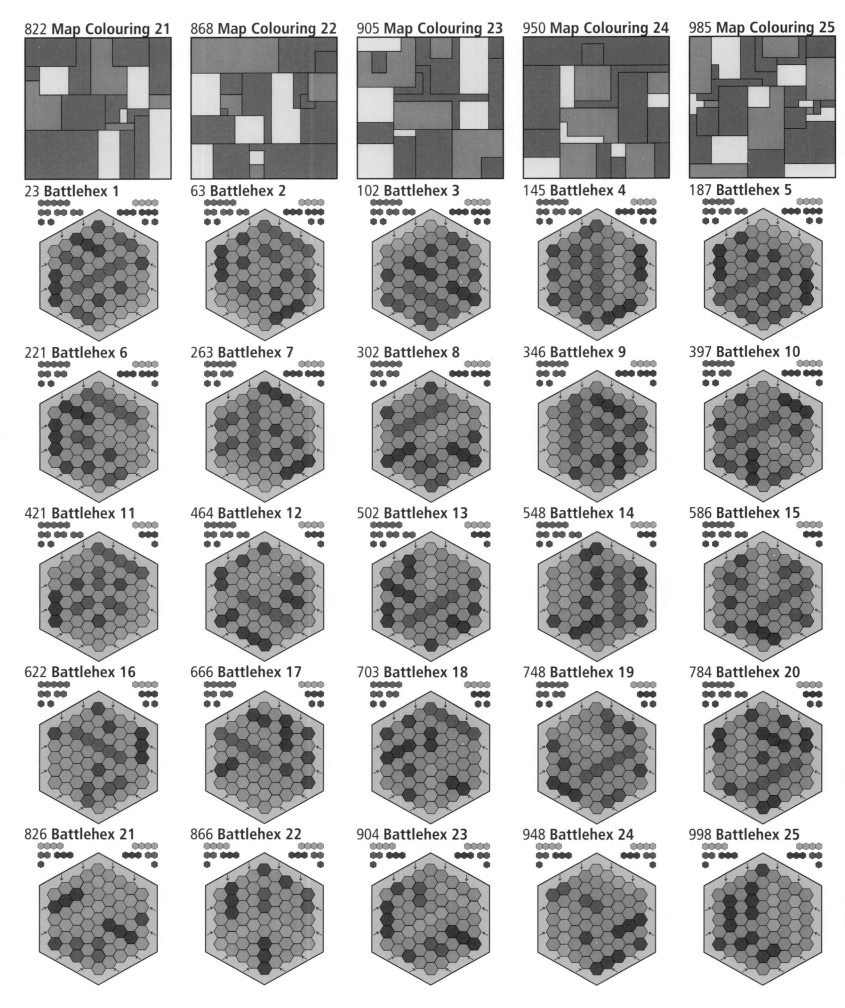

822 **Map Colouring 21** 868 **Map Colouring 22** 905 **Map Colouring 23** 950 **Map Colouring 24** 985 **Map Colouring 25**

23 **Battlehex 1** 63 **Battlehex 2** 102 **Battlehex 3** 145 **Battlehex 4** 187 **Battlehex 5**

221 **Battlehex 6** 263 **Battlehex 7** 302 **Battlehex 8** 346 **Battlehex 9** 397 **Battlehex 10**

421 **Battlehex 11** 464 **Battlehex 12** 502 **Battlehex 13** 548 **Battlehex 14** 586 **Battlehex 15**

622 **Battlehex 16** 666 **Battlehex 17** 703 **Battlehex 18** 748 **Battlehex 19** 784 **Battlehex 20**

826 **Battlehex 21** 866 **Battlehex 22** 904 **Battlehex 23** 948 **Battlehex 24** 998 **Battlehex 25**

28 Match One 1
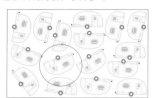

87 Match One 2

127 Match One 3

182 Match One 4
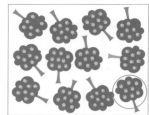

237 Match One 5

286 Match One 6

332 Match One 7

390 Match One 8
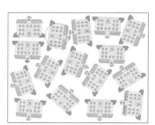

435 Match One 9

474 Match One 10
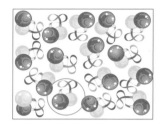

542 Match One 11

581 Match One 12
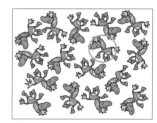

634 Match One 13
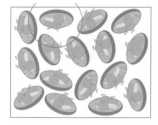

690 Match One 14
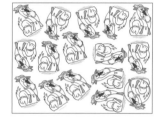

733 Match One 15

795 Match One 16
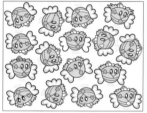

830 Match One 17

880 Match One 18

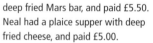

940 Match One 19
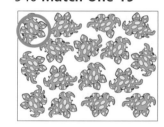

976 Match One 20

29 Suiri 1

Georghe, Duke of Cicea, fed on criminals.
Iancu, Count of Tilead, fed on women.
Janos, Baron of Napoca, fed on the elderly.
Mihas, Lord of Vinatori, fed on foreigners.
Vlad, Prince of Celanu, fed on the wealthy.

81 Suiri 2

Bruce's band, Slopedown, are recording "Black Box", a Prog Rock song.
Rael's band, The Cult of the Void, are recording "Kill the World", a Gothic Rock song.
Leath's band, Neck, are recording "Sudden", an Indie song.
Megan's band, Bellathon, are recording "Canvas Tragedy", an Emo song.
Steve's band, Red Lime, are recording "Juliette", an Alternative Rock song.

134 Suiri 3

Baby Air are a Belgian company that fly to London, but don't allow children.
Connor Airways is an Italian company that flies to Barcelona, but has very expensive food.
EFD is a Portugese company that flies to Frankfurt, but has cramped seats.
Herta Airways is a Danish company that flies to Prague, but suffers delayed departures.
Simplejet are a Dutch company that fly to Paris, but only every other day.

188 Suiri 4

Alistair had a cod supper with a deep fried pizza, and paid £4.00.
Dougal had a haddock supper with deep fried bread, and paid £4.50.
Iain had a sole supper with deep fried scraps, and paid £6.00.
Morton had a skate supper with a deep fried Mars bar, and paid £5.50.
Neal had a plaice supper with deep fried cheese, and paid £5.00.

232 Suiri 5

Adam went to Eton, where he was known as Puffin. He couldn't take off.
James went to Winchester, where he was known as Lasher. He couldn't land.
Justin went to Shrewsbury, where he was known as Loose-Head. He couldn't aim.
Leonard went to Rugby, where he was known as Toasty. He couldn't manoeuvre.
Sebastian went to Harrow, where he was known as Ginger. He couldn't navigate.

283 Suiri 6

Boris is running and on a low carb diet because of a wedding.
Ludmilla is playing tennis and on a low fat diet because of a holiday.
Radka is cycling and on a glycemic index diet because the doctor told her to get fit.
Stanislav is playing squash and on a calorie counting diet because of a presentation.
Vladimir is swimming and in a slimming club diet because of a school reunion.

337 Suiri 7

Dietrich has been married to Birgitta for 7 years, and has bought her lingerie.
Kurt has been married to Petra for 16 years, and has bought her ear-rings.
Michael has been married to Anita for 3 years, and has bought her a camcorder.
Roland has been married to Ingrid for 14 years, and has bought her a ring.

371 Suiri 8

Aladdin is taking potato flour to Damascus in a truck.
Boutros is taking David Hasselhoff albums to Medina in a van.
Iericho is taking cotton to Riyadh in an ambulance.
Jafar is taking silk sheets to Cairo in a car.
Omar is taking DVDs to Bahrain in a 4x4.

430 Suiri 9

Agathi went to SoHo to meet a friend and paid 60 cents.
Eleni went to Macy's to get some exercise, and paid 70 cents.
Filia went to Liberty Island to do some shopping and paid 80 cents.
Lydia went to Central Park for coffee

Volker has been married to Claudia for 5 years, and has bought her a necklace.

and paid 65 cents.
Tina went to Grand Central Station for sight-seeing and paid 75 cents.

482 Suiri 10

Adara went to a Cambodian lodge for the pool.
Gina went to a Thai resort for the forest.
Morna went to a Malaysian chalet for the temple.
Romy went to an Indonesian villa for the shops.
Tisha went to a Mauritanian hotel for the beach.

527 Suiri 11

Alexis had mumps, got ice cream, and wore blue pyjamas.
Billie had tonsilitis, got a visit from a friend, and wore green pyjamas.
Frankie had chicken pox, got jelly, and wore orange pyjamas.
Lee had scarlet fever, got a book, and wore red pyjamas.
Robin had measles, got a toy, and wore yellow pyjamas.

595 Suiri 12

Bjarni bought 10 chocolates and wore a magenta raincoat.
Gunnar bought 6 lollipops and wore a yellow raincoat.
Hertha bought 8 sugar candies and wore a white raincoat.
Ragna bought 12 liquorish lace and wore a cyan raincoat.
Valli bought 4 toffees and wore a black raincoat.

636 Suiri 13

Gertie is knitting socks. She eats digestives and drinks coffee.
Ida is knitting a sweater. She eats ginger snaps and drinks tea.
Kay is knitting a bib. She eats garibaldi biscuits and drinks water.
Lecia is knitting a shawl. She eats butter biscuits and drinks orange juice.
Nessa is knitting a scarf. She eats choc chip cookies and drinks soup.

692 Suiri 14

Antionette is getting blue roses

from Laurent.
Dominique is getting red orchids from Bastien.
Estelle is getting white carnations from Didier.
Maxine is getting pink chrysanthemums from Vincent.
Sabine is getting yellow lilles from Serge.

742 Suiri 15

Dina is having lamb with soup followed by chocolates.
Lili is having duck with noodles followed by ice cream.
May is having pork with stir-fried vegetables followed by cake.
Min is having chicken with rice followed by lychees.
Su is having beef with bean shoots followed by coffee.

781 Suiri 16

Arisa is photographing animals in Berlin and has taken 18 pictures.
Ayame is photographing flowers in Nuremberg and has taken 16

pictures.
Megumi is photographing strangers in Hannover and has taken 14 pictures.
Yukiko is photographing houses in Munich and has taken 17 pictures.
Yuri is photographing churches in Darmstadt and has taken 16 pictures.

829 Suiri 17

Aelle the Red came from Hwicce and ruled in Frilford.
Ceawlin the Just came from Essex and ruled in Chadlington.
Egbert the Bold came from Mercia and ruled in Abingdon.
Offa the Wild came from Sussex and ruled in Asthall.
Redwald the Great came from Wessex and ruled in Cassington.

877 Suiri 18

Donata and Livio met whilst she was oiling her motor scooter. He is going to sing "Amazing".
Eliana and Antonio met whilst she

was buying cucumbers. He is going to sing "Breathe".
Mara and Fabrizio met whilst she was watching football in a cafe. He is going to sing "I Swear".
Monica and Silvio met whilst she was buying cigarettes. He is going to sing "Faithfully".
Serena and Donatello met whilst she was in a cheap winery. He is going to sing "Always".

941 Suiri 19

Buck lives at 2303. He has a green door and likes reading his newspaper outside.
Dave lives at 2305. He has a yellow door and likes sunbathing.
John lives at 2302. He has a blue door and likes washing his car.
Mack lives at 2304. He has a red door and likes barbecues.
Walt lives at 2306. He has a white door and likes playing basketball.

---

31 **Detail Scene 1**
K16, O5, Q36

84 **Detail Scene 2**
N16, F4, Q34

123 **Detail Scene 3**
S38, J10, R15

172 **Detail Scene 4**
S10, I16, E37

226 **Detail Scene 5**
S10, I16, E37

293 **Detail Scene 6**
J35, C34, R31

33 **Detail Scene 7**
P37, R17, C6

378 **Detail Scene 8**
G40, O19, E21

446 **Detail Scene 9**
S10, K23, E36

485 **Detail Scene 10**
H28, D36, H13

530 **Detail Scene 11**
P26, O38, B15

578 **Detail Scene 12**
I8, B26, R6

629 **Detail Scene 13**
P20, N32, D19

685 **Detail Scene 14**
Q24, D27, J4

745 **Detail Scene 15**
K21, N39, P8

776 **Detail Scene 16**
Q27, E34, H7

833 **Detail Scene 17**
M22, F24, H9

886 **Detail Scene 18**
J8, S35, N35

944 **Detail Scene 19**
D8, P12, J35

989 **Detail Scene 20**
P26, O38, B15

---

34 **Identicals 1**

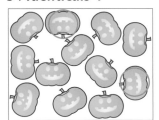

78 **Identicals 2**

138 **Identicals 3**

191 **Identicals 4**

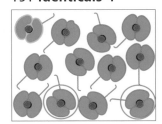

226 **Identicals 5**

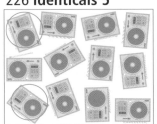

295 **Identicals 6**

329 **Identicals 7**

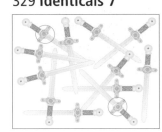

387 **Identicals 8**

444 **Identicals 9**

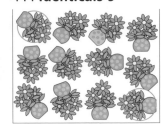

484 **Identicals 10**

541 Identicals 11

575 Identicals 12

643 Identicals 13

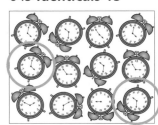

682 Identicals 14

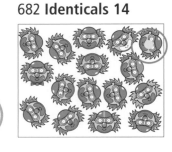

739 Identicals 15

799 Identicals 16

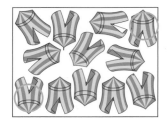

832 Identicals 17

888 Identicals 18

928 Identicals 19

986 Identicals 20

36 Mirror Image 1

89 Mirror Image 2

131 Mirror Image 3

193 Mirror Image 4

235 Mirror Image 5

272 Mirror Image 6

338 Mirror Image 7

385 Mirror Image 8

443 Mirror Image 9

492 Mirror Image 10

538 Mirror Image 11

579 Mirror Image 12

628 Mirror Image 13

697 Mirror Image 14

735 Mirror Image15

775 Mirror Image 16

834 Mirror Image 17

897 Mirror Image 18

931 Mirror Image 19

990 Mirror Image 20

40 Masyu 1

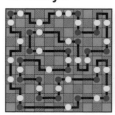

75 Masyu 2

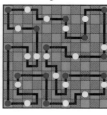

126 Masyu 3

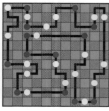

195 Masyu 4

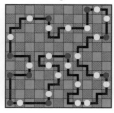

230 Masyu 5

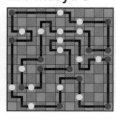

291 Masyu 6

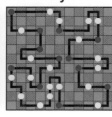

339 Masyu 7

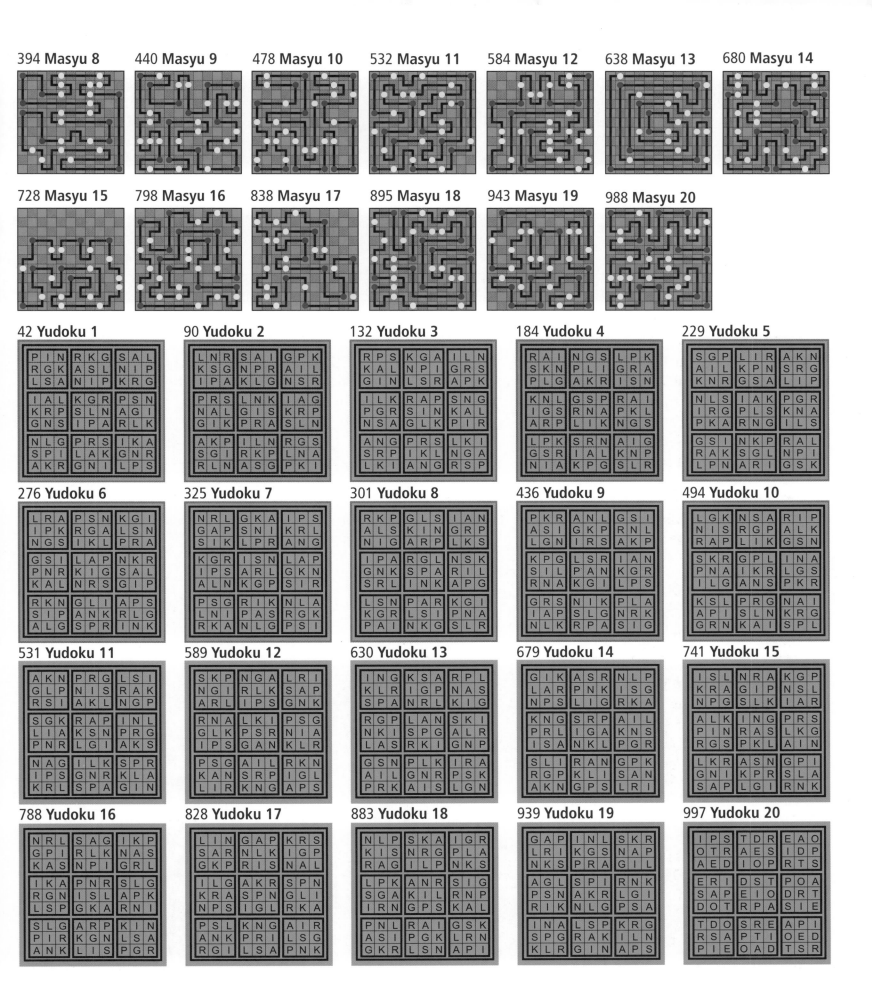

394 Masyu 8 440 Masyu 9 478 Masyu 10 532 Masyu 11 584 Masyu 12 638 Masyu 13 680 Masyu 14

728 Masyu 15 798 Masyu 16 838 Masyu 17 895 Masyu 18 943 Masyu 19 988 Masyu 20

42 Yudoku 1

90 Yudoku 2

132 Yudoku 3

184 Yudoku 4

229 Yudoku 5

276 Yudoku 6

325 Yudoku 7

301 Yudoku 8

436 Yudoku 9

494 Yudoku 10

531 Yudoku 11

589 Yudoku 12

630 Yudoku 13

679 Yudoku 14

741 Yudoku 15

788 Yudoku 16

828 Yudoku 17

883 Yudoku 18

939 Yudoku 19

997 Yudoku 20

46 Silhouettes 1 **119 Silhouettes 2** **170 Silhouettes 3** **249 Silhouettes 4** **316 Silhouettes 5** **369 Silhouettes 6** **449 Silhouettes 7**

519 Silhouettes 8

570 Silhouettes 9 **648 Silhouettes 10** **717 Silhouettes 11** **770 Silhouettes 12** **850 Silhouettes 13** **909 Silhouettes 14** **968 Silhouettes 15**

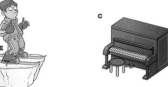

48 Who's Who 1
Pet 1, Ella, belongs to Carol
Pet 2, Georgie, belongs to Alice
Pet 3, Beth, belongs to Ted
Pet 4, Jessie, belongs to Bob

116 Who's Who 2
Baby 1, Heidi, belongs to Georgia.
Baby 2, Isabel, belongs to Jenny.
Baby 3, Daisy, belongs to Erin.
Baby 4, Dana, belongs to Alison.

169 Who's Who 3
Kid 1, Robin, is James's daughter.
Kid 2, Jamie, is Gordon's daughter.
Kid 3, Ashley, is Mark's son.
Kid 4, Blair, is Steve's son.

247 Who's Who 4
Lady 1, Loretta, is married to Lance.

Lady 2, Marlene, is married to Kurt.
Lady 3, Maureen, is married to Nelson.
Lady 4, Mabel, is married to Maurice.

318 Who's Who 5
Student 1, Jon, is Mr. Grey's pupil.
Student 2, Lloyd, is Mr. Broad's pupil.
Student 3, Matt, is Mr. Kent's pupil.
Student 4, Wes, is Mr. Williams's pupil.

367 Who's Who 6
Car 1 belongs to Amanda.
Car 2 belongs to Oliver.
Car 3 belongs to Noel.
Car 4 belongs to Ginny.

448 Who's Who 7
Plant 1 belongs to Brian.
Plant 2 belongs to Roger

Plant 3 belongs to Tony
Plant 4 belongs to Bill

517 Who's Who 8
Teen 1, R.D., is Ada's grandson.
Teen 2, J. J., is Vera's granddaughter.
Teen 3, T.J., is Julius's grandson.
Teen 4, O.P., is Vernon's grandson.

568 Who's Who 9
Secretary 1, Smith, works for Craig.
Secretary 2, Brown, works for Ben.
Secretary 3, Green, works for Paula.
Secretary 4, Jones, works for Judith.

646 Who's Who 10
Drink 1 belongs to Felix.
Drink 2 belongs to Johnny.
Drink 3 belongs to Scott.
Drink 4 belongs to Jimmy.

719 Who's Who 11
Stand 1 belongs to Cate.
Stand 2 belongs to Megan.
Stand 3 belongs to Tony.
Stand 4 belongs to Rod.

772 Who's Who 12
Patient 1, Trevor, is being treated by Dr. Milton.
Patient 2, Ron, is being treated by Dr. Lucas.
Patient 3, Brendon, is being treated by Dr. Jerome.
Patient 4, William, is being treated by Dr. Lester.

847 Who's Who 13
Girl 1, Amy, is going out with Nate.
Girl 2, Nia, is going out with Eric.
Girl 3, Rina, is going out with Loz.
Girl 4, Kerry, is going out with Tod.

908 Who's Who 14
Criminal 1 is Angelo, being hunted by Bob.
Criminal 2 is Mick, being hunted by Ted
Criminal 3 is Buddy, being hunted by Dave
Criminal 4 is Toni, being hunted by Andy.

971 Who's Who 15
Subject 1, Frank, is being interviewed by Jack.
Subject 2, Brad, is being interviewed by Dick.
Subject 3, Eddie, is being interviewed by Roger.
Subject 4, Rocky, is being interviewed by Kitty.

71 Spot the Difference **181 Spot the Difference** **280 Spot the Difference** **376 Spot the Difference** **490 Spot the Difference**

597 Spot the Difference **777 Spot the Difference** **879 Spot the Difference**

687 Spot the Difference

980 Spot the Difference

1000 Spot the Difference 11

70 Killer Sudoku 1

180 Killer Sudoku 2

288 Killer Sudoku 3

389 Killer Sudoku 4

495 Killer Sudoku 5

592 Killer Sudoku 6

689 Killer Sudoku 7

785 Killer Sudoku 8

891 Killer Sudoku 9

984 Killer Sudoku 10

80 Samurai Sudoku 1

197 Samurai Sudoku 2

290 Samurai Sudoku 3

388 Samurai Sudoku 4

481 Samurai Sudoku 5

600 Samurai Sudoku 6

684 Samurai Sudoku 7

789 Samurai Sudoku 8

875 Samurai Sudoku 9

981 Samurai Sudoku 10

85 Super Sudoku 1

194 Super Sudoku 2

275 Super Sudoku 3

379 Super Sudoku 4

479 Super Sudoku 5

574 Super Sudoku 6

691 Super Sudoku 7

796 Super Sudoku 8

885 Super Sudoku 9

993 Super Sudoku 10

86 Differences

190 Differences

278 Differences

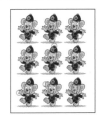

382 Differences

472 Differences

594 Differences

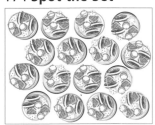

675 Differences

790 Differences

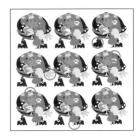

894 Differences

996 Differences

93 Spot the Set

174 Spot the Set

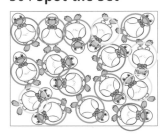

281 Spot the Set

380 Spot the Set

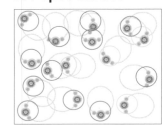

473 Spot the Set

593 Spot the Set

676 Spot the Set

304 Spot the Set

889 Spot the Set

991 Spot the Set

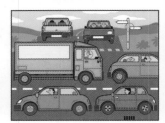

99 Artist's Errors

205 Artist's Errors

544 Artist's Errors

424 Artist's Errors

544 Artist's Errors

653 Artist's Errors

763 Artist's Errors

871 Artist's Errors

973 Artist's Errors

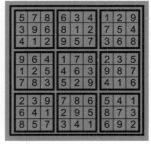

1001 Challenge Sudoku